Pearson Education
Test Prep Series
for

AP® BIOLOGY

Fred W. Holtzclaw
Theresa Knapp Holtzclaw

To accompany:

PEARSON'S CAMPBELL BIOLOGY PROGRAMS

Campbell Biology, 11th Edition, AP® Edition

Campbell Biology in Focus, 2nd Edition, AP® Edition

 Pearson

330 Hudson Street, NY NY 10013

Courseware Portfolio Management Specialist: *Josh Frost*
Courseware Director, Content Development: *Ginnie Simione Jutson*
Managing Producer, Science: *Michael Early*
Content Producer, Science: *Margaret Young*
Production Management and Composition: *Margaret McConnell, Integra*
Interior Design: *Integra*
Illustrators: *Lachina*
Rights & Permissions Manager: *Ben Ferrini*
Manufacturing Buyer: *Stacey J. Weinberger, LSC Communications*
VP Product Marketing: *Christy Lesko*
Executive Product Marketing Manager: *Lauren Harp*
Cover Photo Credits: (Left): *Radius Images/Getty Images;* **(Right):** *Klaus Honal/AGE Fotostock*

5   18

 Pearson

ISBN 10:   0-13-454690-3
ISBN 13: 978-0-13-454690-2

www.PearsonSchool.com/Advanced

Brief Contents

About Your Pearson AP Guide

Pearson Education is the leading education solution provider worldwide. With operations on every continent, we make it our business to understand the changing needs of students at every level, from kindergarten to college. We think that makes us especially qualified to offer this series of Test Prep Workbooks for AP, tied to some of our best-selling programs.

Our reasoning is that as you study for your course, you're preparing along the way for the AP exam. If you can connect the material in the book directly to the exam, it makes the material that much more relevant and enables you to focus your time most efficiently. And that's a good thing!

The AP exam is an important milestone in your education. A high score means you're in a better position for college acceptance and possibly puts you a step ahead with college credits. Our goal is to provide you with the tools you need to succeed.

Good luck!

Revisions to This Edition

Part I: *Introduction to the AP Biology Examination*

- The introduction aligns with and explains the AP Biology Curriculum Framework (CF).
- The seven science practices are introduced.
- The description of the exam and the testing hints are revised to reflect the emphases of the course and information from released exams.
- New command terms and suggestions for writing the essays have been added.

Part II: *A Review of Topics with Sample Questions*

- **You Must Know** boxes are edited to reflect the emphasis seen in recent released exams.
- **What's Important to Know?** boxes are used for material that is not explicitly in the CF but may be used for illustrative examples and explanations.
- Boxes titled **Connect with the Curriculum Framework** target specific information that aligns with the CF.
- Although information about the science practices is woven throughout the book, new boxes titled **Practice the Practice** present information and problems that require use of specific science skills to deal with data or answer questions. Each of these has a solution included in the topic.
- Many new test questions have been added to each topic, including questions that require interpretation of data and application of knowledge.
- New data sets, graphs, and models offer practice with analyzing and drawing conclusions.
- Grid-in questions are included for each topic, as are revised free-response questions that align with released sample exams.
- Over 330 sample questions with explanations are included.

Part III: *The Laboratory*

- This section is heavily revised to reflect the emphasis on inquiry, handling of data, and application of science practices. All 13 investigations are discussed and include hints, explanations, and sample questions.
- Each investigation begins with a brief overview. **You Must Know** boxes are included to emphasize the essential content and skills to be gained as a result of the experience. Additional boxes titled **Science Practices: Can You . . . ?** give students the opportunity to zoom in, make connections, and apply the science practices.
- The College Board formula sheet is included in this edition along with a number of tutorials and problems that take students through sample mathematical applications.
- More than 40 practice questions over lab topics with answers and explanations are included.

Part IV: *Sample Test*

- The sample test has numerous new or significantly revised items to reflect the types of questions students may encounter at exam time.
- Multiple choice, grid-in, and free response questions are included. The test format and number of items conforms to the current AP Exam.

Part V: *Answers and Explanations*

- The format of this section remains similar to past editions, but some explanations stress connections to the curriculum that the student must make and include a description of pertinent knowledge. Many explanations describe the relevant science practice and its required application to correctly answer. Content not included in the main topic outline may be included in this section to enhance understanding.

Part I

Introduction to the AP Biology Examination

This section gives an overview of the Advanced Placement* Program and the AP Biology Examination. Part I introduces the types of questions you will encounter on the exam, explains the procedures used to grade the exam, and provides helpful test-taking strategies. A correlation chart shows where in *Campbell Biology*, Eleventh Edition, by Reece et al., and in *Campbell Biology in Focus*, Second Edition, by Urry et al., you will find key information that commonly appears on the AP Biology Examination. Review Part I carefully before trying the sample test items in Part II and Part III.

The Advanced Placement* Program

You are probably reading this book because you are a student in an Advanced Placement (AP) Biology class, and you want help preparing for the exam. Let us be your guides. Fred and Theresa Holtzclaw have taught AP Biology and worked with the College Board in developing exams and served as graders of the exams for more than 25 years. We know the course well, have been involved with the changes that have been made in it, and have successfully prepared hundreds of our own students for the exam. If you study hard, our hints will give you an edge, and you will be poised for success.

This book will help you in several important ways. The first part of this book introduces you to the AP Biology course and the AP Biology Exam. You'll learn helpful details about the different question formats—multiple-choice, grid-ins, and free-response—that you'll encounter on the exam. In addition, you'll find many test-taking strategies that will help you prepare for the exam. A correlation chart at the end of Part I shows how to use your textbook, *Campbell Biology*, Eleventh Edition, by Reece et al., or *Campbell Biology in Focus*, Second Edition, by Urry et al., to find the information you'll need to know to score well on the AP Biology Exam. By the way, this chart is also useful in helping to identify any extraneous material that won't be tested. Part II of this book contains a review of everything that you learned in your textbook that could be on the AP Biology test. Many questions will be posed along the way so that you can get used to being tested on the concepts in the way that the College Board will test you. The more familiar you are with the AP Biology Exam ahead of time, the more comfortable you'll be on testing day. In Part III, inquiry labs are reviewed, including sample test questions, to check your understanding. In Part IV, there is a practice test for you to try on your own. Part V is where you'll find answers and explanations to all the questions asked in this book.

The AP Program is sponsored by the College Board, a nonprofit organization that oversees college admissions examinations. The AP Program offers 37 different exams in college-level courses to qualified high school students. Over 3,000 colleges and universities around the world grant credit or placement to students who have performed well on AP exams. Each college or university decides whether or not to grant college credit for an AP course, and each bases this decision on what it considers satisfactory grades on AP exams. Depending on what college you attend and what area of study you pursue, your decision to take the AP Biology Exam could save you tuition money. You can contact schools directly to find out their guidelines for accepting AP credits or use College Board's online feature, "AP Credit Policy" (www.collegeboard.com).

Why Take an AP Course?

You may be taking an AP course simply because you like challenging yourself and you are thirsty for knowledge. Another reason may be that you know that colleges look favorably on applicants who have AP courses on their secondary school transcripts. College admissions officers may see your willingness to take these courses as evidence of your work ethic and commitment to your education. Because AP course work is more difficult than average high school work, many admissions officers evaluate AP grades on a higher academic level. For example, if you receive a B in an AP class, it might carry the same weight as an A in a regular-level high school class.

Your AP Biology course prepares you for many of the skills you will need to succeed in college. For example, your teacher may assign a major research paper or require you to perform several challenging laboratory exercises using proper scientific protocol. AP Biology teachers routinely give substantial reading assignments, and students learn how to take detailed lecture notes and participate vigorously in class discussions. Students gain experience with science practices through inquiry and class activities designed to apply these skills. The AP Biology course will challenge you to gather and consider information in new—and sometimes unfamiliar—ways. You can feel good knowing that your hard work in an AP course will give you an advantage as you enter college.

Taking an AP Examination

The AP Biology Exam is given annually in May, and the exams are scored in June. In July the results will be available online for you, your high school, and any colleges or universities you indicated on your answer sheet. Your AP teacher or school guidance counselor can give you information on how to register for an AP exam. Remember, the deadline for registration and payment of exam fees is usually in March, two months before the actual exam date in May. The cost of the exam is subject to change and can differ depending on the number of exams taken. However, in 2016 a single exam costs $92. For students who can show financial need, the College Board will reduce the price by $30, and your school might also waive its regular rebate of $9. Some states pay the exam fee for the student. If you feel you may qualify for reduced rates, ask your school administrators for more information.

To learn more about all things related to AP courses and exams, visit this very helpful website: https://apstudent.collegeboard.org/home. You will always find the latest information here.

AP Biology: Course Goals

The AP Biology course and exam focus on enduring, conceptual understandings and the content that supports them. Factual recall is not as important as being able to use science practices. Knowing content is not enough! You must work on gaining skills all year long. The goal is to help you develop the science skills necessary to be prepared for the study of advanced topics in college science courses.

The emphasis on science practices will help you develop advanced inquiry and reasoning skills. You should be able to design plans to collect and analyze data, make predictions, apply mathematical routines, and connect concepts across domains (levels of organization). Throughout this guide, we will make references to these science practices. Let's be clear: You will still need to master content!

In the AP Biology course, content, inquiry, and reasoning are equally important. The exam will be based on a series of Learning Objectives (LOs), and each LO combines content and science practices. Here is an abbreviated list of the Science Practices from pages 97–102 of the College Board's publication *Course and Exam Description 2015*.

Science Practices for AP Biology

Source: AP Biology—Course and Exam Description. © 2015. The College Board. www.collegeboard.org. Reproduced with permission.

Science Practice 1: The student can use representations and models to communicate scientific phenomena and solve scientific problems.

Science Practice 2: The student can use mathematics appropriately.

Science Practice 3: The student can engage in scientific questioning to extend thinking or to guide investigations within the context of the AP course.

Science Practice 4: The student can plan and implement data collection strategies appropriate to a particular scientific question.

Science Practice 5: The student can perform data analysis and evaluation of evidence.

Science Practice 6: The student can work with scientific explanations and theories.

Science Practice 7: The student is able to connect and relate knowledge across various scales, concepts, and representations in and across domains.

Overview of the Course

The key concepts and related content of the revised AP Biology course and exam are organized around four underlying principles called **Big Ideas**. These encompass the core scientific principles, theories, and processes governing living organisms and biological systems.

Each Big Idea has several **Enduring Understandings**, which are the fundamental concepts you should retain from your course. Each Enduring Understanding has statements of **Essential Knowledge** that you should know. All of the details in the outline are required elements of the course and may be included in the AP Biology Exam. Finally, your teacher may elect to help you learn about biology this year by selecting from many possible **Illustrative Examples**. This is what will make each course unique and allow your teacher to develop a rich course with unique examples of his or her own choosing. For this reason, this guide may cover content that your teacher has not selected. You will need to pick and choose in these areas, realizing that there are many ways a teacher may elect to teach this course.

We took the Curriculum Framework (all 91 pages) and summarized it in an outline that correlates with the concepts in *Campbell Biology,*

Eleventh Edition and *Campbell Biology in Focus* Second Edition. These outlines are found at the front of *Campbell Biology*, (p. vi), and also *Campbell Biology in Focus* (p. ix). Expanded outlines that include Illustrative Examples are available at the Pearson website (www.PearsonSchool.com /AdvancedCorrelations).

It is important for you to know that this outline gives you an idea of the topics that will be covered on the AP exam in May, but the new course will also emphasize Science Practices linked to this content. Facts will not be sufficient! You will need to work with the Science Practices all year long to do well on the exam.

CONNECT WITH THE CURRICULUM FRAMEWORK

Go to the College Board website (https://www.collegeboard.org/) to see a brief summary of the Big Ideas and included topics as well as details on the Science Practices. These are all things you should know and be able to do!

Understanding the AP Biology Examination

The AP Biology Exam takes 3 hours and includes both a 90-minute multiple-choice section and a 90-minute free-response (essay) section that begins with a 10-minute reading period. The multiple-choice section will be one-half of your exam grade, and the free-response section will account for the other half. Both sections include questions that assess students' understanding of the Big Ideas, Enduring Understandings, and Essential Knowledge statements. The exam probably looks like many other tests you've taken. At the core of the examination are questions designed to measure your knowledge and understanding of modern biology. You should be prepared to recall basic facts and concepts, to apply scientific facts and concepts to particular problems, to synthesize facts and concepts, and to demonstrate reasoning and analytical skills by organizing written answers to broad questions. You will hear us repeat this throughout the book: You must be able to *apply* your knowledge. We will give you many chances to practice this in this book.

The AP Biology Exam is very challenging. When you sit down to take the test, you are expected not only to be fluent in the areas of biology that you find fascinating (the ones that probably inspired you to take a special interest in the subject originally), but also to have mastered topics you may find less interesting. Whatever those topics might be—DNA replication, the dizzying details of gene expression, or the immune system—you need to be comfortable with and knowledgeable about all of the AP Biology topics.

Section I, Part A: Multiple-Choice Questions

The first part of the exam consists of 63 standard multiple-choice questions and 6 questions that involve mathematical calculation for which you will grid in a response. You will have 90 minutes to complete Section I. Each of the multiple-choice questions is directly paired with a Learning Objective from the Curriculum Framework. The questions require both an understanding of important concepts and biological processes and the ability to apply information that is given to you in the question. Because of this, the stem of the questions may be longer than many multiple-choice questions you have seen before. This portion of the exam is followed by a 10-minute break—the only official break during the examination. The following chart summarizes this information.

Section	Question Type	Number of Questions	Timing
I	Part A: Multiple Choice	63	90 minutes
	Part B: Grid-In	6	
II	Long Free Response	2	90 minutes (includes suggested 10-minute reading period)
	Short Free Response	6	

Source: AP Biology—Course and Exam Description. © 2015. The College Board. www.collegeboard.org. Reproduced with permission.

Here is a sample item from page 152 of the College Board's *Course and Exam Description 2015*.

A human kidney filters about 200 liters of blood each day. Approximately two liters of liquid and nutrient waste are excreted as urine. The remaining fluid and dissolved substances are reabsorbed and continue to circulate throughout the body. Antidiuretic hormone (ADH) is secreted in response to reduced plasma volume. ADH targets the collecting ducts in the kidney, stimulating the insertion of aquaporins into their plasma membranes and an increased reabsorption of water.

If ADH secretion is inhibited, which of the following would initially result?
  (A) The number of aquaporins would increase in response to the inhibition of ADH.
  (B) The person would decrease oral water intake to compensate for the inhibition of ADH.
  (C) Blood filtration would increase to compensate for the lack of aquaporins.
  (D) The person would produce greater amounts of dilute urine.

Essential Knowledge	3.D.3: Signal transduction pathways link signal reception with cellular response.
Science Practice	1.5: The student can re-express key elements of natural phenomena across multiple representations in the domain.
Learning Objective	3.36: The student is able to describe a model that expresses the key elements of signal transduction pathways by which a signal is converted to a cellular response.

Source: AP Biology—Course and Exam Description. © 2015. The College Board. www .collegeboard.org. Reproduced with permission.

Your course may not have included a study of kidney function, but all the information you need to answer this item is given in the stem. You are told what ADH does and how it is controlled and given the role of aquaporins. It is expected that you can use this information to select the correct answer. If you are certain you know the answer, fill in the corresponding oval on the answer sheet. However, what if you're not certain? The next step is to see if you can eliminate one or more of the choices.

TIP FROM THE READERS
There is no penalty for guessing. *Answer every question!*

Let's look again at the question. The correct answer is D. Choice *A* suggests a response when ADH is inhibited. You must know that this means there is less ADH. The stem tells you that ADH "stimulates the insertion of aquaporins," so you will eliminate this choice. Continue to methodically analyze the other choices, and try to eliminate another choice based on your understanding of the information that is given in the stem. Confidently mark your answer sheet and continue. Remember, answer *every* question!

Lab-Based or Experimental Questions

Another type of question you will see in Section I is the lab-based or experimental question. These questions either present you with a set of data in graph (or other) form, or they describe an experiment and ask you to make predictions, select appropriate data, form hypotheses, analyze data mathematically, and perform other science practices. These questions often occur in groups that use the same data set.

It is known that plant root cells require oxygen in order to obtain ATP. Those who work with plants have long known that it is possible to quickly kill a plant by overwatering. The following graph shows the results of a study of the effect of soil air spaces on plant growth.

1. The data from the above graph show that the plant
   (A) grows fastest when the soil is 5–10% air.
   (B) grows fastest when the soil is 15–20% air.
   (C) grows at the same rate regardless of the soil air percentage.
   (D) grows most slowly when the soil is 5–10% air.

The correct choice is *A*. The graph shows the line with the greatest slope (the highest degree of change over the shortest amount of time) between the percentages 5 and 10. During this time, the plant grows by about $9 - 5 = 4$ grams. Just to be sure, check the amount this plant grows when the soil is 15–20% air. At the start, when the air was 15% air, the plant weighed 12 grams. At the end, when the soil is 20% air, the plant weight is the same—12 grams. Virtually no growth occurred during this time.

Clearly this question requires you to be able to interpret a graph, but at this point in your biology education you should be quite capable of doing that. In order to brush up on the various ways that graphs present information, you might want to review Appendix B of the *AP Biology Investigation Manual*.

2. It is seen from the graph that plant growth is negatively affected by decreased soil oxygen. Which of the following statements best justifies the reason for this effect?
   (A) Plant root cells require oxygen because no photosynthesis occurs underground.
   (B) Plant stem and leaf cells are able to do photosynthesis at a higher rate when there is more oxygen in the soil.
   (C) Water in the soil eliminates oxygen from the soil spaces, so the root cells are unable to produce ATP.
   (D) The rate of cellular respiration is decreased under conditions of high soil moisture.

The correct choice is *C*. This question requires you to recall the reactants and products of photosynthesis and cellular respiration. *All* plant cells do cellular respiration, consuming O_2 in order to produce ATP. Choice *C* justifies (explains) why plant growth is low when there is low soil O_2. Choice *D* restates the information from the graph. Although it is a true statement, it does not justify the reason for this correlation.

Section I, Part B: Grid-In Questions

These questions require you to calculate an answer or determine a value from a graph or data table and enter it in a grid on your answer sheet. Study the following grids and discussion for guidance on how to correctly enter your numerical responses.

Notice that you can bubble your response in any of the boxes, as shown in the samples for 502. Start your answer in any column, space permitting. Unused columns should be left blank. You can see that you are able to indicate negative numbers, fractions, and the location of decimal points. Be sure to follow instructions for the calculation you are to make, and express your answer with the precision that is specified, such as "round to the nearest tenth." If the answer results in a negative number, remember to bubble the minus (–) sign. The final sample grid-in shows you how to express a fractional answer. Fractions only need to be reduced enough to fit in the grid, so 5/10 is acceptable. One detail here is that you should not use mixed numbers such as "3 ¾" because it would be scored as "3 3/4."

You will be able to use a four-function calculator (with square root) during the exam as well as a formula sheet (Appendix B of the *Investigation Manual*) because the emphasis is on your ability to apply mathematical techniques—not memorize formulas. Now try your hand at this sample problem.

Grid-In Question Requiring Calculator Use

The data below demonstrate the frequency of tasters and non-tasters in an isolated population at Hardy-Weinberg equilibrium. The allele for non-tasters is recessive

Tasters	Non-tasters
8235	4328

How many of the tasters in the population are heterozygous for tasting?

Source: AP Biology—Course and Exam Description. © 2015. The College Board. www.collegeboard.org. Reproduced with permission.

To set your mind at ease, the electronic scoring for these responses is set so there may be a range of correct scores to allow for variations in rounding. The acceptable answer for this problem is in the range of 6030–6156, depending on rounding. This question requires that you be able to use the Hardy-Weinberg equation to calculate allelic frequencies.

Section II: Free-Response Questions

At the beginning of Section II of the AP Biology Exam, you will be given a 10-minute period where you may read the questions and plan and outline your responses before you begin writing. Listen carefully as your proctor reads the instructions for this section of the exam. Currently, you are allowed to begin writing as soon as time begins. However, we strongly suggest that you use the initial 10 minutes to read and reread the first two questions. For now, ignore the other essays rather than trying to absorb too much information all at once. However, be sure you continue to follow the steps described in the next paragraph as you tackle each essay on the exam.

Underline key words or phrases such as "Select *two*" or "*Explain* and *predict*" or "Use an example from *each* domain." Use key words to prepare an outline of your response to each of the 10-point questions if time allows. If a graph will be required, decide what type is appropriate and what will go on each axis. During the planning time, you can jot notes on some blank pages, but the instructions are very clear that anything written there will not be graded.

Section II of the AP Biology Exam has eight free-response questions. There are two 10-point questions, three questions worth 4 points each, and three questions worth 3 points each. The long questions will consist of several sections or related tasks and will be evaluated on a 10-point scale. You should allow approximately 20 minutes for a long free-response question.

The 3-point and 4-point questions call for briefer responses. The instructions may say something like "In a sentence or two. . . ." Heed these parameters to use your time wisely. The short free-response questions should be completed in about 6 minutes or so. For *all* free-response questions, you must write your answers out, and you cannot use an outline form. Let's look at an example. What follows will give you an idea about how these questions may appear in your exam booklet.

TIP FROM THE READERS

You may be overwhelmed if you try to read and plan your responses for all eight essays during the initial 10 minutes. We suggest that you focus on the first two essays and then take about 1 minute to plan each of the remaining essays *as you reach them*. Keep your eye on your time, and do not spend longer than suggested on any essay. You can always return to an essay, but your score will most likely be better overall if you give at least a partial answer for each question.

When you open your exam book, here is what you will see:

BIOLOGY

Section II

8 Questions

Planning Time—10 minutes

Writing Time—80 minutes

Directions: Questions 1 and 2 are long free-response questions that require about 22 minutes each to answer and are worth 10 points each. Questions 3–8 are short free-response questions that require about 6 minutes each to answer. Questions 3–5 are worth 4 points each and questions 6–8 are worth 3 points each.

Read each question carefully and completely. Write your response in the space provided for each question. Only material written in the space provided will be scored. Answers must be written out in paragraph form. Outlines, bulleted lists, or diagrams alone are not acceptable.

Here is a sample question for Section II.

1. Water makes up roughly 70% of the human body; cells are roughly 70–95% water, and water covers about three-quarters of the Earth's surface.

   (a) **Describe** the major physical properties of water that make it unique from other liquids.
   (b) **Explain** the properties of water that enable it to travel up through the roots and stems of plants to reach the leaves.

(c) **Explain** why the temperature of the oceans can remain relatively stable and support vast quantities of both plant and animal life when air temperature fluctuates so significantly throughout the year.

Like many free-response questions on the AP Biology Exam, this sample is broken into three distinct parts. Each contains a clear directive. In fact, command terms are printed in boldface to help you focus on exactly how you should answer the question. First, you will need to explain the uniqueness of water by describing its major physical properties. (In your response to this first part of the question, you might wish to include a labeled diagram of the structure of water, complete with electrons and bonds.) Then you must explain the properties of water that allow it to travel from root to leaf. Finally, you should explain the reason(s) why ocean water temperature remains stable and supports plant and animal life—even in the face of great air temperature variations. Of course, limiting your answer by addressing exactly what the question asks will make writing the essay easier for you and earn you a higher score. Always take the time to determine precisely what is being asked before you begin to formulate a concrete thesis and focus on writing your relevant supporting paragraphs.

Grading Procedures for the AP Biology Examination

The raw scores of the AP Biology Examination are converted to the following 5-point scale:

5—Extremely Well Qualified
4—Well Qualified
3—Qualified
2—Possibly Qualified
1—No Recommendation

Some colleges give undergraduate course credit to students who achieve scores of 3 or better on AP exams. Other colleges require students to achieve scores of 4 or 5. You may check the policy for individual colleges on the College Board website (www.collegeboard.com). Here you can also get information about student performance in prior years. Following is a breakdown of how the grading of the AP Biology Exam works.

Section I: Multiple-Choice Questions

The multiple-choice section of the exam is worth 50% of your total score. The raw score of Section I is determined by crediting one point for each correctly answered question. Therefore, it is important to answer each question. *There is no penalty for guessing!*

Section II: Free-Response Questions

Section II counts for 50% of your examination grade. The free-response section is scored by several hundred faculty consultants, including high school teachers and college instructors from all over the country who work in a central location to grade the essays. This period of scoring exams is called the "Reading." To ensure that scoring of all exams is consistent, grading rubrics, or standards, are developed and then faculty consultants are trained in their application. Because of this intense training, group discussion, and supervision, your essay should receive the same score regardless of who reads it. Ongoing internal checks during the Reading ensure this. Each of your essays will be evaluated by a faculty consultant trained to score that single response.

Your answers to the free-response questions must be presented in essay form. Outlines or unlabeled and unexplained diagrams are not given credit. Your performance on any single essay is evaluated independently of the other essays. Do not assume that information provided in one question will be considered during the grading of another essay. You should repeat information from question to question if it is necessary to illustrate your point.

Test-Taking Strategies for the AP Biology Examination

Here are a few tips for preparing in the time leading up to the examination.

▪ The earlier you start studying for the AP Biology Exam, the better. Some students use this AP Biology prep book along with their textbook throughout the course, taking notes in the margin to supplement their teacher's lectures. You should definitely begin serious preparation for the test at least one month in advance.

▪ Each topic in Part II of this book is correlated to *Campbell Biology*, Eleventh Edition, by Reece et al., and *Campbell Focus on Biology*, Second Edition, by Urry et al. For each topic, review your lecture notes, study the figures in your text that explain key concepts, and then make your way through the corresponding section of Part II. If possible, retake your own unit test on the topic, and also answer the questions in this guide for each unit. This will help you identify areas that will require further study. Do not try to reread your text; use it as a tool for those topics that need further study. Pace yourself!

▪ The AP Biology exam will test not only your grasp of essential content but also your ability to think like a scientist and use the Science Practices. We suggest you take advantage of the *Scientific Skills Exercises* and *Inquiry* figures in your text. These will give you practice interpreting graphs and data, which you must be able to do on the AP Biology exam.

AP Review: Lab Essays

The College Board has published a manual with 13 recommended inquiry labs. It is expected that you will complete two labs for each Big Idea during the course of the school year. Your teacher may elect to use some of the labs from the College Board's *AP Biology Investigative Labs*, or others of their choosing. All the laboratories will emphasize the science practices, and you will become more proficient in working and thinking like a scientist only by engaging in this type of work. These labs will often run over multiple days or even weeks and will include components where you learn new techniques and then use them to answer your own experimental questions.

Here is a list of the labs in the College Board's *AP Biology Investigative Labs*.

Source: AP Biology—Investigative Labs: An Inquiry-Based Approach. © 2015. The College Board. www.collegeboard.org. Reproduced with permission.

Big Idea 1: Evolution

Investigation 1: Artificial Selection
Investigation 2: Mathematical Modeling: Hardy-Weinberg
Investigation 3: Comparing DNA Sequences to Understand Evolutionary Relationships with BLAST

Big Idea 2: Cellular Processes: Energy and Communication

Investigation 4: Diffusion and Osmosis
Investigation 5: Photosynthesis
Investigation 6: Cellular Respiration

Big Idea 3: Genetics and Information Transfer

Investigation 7: Cell Division: Mitosis and Meiosis
Investigation 8: Biotechnology: Bacterial Transformation
Investigation 9: Biotechnology: Restriction Enzyme Analysis of DNA

Big Idea 4: Interactions

Investigation 10: Energy Dynamics
Investigation 11: Transpiration
Investigation 12: Fruit Fly Behavior
Investigation 13: Enzyme Activity

It is likely that at least one essay on the exam will be based on an AP investigation, although it may not be one that you have done. Not to fear! Because the questions are based on objectives for the course, your teacher will have prepared you to work with data from a variety of sources, so you will simply need to apply your expertise in scientific thinking acquired over the course to a novel situation. If you have done a similar experiment, this may be helpful—but be sure you read carefully and do not anticipate what is being asked. For example, you may be asked to "Pose a question . . ." or "Predict . . ." or "Describe the results you would expect. . . ." Always do what you are asked!

You might be asked to "design an experiment to determine. . . ." If you performed a lab in your AP class that would answer this question, it is fine to describe this lab. There are a number of items that would generally be included in your design, so consider including each of these:

▌ **State your hypothesis**. Your hypothesis must be testable.
▌ **Identify the variable factor** for the experiment (e.g., temperature).
▌ **Identify a control**. You must explain the control for the experiment.
▌ **Hold all other variables constant**. Explain how you would do this.

- **Manipulate the variable** (for example, one group at 10°C, one at 20°C, and one at 30°C).
- **Measure the results** (for example, cm grown, mass increase in grams).
- **Discuss results expected** as related to hypothesis.
- **Replication or verification**: The experiment must be repeated or large sample sizes must be used.
- **Statistical analysis of data**: You may need to calculate means or determine standard error, for example, or do Chi-square analysis.

> **STUDY TIP** Part III of this guide will discuss all 13 Investigations available from The College Board. Even though you will not do all of these, we suggest you read through all of them. Often lab questions are based on techniques we describe in that section, and if you have a general idea of some common labs and data that can be obtained, it will make answering questions on unfamiliar labs much easier.

Graphing Data

It is likely that you will be asked to graph data. You will need to consider the type of graph that is appropriate for your data. Bar graphs are used when data points are discrete, that is, not related to each other, such as the number of girls in AP Biology vs. the number of boys in AP Biology. Line graphs are used when the data are continuous, such as the change in an individual's height at each birthday. Consider if there is a data point at 0 on the graph. Be sure to extend your line to 0 if there is, but do not take the line to 0 if there is no measurement for that data point. Also,

- Label the graph with a descriptive title.
- Label the x and y axes. Include units (such as "Time in minutes"). Be sure you know which variable is independent and which is dependent.
- Keep all measurement units constant. Each division on the graph must be a unit equal to all the others.
- If you are asked to draw a line to predict what would be shown if some change occurred, be sure that you include a legend for the second line.
- Be able to use or interpret error bars.

Sample Tests

When you are ready to check your preparation, take the sample exam in Part III of this book. Keep track of your time, and try to simulate test conditions. Circle the items you get wrong or could not answer, and keep a list of the subject matter of those questions. The Answers and Explanations section will help you address any errors you have made, so be sure to spend time reviewing the helpful information there. Analyze the items missed to look for patterns— are you having a hard time with the grid-ins or the process of photosynthesis specifically? Spend the next week or so studying the topics in which you are weak. Spend the final days before the test looking through this guide, your class notes, and your textbook to fill in any remaining gaps.

The Day of the Exam

If you have followed this suggested study plan, you should feel well prepared by test day. Plan your schedule so that you get two very good nights of uninterrupted sleep before exam day. The night before the exam, relax, think positive thoughts, and focus on getting a good night's rest. Like some endurance races we have run, success will go to the strong, not necessarily the swift. The AP Biology Exam is a grueling mental exercise, so you need to be rested and well nourished. A little more cramming will *not* help! Below is a brief list of basic tips and strategies to think about before you arrive at the exam site.

1. **Arrive early!** It's a good idea to arrive at the exam site 30 minutes before the start time. On the day of the exam, make sure that you eat a good, nutritious meal. These tips may sound corny or obvious, but your body must be in peak form in order for your brain to perform well. Remember, you are going to need ATP to fuel brain cells at peak efficiency for more than 3 hours.
2. **Bring a photo ID.** (It's essential if you are taking the exam at a school other than your own.) A driver's license or a student ID card will allow you to prove your identity.
3. **Bring at least two sharpened #2 pencils** for the multiple-choice section. Also, bring a clean pencil eraser with you. Many pencils today have cheap erasers that smudge. Invest in a good eraser. The machine that scores Section I of the exam recognizes only marks made by a #2 pencil. Poorly erased responses are often scored incorrectly.
4. **Bring two black ballpoint pens** for the free-response portion of the test. Felt-tip pens run, and pencils and inks of other colors are harder to read.
5. **Bring a watch** with you to the exam. Although many testing rooms have clocks, having your own watch makes it easy to keep close track of your own pace. Watches with calculators or alarms are not permitted in the exam room.
6. **Bring a four-function calculator with square root** (or your school may arrange to have them available). You may be accustomed to using a graphing calculator, but it will be helpful for you to practice using the simpler four-function calculator during the month before the AP exam. The small buttons and different positions for functions may take some practice, and you don't want to be figuring this out during your precious exam minutes. Practice early!

Forbidden Items and Rules of Conduct!

Some items that are forbidden from the testing room are books, notes, laptops, beepers, cameras, and portable listening or recording devices. If you bring a cellular phone with you, be prepared to turn it off and to give it to the test proctor until you are finished with your exam. For a complete list of what not to bring, see the College Board website.

The objects listed above are not allowed in the interest of fairness to all test-takers. Similarly, the test administrators are very clear and very serious about what types of conduct are not allowed during the examination. Below is a list of actions to avoid at all costs because each can result in your immediate dismissal from the exam room.

- Do not consult any outside materials during the 3 hours of the exam period. Remember, the break is technically part of the exam—you are not free to review any materials at that time.
- Do not speak during the exam. If you have a question for the test proctor, raise your hand to get the proctor's attention.
- When you are told to stop working on a section of the exam, you must stop immediately. (*Important hint:* The grid-ins are included in Part I of the exam, so finish them before your break!)
- Do not open your exam booklet before the test begins.
- Never tear a page out of your test booklet or try to remove the exam from the test room.
- Do not behave disruptively—even if you're distressed about a difficult test question or because you've run out of time. Stay calm and make no unnecessary noise.

Section I: Strategies for Multiple-Choice Questions

Obviously, having a firm grasp of biology is the key to doing well on the AP Biology Examination. In addition, being well informed about the exam itself increases your chances of achieving a high score. Below is a list of strategies that you can use to increase your comfort, your confidence, and your chances of excelling on the multiple-choice section of the exam.

- Become as familiar as possible with the format of Section I. The more comfortable you are with the multiple-choice format and with the kinds of questions you'll encounter, the easier the exam will be. Remember, Part II and Part III of this book provide you with invaluable practice on the kinds of multiple-choice questions you will encounter on the AP Biology Exam.
- Every question you answer correctly is a point, so pacing is important. If you have done all the suggested practice tests, you should have a good sense of how to pace yourself. You will have 90 minutes to answer 63 multiple-choice and 6 grid-in questions (about 78 seconds per question). Keep track of time!
- Some of the questions will require calculations or may have complicated data sets. If you encounter a question that will require extra time, leave it blank and make a note. Your goal should be to reach the end of the test, picking up all the points from questions you can answer easily.
- Our students tell us that pacing is very important! They say to never spend too long on an item and then not have time to finish. They report this as their most common error.
- The test is organized with three types of questions: standard multiple-choice, lab sets, and grid-ins. Lab sets are generally the most tedious. When a data table or graph is presented, proceed directly to the related questions. Determine what information is needed to answer the questions, and then return to the data table or graph to seek the information. Sometimes, although the data appear daunting, the questions are actually very easy. Practice doing this!

- Make a light mark in your test booklet next to any questions you can't answer. Return to these questions after you reach the end of Section I. Sometimes questions that appear later in the test will refresh your memory on a particular topic, and you will be able to answer one or more of those earlier questions.
- Always read the entire question carefully, and underline key words or ideas.
- Read each and every one of the answer choices carefully before you make your final selection. When we give our students practice exams, the mistake that troubles them most is when the question is missed because they did not read or mark carefully. Don't let this happen to you!
- Use the process of elimination to help you arrive at the correct answer. Even if you are quite sure of an answer, cross out the letters of incorrect choices in your test booklet as you eliminate them. This cuts down on the incorrect choices and allows you to narrow the remaining choices even further.
- Become completely familiar with the instructions for the multiple-choice questions before you take the exam. By knowing the instructions cold, you'll save yourself the time of reading them carefully on exam day.
- If you finish early, you should go back over as many items as possible to catch any careless errors. This is not the time to second-guess your responses but to be sure you marked the answer you intended and did not misread a question or choice.

> **TIP FROM THE READERS**
> Because so many questions involve graphs and data analysis, budget your time carefully! Practice our suggestion of reading the questions first so you know what information you need. If you spend time trying to understand *all* the information shown by the data, you will run out of time!

Section II: Strategies for Free-Response Questions

Below is a list of strategies that you can use to increase your chances of excelling on the free-response section of the exam.

- You will have a 10-minute period to review the essay questions and make notes before you begin to write your graded responses. During this time, you should organize your thoughts and outline your essays in the space provided. Since the exam now covers eight different questions, our students suggest we advise you to focus primarily on the first two 10-point questions. They tell us that it is almost impossible to work through eight different questions during the 10-minute pre-read time, so they suggest being well-prepared for the longer essays. After the preparation time, you should record your answer on the pages provided for each question in the response book. You have about 20 minutes to spend on each 10-point essay and about 6 minutes for each of the short questions.
- *Read the question; then read the question again!* Be sure you answer the question that is asked and that you address each part of the question. As you read a question, underline any directive words (usually the first word in a question) that indicate how you should answer and focus the material in your essay. Some of the most frequently used directives on the AP Biology Exam are listed

below, along with descriptions of what you need to do in your writing to answer the question.

- *Analyze* (show relationships between events)
- *Compare* (discuss similarities and differences between groups; be sure to address *each* group!)
- *Contrast* (discuss points of difference or divergence between two or more things)
- *Describe* (give a detailed account)
- *Design* (create an experiment and convey its ideas)
- *Predict* (tell what you expect to happen when conditions change; should be scientifically plausible)
- *Justify* (give a scientific basis for why a response is reasonable)
- *Refine* (suggest changes that will improve what has been given)
- *Create a model or representation* (generalize the information or portray it graphically)

TIP FROM THE READERS

Explain is an important term that has very specific requirements! Here are the components of a scientific explanation:

1. Make a *claim* (an assertion or conclusion)
2. Provide *evidence* (scientific data that support the claim)
3. Give *reasoning* (link the evidence to the claim)

Here is an example of a question and how you might answer it:

Explain when chromosome number is reduced in meiosis.
Chromosome number is reduced in the first meiotic division (CLAIM) because at that time homologous pairs are separated (EVIDENCE). At this point there is only one chromosome from each pair of parental chromosomes, although it consists of replicated sister chromatids (REASONING).

In the grading of the AP Biology Exam, we can tell you that it is *essential* to include all three components of a scientific explanation.

- Reread the question as many times as necessary to make sure you cover each aspect of the topic. Free-response questions frequently have several parts, so you will need to take this into account as you outline your ideas.
- Write an essay! As the exam states clearly in the directions to free-response questions, a diagram or graph by itself is never an acceptable way to answer a free-response question. However, you should think about whether you could use a labeled diagram or graph to develop your written answer in some useful way.
- The essay you craft for this exam is not the same type of essay you should write for an English course. Yes, it should be well-organized; however, introductory sentences and conclusions are absolutely not necessary. Readers are

interested in what you know and how well you express your knowledge. Spend your time packing the essay with the biological information you have worked so hard to learn.

▍ If the question has several parts, answer the parts in the sequence given. We suggest that you skip a line between sections (a, b, c, etc.) so it is very clear that you have addressed each part of the question. Use a letter or some other indication for each part so that the faculty consultant does not overlook a section of your response.

▍ If you are asked to perform a calculation, be sure to show the steps you used to arrive at your answer. You have heard this before: Show your work!

▍ If you cannot remember a specific term, describe the structure or process.

▍ Define any scientific term you use that is directly related to your response. For example, if you discuss hydrogen bonding and how it relates to properties of water, be sure to explain what hydrogen bonds are, and then describe or define adhesion, cohesion, and so on.

▍ Your handwriting can affect your results. Although faculty consultants make every attempt to read each essay, sometimes it is impossible to decipher messy handwriting. When your handwriting is poor, the reader may lose concentration or patience and miss an important word or phrase.

▍ Don't leave any part of any essay blank. Every essay point is worth approximately 1.5 times as much as each multiple-choice point.

▍ If time allows, proofread your essays. Don't worry about crossing out material—readers understand that your responses are first drafts and that you are writing down ideas under the pressure of time. A single line through the material you wish to omit is sufficient. However, anything that you cross out will not be graded!

A Sample Free-Response Question and How to Approach It

The success of your free-response essays will depend a great deal on how clearly and extensively you answer the questions posed. Of course, the structure of your essays will depend entirely on your knowledge of the subjects at hand. Take a look at an example of a free-response question below.

1. In cancer, the cell's reproductive machinery experiences a loss of control that makes cancer cells reproduce continually and eventually form a tumor.
   (A) **Describe** three DNA-related cellular events that could lead to the loss of cell division control that contributes to cancer.
   (B) **Describe two** ways in which tumors can disrupt normal function of the body.
   (C) **Predict** two cell processes that could be targeted to find a cure for cancer, and include a biological explanation for each.

In order to answer this question, you should isolate exactly what it is that you must answer. You may want to underline the relevant information in the question to remind yourself of your focus. *Circle* the number of examples you are to use in any response because this is all the reader will give you credit for doing. Go with your best choices only! To answer part (a), you'll need to identify three appropriate DNA-related cellular events. Here are three likely choices:

1. A mutation or change in the original DNA sequence
2. Errors in DNA replication that go undetected by the cell's proofreading devices
3. A translocation error

Under each of the three events, you should list any and all details you remember about those events to use in your description. When you flesh out these details, you'll need to clearly connect them to the concept of the loss of cell division control leading to cancer.

To answer part (b), list the two best reasons you can think of as to why tumors are harmful to the body. Do not bother with more! Remember, only your first two responses will be graded. These might include cancerous cells' ability to metastasize; tumors' ability to occur almost anywhere in the body; tumors' tendency to block the flow of blood when they grow near blood vessels; or disruption of the natural function of an organ in the body. Discuss how each of your choices can alter the natural function of any organ in the body and how that will endanger homeostasis.

To answer part (c), you'll need to consider first what causes cancer. Then you must think creatively in order to predict reasonable approaches to dealing with each specific cause.

AP Biology Concepts at a Glance

On the College Board website (https://www.collegeboard.org/), you will find the Essential Knowledge statements from the AP Biology Curriculum Framework. These represent the content that you should know, although all questions will link this knowledge to a science practice.

Part II

A Review of Topics with Sample Questions

Part II corresponds to *Campbell Biology*, Eleventh Edition, by Reece et al. as well as *Biology in Focus,* Second Edition, by Urry, Cain, et al. The content is divided into 10 broad topics, and within each topic there are bold headings. Each of these topics is aligned with material in the textbooks by reference to the concepts where it is found. You will find an overview of important information and sample multiple-choice, grid-in, and free-response questions. The content necessary to do well on the AP Biology Exam is included in the bulleted information, but you will need to rely on sample questions and your teacher's instruction to reinforce the science practices. Some of the included material may be outside the scope of the AP exam, but we have included it because your teacher may use it to help you better understand the richness of biology. You can find answers and explanations to the questions in Part V. Be sure to review the answers thoroughly to prepare yourself for the range of questions you will encounter on the AP Biology Exam.

The Chemistry of Life

The Chemical Context of Life
(Biology, *11e: Chapters 2, 3;* Focus, *2e: Chapter 2*)

WHAT'S IMPORTANT TO KNOW?
Some of this material is considered prior knowledge for the AP Biology Exam. However, you will need to know this information to proceed with the required topics, so we include what is most important in this area.

YOU MUST KNOW

- The three subatomic particles and their significance.
- The types of chemical bonds and how they form.
- The importance of hydrogen bonding to the properties of water.
- Four unique properties of water and how each contributes to life on Earth.
- How to interpret the pH scale.
- How changes in pH can alter biological systems.
- The importance of buffers in biological systems.

Matter consists of chemical elements in pure form and in combinations called compounds (Biology, *11e: 2.1;* Focus, *2e: 2.1*)

▌ **Matter** is anything that takes up space and has mass.

▌ An **element** is a substance that cannot be broken down into other substances by chemical reactions. *Examples*: gold, copper, carbon, and oxygen.

▌ A **compound** is a substance consisting of two or more elements combined in a fixed ratio. *Examples*: water (H_2O) and table salt (NaCl).

▌ **C, H, O, N** make up 96% of living matter. About 25 of the 92 natural elements are known to be essential to life.

▌ **Trace elements** are those required by an organism in only minute quantities. *Examples*: iron and iodine.

An element's properties depend on the structure of its atoms (Biology, *11e: 2.2;* Focus, *2e: 2.2*)

▌ **Atoms** are the smallest units of an element that retain the property of the element. Atoms are made up of neutrons, protons, and electrons.

- **Protons** are positively charged particles found in the nucleus of the atom.
- **Electrons** are negatively charged particles that are found in electron shells around the nucleus. They determine the chemical properties and reactivity of the element.
- **Neutrons** are particles with no charge. They are found in the nucleus. Their number can vary in a given element, resulting in isotopes.
- **Isotopes** are forms of an element with differing numbers of neutrons. *Example:* ^{12}C and ^{14}C are isotopes of carbon. Both have 6 protons, but ^{12}C has 6 neutrons, whereas ^{14}C has 8 neutrons.
- Radioactive isotopes are widely used in medicine for both diagnosis and treatment. Radiometric data uses the rate of decay or half-life of certain isotopes to determine the ages of fossils and rock strata.
- The **atomic number** is the number of protons an element possesses. This number is unique to every element. (See Figure 1.1.)
- The **mass number** of an element is the sum of its protons and neutrons.

Figure 1.1   An element of the periodic table

The formation and function of molecules depend on chemical bonding between atoms (Biology, *11e: 2.3*; Focus, *2e: 2.3*)

- **Chemical bonds** are interactions between the valence electrons of different atoms. Atoms are held together by chemical bonds to form molecules.
- A **covalent bond** occurs when valence electrons are shared by two atoms.

  - **Nonpolar covalent bonds** occur when the electrons being shared are shared equally between the two atoms. *Examples*: O═O, H—H.
  - Atoms vary in their *electronegativity*, a tendency to attract electrons of a covalent bond. Oxygen and nitrogen are strongly electronegative.
  - In **polar covalent bonds**, one atom has greater electronegativity than the other, resulting in an unequal sharing of the electrons. Water (H_2O) is formed with polar covalent bonds. This results in the region around the oxygen atom being slightly negative, whereas the regions around the hydrogen atoms are slightly positive. *Example*: Refer to Figure 1.2 and note that within each molecule of H_2O the electrons are shared unequally, forming areas of partial negative and positive charges.

- **Ionic bonds** are chemical bonds resulting from the attraction between oppositely charged ions. Table salt is formed by ionic bonds between positively charged sodium ions and negatively charged chlorine ions.
- **Hydrogen bonds** are relatively weak bonds that form between the partial positively charged hydrogen atom of one molecule and the strongly electronegative

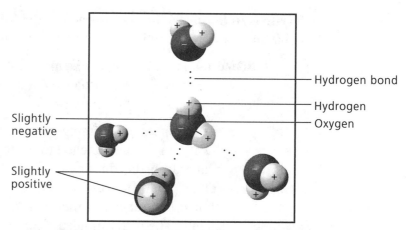

Figure 1.2 Hydrogen bonds between water molecules

oxygen or nitrogen of *another* molecule. Go to Figure 1.2 and circle each hydrogen bond. How many hydrogen bonds can be formed by a single water molecule? Hydrogen bonds play a major role in the three-dimensional shape of proteins and nucleic acids.

▎ **Van der Waals interactions** are very weak, transient connections that are the result of asymmetrical distribution of electrons within a molecule. These weak interactions contribute to the three-dimensional shape of molecules.

Chemical reactions make and break chemical bonds (Biology, *11e: 2.4;* Focus, *2e: 2.4*)

▎ A **chemical reaction** shows the **reactants**, which are the starting materials, with an arrow to indicate their conversion into the **products**, the ending materials.

Example: $6\ CO_2 + 6\ H_2O$ (reactants) $\longrightarrow C_6H_{12}O_6 + 6\ O_2$ (products)

▎ The previous chemical reaction also shows the number of molecules involved. This is the coefficient in front of each molecule. Note that the number of atoms of each element is the same on each side of the reaction.

▎ Some chemical reactions are reversible, which is indicated with a double-headed arrow: $3\ H_2 + N_2 \rightleftharpoons 2\ NH_3$.

Hydrogen bonding gives water properties that help make life possible on Earth (Biology, *11e: 3.1–3.2;* Focus, *2e: 2.5*)

▎ The **structure of water** is the key to its special properties. Water is made up of one atom of oxygen and two atoms of hydrogen, bonded to form a molecule.

▎ Water molecules are **polar**. The oxygen region of the molecule has a partial negative charge, and each hydrogen region has a partial positive charge.

▎ **Hydrogen bonds** form between water molecules. The slightly negative oxygen atom from one water molecule is attracted to the slightly positive hydrogen end of *another* water molecule.

▎ Each water molecule can form a maximum of four hydrogen bonds at a time. (Refer to Figure 1.2.)

▌ **Hydrogen bonds** are the key to each of the following properties of water and what makes water so unique.

1. **Cohesion** is the linking of like molecules. Think "water molecule joined to water molecule" and visualize a water strider being able to walk on top of a pond because of the *surface tension* resulting from this property.

   - **Adhesion** is the clinging of one substance to another. Think "water molecule attached to some other molecule," such as water droplets adhering to a glass windshield.
   - **Transpiration** is the movement of water molecules up the very thin xylem tubes and their evaporation from the stomata in plants. The water molecules cling to each other by *cohesion* and to the walls of the xylem tubes by *adhesion*.

2. Moderation of temperature is possible because of water's high specific heat.

   - **Specific heat** is the amount of heat required to raise or lower the temperature of a substance by 1°C. Relative to most other materials, the temperature of water changes less when a given amount of heat is lost or absorbed. This high specific heat makes the temperature of Earth's oceans relatively stable and able to support vast quantities of both plant and animal life.

3. Insulation of bodies of water happens when there is floating ice.

   - Water is less dense as a solid than it is as a liquid, whereas the opposite is true of most other substances. Because ice is less dense than liquid water, ice floats. This keeps larger bodies of water from freezing solid, allowing life to exist in ponds, lakes, and even oceans.

4. Water is an important *solvent*. (The substance that something is dissolved in is called the *solvent*, whereas the substance being dissolved is the *solute*. Together they are called the *solution*.)

   - **Hydrophilic** substances are water soluble. These include ionic compounds, polar molecules (for example, sugars), and some proteins.
   - **Hydrophobic** substances, such as oils, are nonpolar and do not dissolve in water.

Acidic and basic conditions affect living organisms (Biology, 11e: 3.3; Focus, 2e: 2.5)

▌ The **pH** scale runs between 0 and 14 and measures the relative acidity and alkalinity of aqueous solutions. (See Figure 1.3.)

Figure 1.3   pH scale

- **Acids** have an excess of H^+ ions and a pH below 7.0. $[H^+] > [OH^-]$
- **Bases** have an excess of OH^- ions and a pH above 7.0. $[H^+] < [OH^-]$
- Pure water is neutral, which means it has a pH of 7.0. $[H^+] = [OH^-]$
- **Buffers** are substances that minimize changes in pH. They accept H^+ from a solution when hydrogen molecules are in excess and donate H^+ when hydrogen molecules are depleted. Buffering compounds are essential in living tissues to minimize pH changes.
- **Carbonic acid (H_2CO_3)** is an important buffer in living systems. It moderates pH changes in blood plasma and the ocean.

Carbon and the Molecular Diversity of Life
(Biology, *11e: Chapters 4, 5;* Focus, *2e: Chapter 3*)

YOU MUST KNOW

- The properties of carbon that make it so important.
- The role of **dehydration reactions** in the formation of organic compounds and **hydrolysis** in the digestion of organic compounds.
- How the sequence and subcomponents of the four groups of organic compounds determine their properties.
- The cellular functions of carbohydrates, lipids, proteins, and nucleic acids.
- How changes in these organic molecules would affect their function.
- The four structural levels of proteins and how changes at any level can affect the activity of the protein.
- How proteins reach their final shape (**conformation**), the **denaturing** impact that heat and pH can have on protein structure, and how these changes may affect the organism.
- Directionality influences structure and function of polymers, such as nucleic acids (5′ and 3′ ends) and proteins (amino and carboxyl ends).

Carbon and molecular diversity (Biology, *11e: 4.1–4.3;* Focus, *2e: 3.1*)

- The major elements of life are C, H, O, N, S, and P—sometimes recalled with an acronym that forms a person's name: ***P.S. COHN***.
- *All* **organic compounds** contain carbon, and most also contain hydrogen.
- Carbon is unparalleled in its ability to form molecules that are large, complex, and diverse. Why?
    - It has 4 valence electrons.
    - It can form up to 4 covalent bonds.
    - These bonds can be single, double, or triple covalent bonds.
    - It can form large molecules.
    - These molecules can be chains, ring-shaped, or branched.
- **Isomers** are molecules that have the same molecular formula but differ in their arrangement of these atoms. These differences can result in molecules

that are very different in their biological activities. *Examples*: glucose and fructose (both have the molecular formula of $C_6H_{12}O_6$).

- The distinctive properties of an organic molecule depend not only on the arrangement of its carbon skeleton but also on the various functional groups attached to that skeleton.
- The **functional groups** attached to the carbon skeleton have diverse properties. The behavior of organic molecules is dependent on the identity of their functional groups.
- The following are some common functional groups:

Functional Group Name/Structure	Organic Molecules with the Functional Group and Items of Note about the Functional Group
Hydroxyl, —OH	Alcohols such as ethanol, methanol; helps dissolve molecules such as sugars
Carboxyl, —COOH	Carboxylic acids such as fatty acids and sugars; acidic properties because it tends to ionize; source of H^+ ions
Carbonyl, >CO	Ketones and aldehydes such as sugars
Amino, —NH₂	Amines such as amino acids
Phosphate, PO₃	Organic phosphates, including ATP, DNA, and phospholipids
Sulfhydryl, —SH	Found in the amino acid cysteine; forms disulfide bridges in proteins
Methyl, —CH₃	Addition of a methyl group affects expression of genes

Macromolecules are polymers, built from monomers (Biology, *11e: 5.1;* Focus, *2e: 3.2*)

- **Polymers** are long chain molecules made of repeating subunits called **monomers**. *Examples*: Starch is a polymer composed of glucose monomers. Proteins are polymers composed of amino acid monomers. (See Figure 1.4.)
- **Dehydration reactions** create polymers from monomers. Two monomers are joined by removing one molecule of water. *Example*: $C_6H_{12}O_6 + C_6H_{12}O_6 \rightarrow C_{12}H_{22}O_{11} + H_2O$.
- **Hydrolysis** occurs when water is added to split large molecules. This reaction is the reverse of dehydration.

Figure 1.4   Synthesis and breakdown of polymers

Carbohydrates serve as fuel and building material (Biology, *11e: 5.2;* Focus, *2e: 3.3*)

- **Carbohydrates** include both simple sugars (glucose, fructose, galactose, etc.) and polymers such as starch made from these and other subunits. All carbohydrates exist in a ratio of 1 carbon:2 hydrogen:1 oxygen or CH_2O.
- **Monosaccharides** are the monomers of carbohydrates. *Examples*: glucose ($C_6H_{12}O_6$) and ribose ($C_5H_{10}O_5$). Notice the 1:2:1 ratio discussed in the previous bullet point.
- **Polysaccharides** are polymers of monosaccharides. *Examples*: starch, cellulose, and glycogen.
- Both starches and cellulose are composed of glucose monomers, but the different ring forms (alpha and beta) and linkages between them result in very

different functions. For example, you can digest starch, which has 1–4 alpha linkages, and not cellulose, which has 1–4 beta linkages. Keep this in mind: *Change the structure, change the function!*

▌ Two functions of polysaccharides are **energy storage** and **structural support**.

1. Energy-storage polysaccharides

- **Starch** is a storage polysaccharide found in plants (for example, potatoes).
- **Glycogen** is a storage polysaccharide found in animals (vertebrate muscle cells and liver cells).

2. Structural support polysaccharides

- **Cellulose** is a major component of plant cell walls.
- **Chitin** is found in the exoskeleton of arthropods, such as lobsters and insects, and the cell walls of fungi. It gives cockroaches their "crunch."

Lipids are a diverse group of hydrophobic molecules (Biology, *11e: 5.4;* Focus, *2e: 3.4*)

▌ Lipids are all **hydrophobic**. They aren't polymers because they are assembled from a variety of components. *Examples*: **waxes, oils, fats,** and **steroids**.

▌ **Fats** (also called triglycerides) are made up of a **glycerol** molecule and three **fatty acid** molecules.

▌ **Fatty acids** include hydrocarbon chains of variable lengths. These chains are nonpolar and therefore hydrophobic.

▌ **Saturated fatty acids**

- ▬ have no double bonds between carbons
- ▬ tend to pack solidly at room temperature
- ▬ are linked to cardiovascular disease
- ▬ are commonly produced by animals
- ▬ *Examples*: butter and lard

▌ **Unsaturated fatty acids**

- ▬ have some C=C (carbon double bonds); this results in kinks
- ▬ tend to be liquid at room temperature
- ▬ are commonly produced by plants
- ▬ *Examples*: corn oil and olive oil

▌ **Functions of lipids**

- ▬ *Energy storage*: Fats store more than twice as many calories per gram as carbohydrates!
- ▬ *Protection* of vital organs and *insulation*: In humans and other mammals, fat is stored in adipose cells.

▌ **Phospholipids** make up cell membranes. They

- ▬ have a hydrophilic (polar) head that includes a phosphate group.
- ▬ have two fatty acid tails, which are hydrophobic.

■ are arranged in a bilayer in forming the cell membrane, with the hydrophilic heads pointing toward the watery cytosol or extracellular environment and hydrophobic tails sandwiched in between (Figure 1.5).

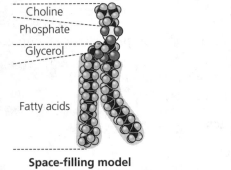
Choline
Phosphate
Glycerol
Fatty acids
Space-filling model

WATER
Hydrophilic head
Hydrophobic tails
Phospholipid symbol
Hydrophobic tails
Hydrophilic head
Phospholipid bilayer

Figure 1.5   The structure of a phospholipid

■ **Steroids** are made up of four rings that are fused together.

■ **Cholesterol** is a steroid. It is a common component of cell membranes.
■ **Estrogen** and **testosterone** are steroid hormones.

Proteins include a diversity of structures, resulting in a wide range of functions (Biology, *11e: 5.4;* Focus, *2e: 3.5*)

■ **Proteins** are polymers made up of amino acid monomers.
■ **Amino acids** contain a central carbon bonded to a carboxyl group (COOH) at one end, an amino group (NH_2) at the other end, a hydrogen atom, and an R group (variable group or side chain). (See Figure 1.6.)
■ **Peptide bonds** link amino acids. They are formed by dehydration synthesis between the amino and carboxyl groups of adjacent monomers.
■ **There are four levels of protein structure** (Figure 1.7):

α carbon
R
H
H
N
C
C
O
OH
H
Amino group
Carboxyl group

Figure 1.6   The structure of an amino acid

■ **Primary structure** is the unique sequence in which amino acids are joined.
■ **Secondary structure** refers to one of two three-dimensional shapes that are the result of hydrogen bonding between members of the polypeptide backbone (not the amino acid side chains).

■ **Alpha (α) helix** has a coiled shape, much like a slinky.
■ **Beta (β) pleated sheet** has an accordion shape.

■ **Tertiary structure** has a complex globular shape resulting from interactions between the side chains (R groups), such as hydrophobic interactions, van der Waals interactions, hydrogen bonds, and disulfide bridges.

■ Globular proteins such as enzymes are held in position by these R group interactions.

■ **Quaternary structure** refers to the association of two or more polypeptide chains into one large protein. Hemoglobin is a globular protein with quaternary structure because it is composed of four polypeptide chains.

Primary structure   Secondary structure   Tertiary structure   Quaternary structure

Figure 1.7   Levels of protein structure

- **Protein shape is crucial to protein function.** When a protein does not fold properly, its function is changed. This can be the result of a single amino acid substitution, such as in the abnormal hemoglobin typical of sickle-cell disease.

- A protein is **denatured** when it loses its shape and ability to function because of **heat**, a **change in pH**, or some other disturbance. Keep this in mind: *Change the structure, change the function!*

CONNECT WITH THE CURRICULUM FRAMEWORK

Here is LO 4.1: The student is able to explain the connection between the sequence and the subcomponents of a biologic polymer and its properties. How can you prepare for questions on this objective?

Consider each category of organic compound. Describe a specific change that might occur in a molecule in each category, and explain how this might affect the original function of the molecule.

Nucleic acids store, transmit, and help express hereditary information (Biology, *11e: 5.5*; Focus, *2e: 3.6*)

Figure 1.8   The components of nucleic acids

- **DNA** (deoxyribonucleic acid) and **RNA** (ribonucleic acid) are the two nucleic acids. Their monomers are nucleotides.

- **Nucleotides** are made up of three parts (Figure 1.8):

  - **Nitrogenous base** (adenine, thymine, cytosine, and guanine in DNA; adenine, uracil, cytosine, and guanine in RNA)
  - **Pentose** (5-carbon) **sugar** (deoxyribose in DNA or ribose in RNA)
  - **Phosphate group**

- **DNA** is the molecule of heredity.

  - It is a double-stranded helix.
  - Its nucleotides are adenine, thymine, cytosine, and guanine.
  - Adenine nucleotides will hydrogen bond to thymine nucleotides; cytosine nucleotides will hydrogen bond to guanine nucleotides.

- **RNA** is single-stranded. Its nucleotides are adenine, uracil, cytosine, and guanine. Note that it does not have thymine.

■ Nucleic acids have directionality, determined by the 3′ and 5′ carbons of the sugar. This will determine the direction of DNA replication and transcription (5′ to 3′).

SUMMARY TABLE

Macromolecules/Polymers	Monomers/Components	Examples	Functions
Carbohydrates	Monosaccharides	Sugars, starch, glycogen, cellulose	Energy, energy storage, structural
Lipids	Fatty acids and glycerol	Fats, oils	Important energy source, insulation, phospholipids of plasma membrane
Proteins	Amino acids	Hemoglobin, lipase	Enzymes, movement, membrane receptors
Nucleic acids	Nucleotides (sugar, phosphate group, nitrogenous base)	DNA, RNA	Genetic information, code for amino acid sequences

Level 1: Knowledge/Comprehension Questions

The Level 1, Knowledge/Comprehension, questions review essential content knowledge but don't represent the type of question you will see on the AP Exam. The Level 2, Application/Synthesis, questions are similar to those you will see on the exam.

1. Which list of components characterizes RNA?
   (A) a phosphate group, deoxyribose, and uracil
   (B) a phosphate group, ribose, and uracil
   (C) a phosphate group, ribose, and thymine
   (D) a phosphate group, deoxyribose, and uracil

2. Which of the following molecules would contain a polar covalent bond?
   (A) Cl_2
   (B) NaCl
   (C) H_2O
   (D) CH_4

3. Which of the following statements regarding carbon is *false*?
   (A) Carbon has the capacity to form polar covalent bonds with hydrogen.
   (B) Carbon has the ability to form covalent bonds with up to four other atoms.
   (C) Carbon has the capacity to form single and double bonds.
   (D) Carbon has the ability to bond together to form extensive branched or unbranched "carbon skeletons."

4. Because of the unique properties of water associated with hydrogen bonding, water evaporates from pores on the leaves of plants and draws up water molecules in a continuous chain from the roots up through the vascular tissues of plants. Which of these groups of terms describes the process and properties of water that explain this?
   (A) adhesion, cohesion, and translocation
   (B) adhesion, cohesion, and transcription
   (C) cohesion, hybridization, and transpiration
   (D) cohesion, adhesion, and transpiration

Directions: Questions 5–8 consist of four lettered choices followed by a list of numbered phrases or sentences. For each numbered phrase or sentence, select the one choice that is most closely related to it. Each choice may be used once, more than once, or not at all.

Questions 5–8
   (A) Lipids
   (B) Peptide bonds
   (C) Alpha helix
   (D) Cellulose

5. The major class of biological molecules that are not polymers

6. Linkages between the monomers of proteins

7. A secondary structure of proteins

8. A structural carbohydrate found in plants

9. Hydrolysis is involved in which of the following?
   (A) formation of starch, a polysaccharide, from monomers of glucose
   (B) hydrogen bond formation between nitrogen bases of nucleic acids
   (C) peptide bond formation between amino acids to form a protein
   (D) the digestion of sucrose, a disaccharide to its monomers of glucose and fructose

10. The process by which protein conformation is lost or broken down is
    (A) dehydration synthesis.
    (B) translation.
    (C) denaturation.
    (D) hydrolysis.

11. An organic compound that is composed of carbon, hydrogen, and oxygen in a 1:2:1 ratio is known as a
    (A) lipid.
    (B) carbohydrate.
    (C) protein.
    (D) nucleic acid.

12. Which of the macromolecules below could form structural parts of the cell, be enzymes, or be involved in cell movement or communication?
    (A) nucleic acids
    (B) proteins
    (C) lipids
    (D) carbohydrates

13. The plasma membrane is composed of several different macromolecules. Which macromolecule serves as the fluid interface between the intracellular and extracellular environments?
    (A) proteins
    (B) phospholipids
    (C) carbohydrates
    (D) cholesterol

14. The partial negative charge at one end of a water molecule is attracted to a partial positive charge of another water molecule. What is this type of attraction called?
    (A) a polar covalent bond
    (B) an ionic bond
    (C) a hydration shell
    (D) a hydrogen bond

15. Polymers of carbohydrates and proteins are all synthesized from monomers by which of the following processes?
    (A) the joining of monosaccharides
    (B) hydrolysis
    (C) dehydration reactions
    (D) ionic bonding of monomers

16. If the pH of a solution is decreased from 7 to 6, it means that the concentration of
    (A) H^+ has decreased to 1/10 of what it was at pH 7.
    (B) H^+ has increased to 10 times what it was at pH 7.
    (C) OH^- has increased to 10 times what it was at pH 7.
    (D) OH^- has increased to 1/7 of what it was.

17. Recall the structure of a typical amino acid and how the molecule has two distinct "ends." Which two functional groups are always found in amino acids?
    (A) amine and sulfhydryl
    (B) hydroxyl and carboxyl
    (C) carboxyl and amine
    (D) phosphate group and nitrogenous base

Level 2: Application/Analysis/Synthesis Questions

1. The hydrogen bonds shown in this figure are each between

   Hydrogen bond

   (A) two hydrogen atoms.
   (B) two oxygen atoms.
   (C) an oxygen and a hydrogen atom of the same water molecule.
   (D) an oxygen and a hydrogen atom of different water molecules.

2. The tremendous variation and unique properties of proteins are most likely a result of
   (A) interactions between R groups of the amino acids.
   (B) hydrogen bonds linking amino acids.
   (C) the utilization of hundreds of different amino acids in the primary structure of the protein.
   (D) peptide bonds linking amino and carboxyl groups.

Question 3 refers to the following art.

3. If the dipeptide in the figure were to be digested, how would it be reduced to amino acids?
   (A) by a dehydration reaction, which removes water
   (B) by reduction in digestive fluid pH in the stomach
   (C) through the removal of functional groups at either end
   (D) through a hydrolysis reaction in which water is added

4. A globular blood protein that transports vitamin A is 127 amino acids long. How many water molecules were produced in the synthesis of the protein, and by what chemical process were the amino acids joined together?
   (A) 127; hydrolysis
   (B) 127; dehydration
   (C) 126; hydrolysis
   (D) 126; dehydration

After reading the following paragraph, answer questions 5 and 6.

You're the manager of a factory that produces enzyme-washed blue jeans (the enzymes lighten the color of the denim, giving a faded appearance). When the most recent batch of fabric came out of the enzyme wash, however, the color wasn't light enough to meet your standards. Your quality control laboratory wants to do some tests to determine why the wash enzymes didn't perform as expected.

5. Which hypothesis is most likely to be productive for the initial investigation?
   (A) The nucleotide chain of the enzymes may be incorrectly formed.
   (B) The dye in the fabric may have hydrolyzed the fatty acids in the enzymes.
   (C) The polysaccharides in the enzymes may have separated in the wash water.
   (D) The three-dimensional amino acid structure of the enzyme may have been altered.

6. Based on your understanding of enzyme structure, which of the following would you recommend that the lab also investigate?
   (A) the temperature of the liquid in the washing vat
   (B) washing the blue jeans in smaller vats
   (C) the manufacturer of the fabric
   (D) switching to another product for the enzyme wash

7. The molecular formula for glucose is $C_6H_{12}O_6$. What would be the molecular formula for a polymer made by joining 10 glucose molecules together by dehydration reactions?
   (A) $C_{60}H_{120}O_{60}$
   (B) $C_6H_{12}O_6$
   (C) $C_{60}H_{102}O_{51}$
   (D) $C_{60}H_{100}O_{50}$

8. Which of the following pairs of base sequences could form a short stretch of a normal double helix of DNA?
   (A) 5′-AGCA-3′ with 3′-UCGU-5′
   (B) 5′-AGCT-3′ with 5′-TCGA-3′
   (C) 5′-GCGC-3′ with 5′-TATA-3′
   (D) 5′-ATGC-3′ with 5′-GCAT-3′

9. Water is an excellent solvent. Select the property that justifies this statement.
   (A) As a polar molecule, it can surround and dissolve ionic and polar molecules.
   (B) It forms ionic bonds with ions, hydrogen bonds with polar molecules, and hydrophobic interactions with nonpolar molecules.
   (C) It forms hydrogen bonds with itself so cohesion is possible.
   (D) It is liquid and will adhere to many substances.

10. If three molecules of a fatty acid (each with a formula of $C_{16}H_{22}O_2$) are joined to a molecule of glycerol ($C_3H_8O_3$), the resulting molecule would have the formula
   (A) $C_{48}H_{66}O_6$.
   (B) $C_{48}H_{60}O_3$.
   (C) $C_{51}H_{68}O_6$.
   (D) $C_{51}H_{74}O_9$.

Use the following data chart and reading to answer questions 11–15.

Analyzing Polypeptide Sequence Data

Species	Alignment of Amino Acid Sequences of β-globin					
Human	1 VHLTPEEKSA	VTALWGKVNV	DEVGGEALGR	LLVVYPWTQR	FFESFGDLST	PDAVMGNPKV
Monkey	1 VHLTPEEKNA	VTTLWGKVNV	DEVGGEALGR	LLLVYPWTQR	FFESFGDLSS	PDAVMGNPKV
Gibbon	1 VHLTPEEKSA	VTALWGKVNV	DEVGGEALGR	LLVVYPWTQR	FFESFGDLST	PDAVMGNPKV
Human	61 KAHGKKVLGA	FSDGLAHLDN	LKGTFATLSE	LHCDKLHVDP	ENFRLLGNVL	VCVLAHHFGK
Monkey	61 KAHGKKVLGA	FSDGLNHLDN	LKGTFAQLSE	LHCDKLHVDP	ENFRLLGNVL	VCVLAHHFGK
Gibbon	61 KAHGKKVLGA	FSDGLAHLDN	LKGTFAQLSE	LHCDKLHVDP	ENFRLLGNVL	VCVLAHHFGK
Human	121 EFTPPVQAAY	QKVVAGVANA	LAHKYH			
Monkey	121 EFTPQVQAAY	QKVVAGVANA	LAHKYH			
Gibbon	121 EFTPQVQAAY	QKVVAGVANA	LAHKYH			

Data from http://www.ncbi.nlm.nih.gov/protein/AAA21113.1 (Human);
http://www.ncbi.nlm.nih.gov/protein/122634 (rhesus monkey);
http://www.ncbi.nlm.nih.gov/protein/122616 (gibbon)

DNA and polypeptide sequences from closely related species are more similar to each other than sequences from more distantly related species. In the alignment shown here, the letters give the sequences of the 146 amino acids in β-globin from humans, rhesus monkeys, and gibbons. Because a complete sequence would not fit on one line, the sequences are broken into segments. The sequences for the three different species are aligned for ease of comparison. For example, you can see that, for all three species, the first amino acid is "V" (valine) and the 146th amino acid is "H" (histidine).

Scan the aligned sequences, letter by letter, noting any positions where the amino acids in the monkey or gibbon sequences do not match the human sequence.

11. How many amino acids differ between the monkey and the human sequences?
(A) 2
(B) 6
(C) 8
(D) 10

12. What percentage of monkey β-globin amino acids is *identical* to the human sequence? (This is called the percentage identity between the monkey and human β-globin sequences.)
(A) 5.48%
(B) 94.5%
(C) 95.9%
(D) 98.6%

13. Using the same procedure, notice that humans and gibbons differ in amino acids at two locations. What percentage of gibbon β-globin amino acids is *identical* to the human sequence? (This is called the percentage identity between the gibbon and human β-globin sequences.)
(A) 1.37%
(B) 94.5%
(C) 95.9%
(D) 98.6%

14. Based on the β-globin alignment, identify the best hypothesis about how humans are related to monkeys and gibbons.
    (A) Gibbons are more closely related to humans than monkeys are because the gibbon β-globin sequence is a closer match with the human sequence.
    (B) Monkeys are more closely related to humans than gibbons are because the monkey β-globin sequence has the lower percentage identity with humans.
    (C) Both monkeys and gibbons are equally unrelated to humans because neither monkeys nor gibbons have the exact same β-globin sequence as humans.
    (D) Both monkeys and gibbons are equally related to humans because they both have less than a 10% difference in β-globin sequence with humans.

15. What other evidence could you use to analyze evolutionary relatedness among gibbons, monkeys, and humans?
    (A) the amino acid sequences of other proteins from gibbons, monkeys, and humans
    (B) the β-globin amino acid sequence from gorillas
    (C) the frequency of albinism (mutants that lack hair and skin pigment) in populations of gibbons, monkeys, and humans
    (D) the amount of habitat overlap among gibbons, monkeys, and humans

Grid-in Questions

The following questions require a numerical response.

1. If nine molecules of a monosaccharide with the formula $C_6H_{12}O_6$ are assembled to produce a complex carbohydrate, how many atoms of hydrogen will be in the final polymer? Answer to the nearest whole number.

2. What is the difference between the number of H^+ ions in a solution with a pH of 2 compared with a solution at a pH of 6? If appropriate, include a negative sign in your answer.

Free-Response Question

1. *The selectively permeable plasma membrane is composed of phospholipids and protein, which allow for its unique functions.*

   (a) **Describe** the structure and properties of phospholipids and *explain* the important roles of phospholipids in the plasma membrane.
   (b) **Predict** how the normal function of the plasma membrane would be altered if all phospholipids were saturated, resulting in fatty acid tails without kinks or bends. **Explain** the effect this would have on plants located in very cold regions.
   (c) **Proteins** are an important component of the cell membrane. **Describe** two specific functions of proteins in the membrane.
   (d) **Explain** the role of each type of protein you select for Part C based on the structure and properties of a protein.

The Cell

A Tour of the Cell

(Biology, *11e: Chapter 6;* Focus, *2e: Chapter 4*)

> **YOU MUST KNOW**
>
> - Three differences between prokaryotic and eukaryotic cells.
> - The structure and function of organelles common to plant and animal cells.
> - The structure and function of organelles found only in plant cells or only in animal cells.
> - How different cell types show differences in subcellular components.
> - How internal membranes and organelles contribute to cell functions. (LO 2.13)
> - How cell size and shape affect the overall rate of nutrient intake and waste elimination. (LO 6.2)

Eukaryotic cells have internal membranes that compartmentalize their functions (Biology, *11e: 6.2;* Focus, *2e: 4.2*)

▮ The following table organizes the major characteristics of prokaryotic and eukaryotic cells.

Characteristics	Prokaryotic Cells	Eukaryotic Cells
Plasma membrane	Yes	Yes
Ribosomes	Yes	Yes
Membrane-bound organelles in cytosol	No	Yes
Nucleus	No	Yes
Size	1 µm–10 µm	10 µm–100 µm

▮ Prokaryotic cells are found in the domains Bacteria and Archaea. Members of the domain Eukarya have eukaryotic cells. Animals, fungi, plants, and protists all have eukaryotic cells.

▮ Three key details to remember about prokaryotic cells include the following:

- ▪ The single circular chromosome is found in a region called the nucleoid, but there is no nuclear membrane and therefore no true nucleus.
- ▪ No membrane-bound organelles are found in the cytosol. (There are ribosomes, but they are not membrane bound.)
- ▪ From the preceding table, notice how much smaller prokaryotes are than eukaryotes.

▌ Three corresponding details about eukaryotic cells:

  ▪ A membrane-enclosed nucleus contains the cell's linear chromosomes.
  ▪ Many membrane-bound organelles are found in the cytoplasm.
  ▪ On average, eukaryotes are much larger than prokaryotes.

▌ Use Figures 2.1 and 2.2 to locate each component of a plant or animal cell as they are reviewed. Notice if the cell structure is found only in animal cells, only in plant cells, or in both plant and animal cells (see Figures 6.8 and 6.9, 11e).

▌ The **plasma membrane** forms the boundary for a cell. It is selectively permeable and permits the passage of materials into and out of the cell.

▌ The plasma membrane is made up of *phospholipids*, *proteins*, and associated *carbohydrates*. These molecules determine the functions of the membrane.

▌ The *surface-area-to-volume ratio* becomes less favorable as a cell increases in size. The total volume grows proportionately more than the surface area. Because a cell acquires resources through the plasma membrane, cell size is limited.

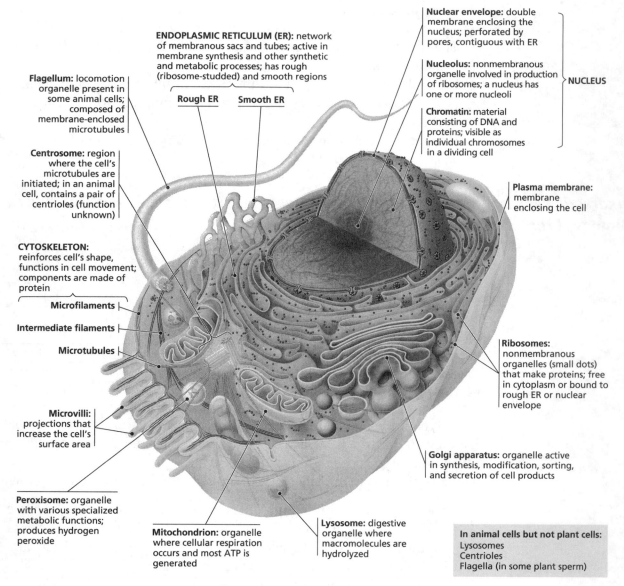

Figure 2.1   Animal Cell Structure

NUCLEUS
- Nuclear envelope
- Nucleolus
- Chromatin

Centrosome: region where the cell's microtubules are initiated; lacks centrioles in plant cells

Rough endoplasmic reticulum

Smooth endoplasmic reticulum

Ribosomes (small dots)

Central vacuole: prominent organelle in older plant cells; functions include storage, breakdown of waste products, hydrolysis of macromolecules; enlargement of vacuole is a major mechanism of plant growth

Tonoplast: membrane enclosing the central vacuole

Golgi apparatus

Microfilaments

Intermediate filaments ⎫ **CYTOSKELETON**

Microtubules

Mitochondrion

Peroxisome

Plasma membrane

Cell wall: outer layer that maintains cell's shape and protects cell from mechanical damage; made of cellulose, other polysaccharides, and protein

Wall of adjacent cell

Chloroplast: photosynthetic organelle; converts energy of sunlight to chemical energy stored in sugar molecules

Plasmodesmata: channels through cell walls that connect the cytoplasms of adjacent cells

In plant cells but not animal cells:
Chloroplasts
Central vacuole and tonoplast
Cell wall
Plasmodesmata

Figure 2.2   Plant Cell Structure

▌ You could be asked to calculate a surface-area-to-volume ratio. Do the grid-in question at the end of this topic for practice. The answers section will have the correct answer and an explanation for how to do the problem.

CONNECT WITH THE CURRICULUM FRAMEWORK

Big Idea 2

1. Be able to calculate surface-area-to-volume ratios for various cell sizes and shapes. Can you use this information to predict relative rates of diffusion into/out of the cell?

2. Explain how each of the following structures enhance exchange of molecules: root hairs, microvilli, and cristae of mitochondria.

The eukaryotic cell's genetic instructions are housed in the nucleus and carried out by the ribosomes (Biology, *11e: 6.3;* Focus, *2e: 4.3*)

▌ The **nucleus** has the following key characteristics:

  ▪ The nucleus contains most of the cell's DNA. Within the nucleus, DNA is the template to make messenger RNA (mRNA), which contains the code to produce a protein.

  ▪ The nucleus is the most noticeable organelle in the cell because of its large relative size. It is surrounded by a double membrane, the **nuclear envelope**. Note that the nuclear envelope is continuous with the rough endoplasmic reticulum. The nuclear envelope has pore structures that regulate what may enter or leave the nucleus.

  ▪ **Chromatin** is the complex of DNA and protein housed in the nucleus that is formed from the chromosomes. As a cell gets ready for cell division, the diffuse threads of chromatin condense into visible chromosomes.

  ▪ The **nucleolus** is a region of the nucleus where ribosomal RNA (rRNA) is synthesized and complexes with proteins to form ribosomal subunits.

▌ **Ribosomes** are protein factories. They are composed of rRNA and protein and are sites of protein synthesis in the cell. Each ribosome consists of a large and a small subunit.

  ▪ *Free ribosomes* float in the cytosol and generally produce proteins that are used within the cell.

  ▪ *Bound ribosomes* are attached to the endoplasmic reticulum and make proteins destined for export from the cell.

CONNECT WITH THE CURRICULUM FRAMEWORK

Big Idea 2

Consider what cell features might be present in abundance or absent in certain cells based on their functions. Questions at the end of this chapter will test your understanding of this topic.

The endomembrane system regulates protein traffic and performs metabolic functions in the cell (Biology, *11e: 6.4;* Focus, *2e: 4.4*)

▌ **Endoplasmic reticulum (ER)** makes up more than half the total membrane structure in many cells. The ER is a network of membranes and sacs whose internal area is called the *cisternal space*. There are two types of ER:

  ▪ **Smooth ER** has four primary functions: synthesis of lipids, metabolism of carbohydrates, detoxification of drugs and poisons, and storage of calcium ions. These functions vary by cell type.

  ▪ **Rough ER** is so called because its associated ribosomes make the structure appear rough under the microscope. Ribosomes associated with the ER synthesize proteins that are generally secreted by the cell. As the proteins are produced by the ER-bound ribosomes, the polypeptide chains travel across the ER membrane and into the cisternal space. Within the cisternal space, the proteins reach conformation and are packaged into *transport vesicles,* which bud off the ER and move toward the Golgi apparatus.

- The **Golgi apparatus** operates something like a warehouse: Proteins from the transport vesicles are received, sorted, and shipped. As Figures 2.1 and 2.2 show, the Golgi apparatus consists of flattened sacs of membranes arranged in stacks. Golgi stacks have polarity; the *cis* face receives vesicles, whereas the *trans* face ships vesicles. Products of the ER are modified here, and the Golgi apparatus is extensive in cells specialized for secretion.

- **Lysosomes** are membrane-bound sacs of hydrolytic enzymes that can digest large molecules, including proteins, polysaccharides, fats, and nucleic acids. They have digestive enzymes that break down macromolecules to organic monomers that are released into the cytosol and thus recycled by the cell. The digestive or hydrolytic enzymes work best in the acidic environment found in lysosomes. If a lysosome breaks open or leaks, the enzymes are not very active in the neutral pH of the cell. This is a good example of the importance of cell compartmentalization.

- **Vacuoles** are large vesicles that perform a variety of functions in different kinds of cells. *Food vacuoles* such as those formed by phagocytosis in protists are one example, and *contractile vacuoles* that maintain water balance in *Paramecia* and other protists are another example.

- **Central vacuoles** in plant cells may concentrate and contain compounds not found in the cytosol. A large central vacuole is one of the striking differences between plant and animal cells. In plants, a vacuole can make up as much as 80% of the volume of the cell.

Mitochondria and chloroplasts change energy from one form to another (Biology, *11e: 6.5;* Focus, *2e: 4.5*)

- **Mitochondria** are the sites of cellular respiration, the metabolic process that uses oxygen to generate ATP by extracting energy from sugars, fats, and other fuels. Mitochondria are found in both plant and animal cells. Study Figure 2.3 to learn the structure.

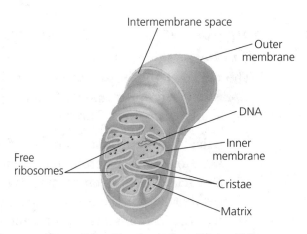

Figure 2.3   Structure of a mitochondrion

- Mitochondria consist of an *outer* and *inner membrane*. The inner membrane is highly folded. These *cristae* (folds) increase the surface area, enhancing the productivity of cellular respiration.
- The inner compartment, the *mitochondrial matrix*, is fluid filled, and many of the reactions of cellular respiration occur here.
- The mitochondrial matrix contains mitochondrial DNA as well as ribosomes.

- **Chloroplasts,** found in plants and algae, are the sites of photosynthesis. The chloroplasts' stroma contains their own DNA and ribosomes.
- The *endosymbiont theory* proposes that mitochondria and chloroplasts share a similar origin. This theory states that these organelles descended from pro-karyotic cells once engulfed by ancestors of eukaryotic cells. There are several pieces of evidence for this:

  - Both organelles have a double-membrane structure.
  - Both organelles have their own ribosomes and circular DNA molecules.
  - Both reproduce independently within the cell.

- **Peroxisomes** are single-membrane-bound compartments in the cell responsible for various metabolic functions that involve the transfer of hydrogen from compounds to oxygen, producing hydrogen peroxide (H_2O_2). Peroxisomes break down fatty acids to be sent to the mitochondria for fuel and detoxify alcohol by transferring hydrogen from the poison to oxygen.
- This is an excellent example of how the cell's compartmental structure is crucial to its functions. (EK 2.B.3) The enzymes that produce hydrogen peroxide and those that dispose of this toxic compound are separate from other cellular components that could be damaged.

WHAT'S IMPORTANT TO KNOW?

The information that follows about the cytoskeleton and cell junctions is not included in the Essential Knowledge for the AP Biology Exam, although your teacher may select illustrative examples from this material. Knowledge of this information will help you understand vital processes such as cell motility and division.

The cytoskeleton is a network of fibers that organizes structures and activities in the cell (Biology, *11e: 6.6;* Focus, *2e: 4.6*)

- The **cytoskeleton** is a network of protein fibers that runs throughout the cytoplasm, where it is responsible for support, motility, and regulation in some biochemical activities. Three types of fibers make up the cytoskeleton:

  - **Microtubules**, made of the protein tubulin, are the largest of the cytoskeleton fibers. Microtubules shape and support the cell and also serve as tracks along which organelles equipped with *motor molecules* can move. Microtubules also separate chromosomes during mitosis and meiosis (forming the spindle) and are the structural components of cilia and flagella (found primarily in animal cells).

- **Microfilaments** are composed of the protein *actin*. Much smaller than microtubules, microfilaments function in smaller-scale support. When coupled with the motor molecule *myosin*, microfilaments can be involved with movement. *Examples:* amoeboid movement, cytoplasmic streaming, and contraction of muscle cells.
- **Intermediate filaments** are slightly larger than microfilaments and smaller than microtubules. Intermediate fibers are more permanent fixtures in the cell, where they are important in maintaining the shape of the cell and fixing the position of certain organelles.

- **Centrosomes** are part of a region located near the nucleus from which microtubules grow (the area is also called the *microtubule-organizing center*). Centrosomes contain centrioles in animal cells.
- **Centrioles** are located within the centrosomes of animal cells, where they replicate before cell division.
- A specialized arrangement of microtubules is responsible for the beating of flagella and cilia.

- **Flagella** are usually long and few in number. Many unicellular eukaryotic organisms are propelled through the water by flagella, as are the sperm of animals, algae, and some plants.
- **Cilia** are usually much shorter and more numerous than flagella. Cilia can also be used in locomotion or, when held in place as part of a tissue layer, can move fluid over the surface of the tissue. For example, the lining of the trachea moves mucus-trapped debris out of the lungs in this manner.

- Although different in length, number per cell, and beating pattern, cilia and flagella share a common ultrastructure. Nearly all eukaryotic cilia and flagella have nine pairs of microtubules surrounding a central core of two microtubules. This arrangement is referred to as the "9 + 2" pattern.

Extracellular components and connections between cells help coordinate cellular activities (Biology, *11e: 6.7;* Focus, *2e: 4.7*)

- The **cell wall** of a plant protects the plant and helps maintain its shape. It is outside the plasma membrane. The primary component of cell walls is the carbohydrate *cellulose*.
- Prokaryotes and fungi also have cell walls, although they are not formed of cellulose.
- **Plasmodesmata** are channels that perforate adjacent plant cell walls and allow the passage of some molecules from cell to cell.
- The **extracellular matrix (ECM)** of animal cells is situated just outside the plasma membrane; it is composed of glycoproteins secreted by the cell (most prominent of which is collagen). The ECM greatly strengthens tissues and serves as a conduit for transmitting external stimuli into the cell, which can turn genes on and modify biochemical activity.
- Animal cells have three types of intercellular junctions:

- **Tight junctions** are sections of animal cell membrane where two neighboring cells are fused, making the membranes watertight.

- **Desmosomes** fasten adjacent animal cells together, functioning like rivets to fasten cells into strong sheets.
- **Gap junctions** provide channels between adjacent animal cells through which ions, sugars, communication molecules, and other small molecules can pass.

STUDY TIP Know the structure and function of each organelle and whether it is found in a plant cell or an animal cell, or both. Be able to predict and justify how a change in a cellular organelle would affect the function of the entire cell or organism.

Membrane Structure and Function
(Biology, *11e: Chapter 7*; Focus, *2e: Chapter 5*)

YOU MUST KNOW

- Why membranes are selectively permeable.
- The role of phospholipids, proteins, and carbohydrates in membranes.
- How water will move when a cell is placed in an isotonic, hypertonic, or hypotonic solution and be able to predict the effect of different environments on the organism.
- How electrochemical gradients and proton gradients are formed and function in cells.

Cellular membranes are fluid mosaics of lipids and proteins
(Biology, *11e: 7.1*; Focus, *2e: 5.1*)

- The **plasma membrane** is *selectively permeable*; that is, it allows some substances to cross it more easily than others.
- Membranes are predominantly made of phospholipids and proteins held together by weak interactions that cause the membrane to be fluid. The *fluid mosaic model* of the cell membrane describes the membrane as fluid, with proteins embedded in or associated with the phospholipid bilayer. Figure 2.4 shows the current model of an animal cell's plasma membrane. Find each part of the membrane according to the following description of the three primary organic molecules of the membrane:

  - The **phospholipids** in the membrane provide a hydrophobic barrier that separates the cell from its liquid environment. The hydrophilic phosphate portions of the phospholipids are oriented toward the aqueous inside and outside environments of cells, whereas the hydrophobic fatty acids face each other in a double layer (the *bilayer*) in the interior. Hydrophilic molecules cannot easily enter the cell, but hydrophobic molecules can enter much more easily—hence the selectively permeable nature of the membrane.
  - There are **proteins** completely embedded in the membrane, including some that span the membrane completely. These may serve as transport channels to move materials across the hydrophobic interior

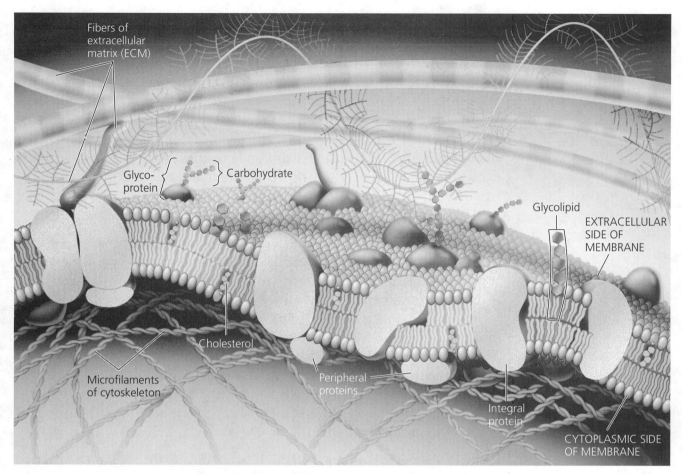

Figure 2.4   Structure of an animal cell's plasma membrane

of the phospholipid bilayer or as molecular receptors to bind to signaling molecules (ligands). Peripheral proteins are loosely bound to the membrane's surface. An example would be a G protein, which can move along the membrane when a ligand binds a G protein-coupled receptor. (See Figure 2.6 on page 54.)

- **Carbohydrates** on the membrane are crucial in cell-cell recognition, which is important in the sorting of cells into tissues in an animal embryo and is also the basis for rejection of foreign cells by the immune system.

Membrane structure results in selective permeability (Biology, *11e: 7.2;* Focus, *2e: 5.2*)

- Nonpolar molecules—such as hydrocarbons, carbon dioxide, and oxygen—are hydrophobic and can dissolve in the hydrophobic interior of the phospholipid bilayer and cross the membrane easily.
- The hydrophobic core of the membrane impedes the passage of ions and polar molecules, which are hydrophilic. However, hydrophilic substances can avoid the lipid bilayer by passing through **transport proteins** that span the membrane (see Figure 2.4).
- Perhaps the most important molecule to move across the membrane is water. Water moves through special transport proteins termed **aquaporins**. Aquaporins greatly accelerate the speed (three billion water molecules per aquaporin per second!) at which water can cross membranes.

Passive transport is diffusion of a substance across a membrane with no energy investment (Biology, *11e: 7.3*; Focus, *2e: 5.3*)

▌ In **passive diffusion,** a substance travels from where it is more concentrated to where it is less concentrated, diffusing down its **concentration gradient**. Hydrocarbons, carbon dioxide, and oxygen (O_2) are hydrophobic substances that can pass easily across the cell membrane by passive diffusion. This type of diffusion does not require work to be done, and it relies only on the thermal motion energy intrinsic to the molecule in question. It is called "passive" because the cell expends no energy in moving the substances.

▌ The diffusion of water across a selectively permeable membrane is **osmosis**. A cell has one of three water relationships with the environment around it.

- ▪ In an **isotonic solution**, there will be no net movement of water across the plasma membrane. Water crosses the membrane at the same rate in both directions.
- ▪ In a **hypertonic solution**, a cell will lose water to its surroundings. The *hyper-* prefix refers to more solutes in the water around the cell–hence the movement of water to the higher (hyper) concentration of solutes. In this case, the cell loses water to the environment, shrivels, and may die.
- ▪ In a **hypotonic solution**, water will enter the cell faster than it leaves. The *hypo-* prefix refers to fewer solutes in the water around the cell— hence the movement of water into the cell where solutes are more heavily concentrated. In this case, the cell will swell and may burst.

▌ Be sure to watch the wording: Is the cell hypertonic to the solution it is placed in, or is the surrounding solution hypertonic to the cell? In the first example, water moves into the cell, whereas in the second example water moves out of the cell. Remember this: Water moves *from* a hypotonic solution *to* a hypertonic solution. **Hypo→Hyper**

> **STUDY TIP** It is likely that you will do an investigation or lab that focuses on osmosis and diffusion. Work with these ideas until you can predict the direction of water movement based on the concentration of solutes inside and outside the cell.

▌ **Ions** and **polar molecules** cannot pass easily across the membrane. The process by which ions and hydrophilic substances diffuse across the cell membrane with the help of transport proteins is called **facilitated diffusion**. Transport proteins are specific (like enzymes) for the substances they transport. They work in one of two ways:

- ▪ They provide a hydrophilic channel through which the molecules in question can pass.
- ▪ They bind loosely to the molecules in question and carry them through the membrane.

Active transport uses energy to move solutes against their gradients
(Biology, *11e: 7.4*; Focus, *2e: 5.4*)

▌ In **active transport**, substances are moved against their concentration gradient—that is, from the region where they are *less* concentrated to the region where they are *more* concentrated. This type of transport requires energy, usually in the form of ATP.

▌ A common example of active transport is the **sodium-potassium pump**. This transmembrane protein pumps sodium out of the cell and potassium into the cell. The sodium-potassium pump is necessary for proper nerve transmission and is a major energy consumer in your body as you read this.

▌ The inside of the cell is negatively charged compared with outside the cell. The difference in electric charge across a membrane is expressed in voltage and termed the **membrane potential**. Because the inside of the cell is negatively charged, positively charged ions on the outside, such as sodium, are attracted to the negative charges inside the cell. Thus, two forces drive the diffusion of ions across a membrane:

  ▪ *A chemical force*, which is the ion's concentration gradient.
  ▪ *A voltage gradient* across the membrane, which attracts positively charged ions and repels negatively charged ions.

This combination of forces acting on an ion forms an **electrochemical gradient**.

> **STUDY TIP** Both photosynthesis and cellular respiration, the topics of two upcoming chapters, utilize electrochemical (proton) gradients as potential energy sources to generate ATP. By carefully studying electrochemical gradients now, you will be in a good position to understand more complex processes later.

▌ In **cotransport**, an ATP pump that transports a specific solute indirectly drives the active transport of other substances. In this process, the substance that was initially pumped across the membrane—an H^+ pumped by a proton pump, for example—can do work as it moves back across the membrane by diffusion and brings with it a second compound, such as sucrose, against its gradient.

PRACTICE THE PRACTICE: Interpreting Diagrams and Making Predictions

To review transport, try your hand at the following questions using Figure 2.5.

1. Which figure (I, II, III, or IV) represents *active transport?* There are two ways you should be able to tell.
2. Which figure shows *simple diffusion?*
3. Which figure shows *facilitated diffusion* with a *carrier protein?*
4. Which figure shows *facilitated diffusion* with a *channel protein?*
5. Predict the effect many additional triangle-shaped molecules to the lower portion of Diagram A would have on the net movement of molecules through Figure II.
6. Modify Figure I to show net equilibrium.

You can find answers on the next page.

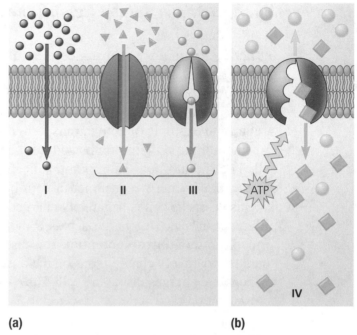

Figure 2.5   Passive and active transport

Bulk transport across the plasma membrane occurs by exocytosis and endocytosis (Biology, *11e: 7.5;* Focus, *2e: 5.5*)

▌ Large molecules are moved across the cell membrane through exocytosis and endocytosis.

- ▪ In **exocytosis**, vesicles from the cell's interior fuse with the cell membrane, expelling their contents.
- ▪ In **endocytosis**, the cell forms new vesicles from the plasma membrane; this is basically the reverse of exocytosis, and this process allows the cell to take in macromolecules. Examples of endocytosis include the engulfing of foreign particles by white blood cells or amoebas.

Answers to questions for Figure 2.5:

1. IV (It shows the use of ATP and molecules being moved against a concentration gradient.)
2. I
3. III
4. II
5. The net movement of molecules through Figure II would stop when there are more molecules in the lower compartment as molecules move from a region of high concentration to a region of lower concentration.
6. Your diagram should show numerous round molecules in the lower compartment and arrows in both directions. At equilibrium, molecules continue to move.

Cell Communication

(Biology, *11e: Chapter 11;* Focus, *2e: 5.6*)

> ## YOU MUST KNOW
>
> - The three stages of cell communication: reception, transduction, and response.
> - How a receptor protein recognizes signal molecules and starts transduction.
> - How a cell signal is amplified by a phosphorylation cascade.
> - An example of a second messenger and its role in a signal transduction pathway.
> - How a cell response in the nucleus turns on genes, whereas in the cytoplasm a response activates enzymes.
> - Why apoptosis is important to normal functioning of multicellular organisms.

External signals are converted to responses within the cell (Biology, *11e: 11.1;* Focus, *2e: 5.6*)

▌ In signaling, animal cells communicate by direct contact or by secreting local regulators, such as growth factors or neurotransmitters. There are three stages of cell signaling.

   ▪ **Reception**—the target cell's detection of a signal molecule coming from outside the cell

   ▪ **Transduction**—the conversion of the signal to a form that can bring about a specific cellular response

   ▪ **Response**—the specific cellular response to the signal molecule

Reception: A signaling molecule binds to a receptor protein, causing it to change shape (Biology, *11e: 11.2;* Focus, *2e: 5.6*)

▌ The binding between a signal molecule (**ligand**) and a **receptor** is highly specific. A conformational change in a receptor is often the initial transduction of the signal. Receptors are found in two places:

   ▪ **Intracellular receptors** are found inside the plasma membrane in the cytoplasm or nucleus. The signal molecule must cross the plasma membrane and therefore must be hydrophobic, like the steroid hormone testosterone.

   ▪ **Plasma membrane receptors** bind to water-soluble ligands.

▌ A **G-protein-coupled receptor** is a membrane receptor that works with the help of a **G protein**. Examine Figure 2.6 to review how these receptors work.

   ▪ Step 1: The ligand or signaling molecule has bound to the G-protein-coupled receptor. This causes a conformational change in the receptor so that it may now bind to an inactive G protein, causing a GTP (guanosine triphosphate) to displace the GDP (guanosine diphosphate). This activates the G protein.

- Step 2: The G protein binds to a specific enzyme and activates it. When the enzyme is activated, it can trigger the next step in a pathway leading to a cellular response. All the molecular shape changes are temporary. To continue the cellular response, new signal molecules are required.

CONNECT WITH THE CURRICULUM FRAMEWORK

Big Idea 3/EK 3.D: Cells communicate by generating, transmitting, and receiving chemical signals.

Cell-to-cell communication is found in all biological systems and shared across evolutionary lines of descent. Three examples of chemical signaling pathways include G-protein-coupled receptors, ligand-gated ion channels, and receptor tyrosine kinases. Be able to describe one of these pathways, including how a signal is converted into a cellular response. (LO 3.33, LO 3.36)

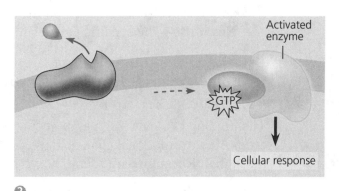

Figure 2.6   G protein-coupled receptor

- The **receptor tyrosine kinases** are a second type of membrane protein. Examine Figure 2.7 to review how these proteins function (this is not discussed in *Focus* but is explained next).

  - Step 1 shows the binding of signal molecules to the receptors and the subsequent formation of a dimer. In the dimer configuration, each tyrosine kinase adds a phosphate from an ATP molecule. (Kinases are enzymes that phosphorylate their substrate.)

1

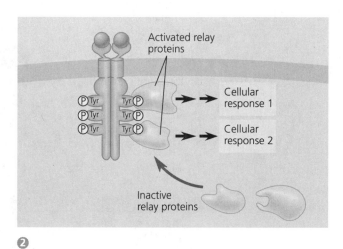

2

Figure 2.7   Receptor tyrosine kinase

- ■ Step 2 shows the fully activated receptor protein as it initiates a unique cellular response for each phosphorylated tyrosine.
- ■ The ability of a single ligand to activate multiple cellular responses is a key difference between G-protein-coupled receptors and receptor tyrosine kinases.

▮ Specific signal molecules cause **ligand-gated ion channels** in a membrane to open or close, regulating the flow of specific ions. When the ligand opens the gate and ions flow into the cell, the change in ion concentration can result in a change in cell activity. See Figure 2.8.

Transduction: Cascades of molecular interactions relay signals from receptors to target molecules in the cell (Biology, *11e: 11.3;* Focus, *2e: 5.6*)

▮ Signal transduction pathways often involve a **phosphorylation cascade**. Because the pathway is usually a multistep one, the possibility of greatly amplifying the signal exists. At each step, enzymes called **protein kinases** phosphorylate and thereby activate many proteins at the next level. This cascade of phosphorylation greatly enhances the signal, allowing for a large cellular response.

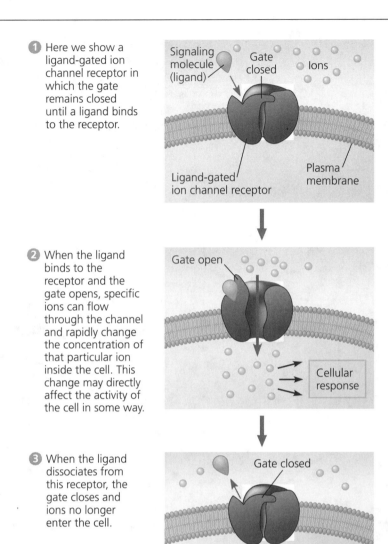

① Here we show a ligand-gated ion channel receptor in which the gate remains closed until a ligand binds to the receptor.

Signaling molecule (ligand) Gate closed Ions

Ligand-gated ion channel receptor Plasma membrane

② When the ligand binds to the receptor and the gate opens, specific ions can flow through the channel and rapidly change the concentration of that particular ion inside the cell. This change may directly affect the activity of the cell in some way.

Gate open

Cellular response

③ When the ligand dissociates from this receptor, the gate closes and ions no longer enter the cell.

Gate closed

Figure 2.8   Ion channel receptors

> ▌ **Protein phosphatases** are enzymes that remove phosphate groups and inactivate proteins that were activated by kinases. Thus, the signal can be turned *on* by kinases and *off* by phosphatases.
>
> ▌ Not all components of signal transduction pathways are proteins. Many signaling pathways involve small nonprotein water-soluble molecules or ions called **second messengers**. *Calcium ions* and *cyclic AMP* (adenosine monophosphate) are two common second messengers. The second messengers, once activated, can initiate a phosphorylation cascade, resulting in a cellular response.

Response: Cell signaling leads to regulation of transcription or cytoplasmic activities (Biology, *11e: 11.4;* Focus, *2e: 5.6*)

> ▌ Many signaling pathways ultimately regulate protein synthesis, usually by turning specific genes on or off in the nucleus. Often, the final activated molecule in a signaling pathway functions as a transcription factor.
>
> ▌ In the cytoplasm, signaling pathways often regulate the activity of proteins rather than their synthesis. For example, the final step in the signaling pathway may affect the activity of enzymes or cause cytoskeleton rearrangement.

Apoptosis integrates multiple cell-signaling pathways
(Biology, *11e: 11.5*; Focus, *2e: 16.1*)

▌ An elaborate example of cell signaling is a program of controlled cell suicide called **apoptosis**. During apoptosis, the cell is systematically dismantled and digested. This protects neighboring cells from damage that would occur if a dying cell merely leaked out its digestive and other enzymes.

- ▪ Apoptosis is triggered by signals that activate a cascade of "suicide" proteins in the cells.
- ▪ In vertebrates, apoptosis is a normal part of development and is essential for a normal nervous system, for the operation of the immune system, and for normal morphogenesis of hands and feet in humans.

> **STUDY TIP** Cell signaling has emerged as an important topic that explains cell interactions. Devote study time to understanding how reception, transduction, and response collectively result in cell communication. As you study further in biology, you will find that errors in cell signaling and failures to trigger apoptosis underlie many types of cancer. Can you select a single aspect of cell signaling and explain how its alteration could trigger uncontrolled cell growth?

The Cell Cycle
(Biology, *11e: Chapter 12;* Focus, *2e: Chapter 9*)

> **YOU MUST KNOW**
> - The structure of the replicated chromosome.
> - The events that occur in interphase of the cell cycle (G_1, S, and G_2).
> - The role of cyclins and cyclin-dependent kinases in the regulation of the cell cycle.
> - Ways in which the normal cell cycle is disrupted to cause cancer or halted in certain specialized cells.
> - The features of mitosis that result in the production of genetically identical daughter cells including replication, alignment of chromosomes (metaphase), and separation of chromosomes (anaphase).

Most cell division results in genetically identical daughter cells
(Biology, *11e: 12.1*; Focus, *2e: 9.1*)

▌ The **cell cycle** is the life of a cell from the time it is first formed from a dividing parent cell until its own division into two cells.

A cell's endowment of DNA—its genetic information—is called its **genome**. Before the cell can divide, the cell's genome must be copied.

■ All eukaryotic organisms have a characteristic number of chromosomes in their cell nuclei. As an example, human **somatic cells** (all body cells except gametes) have 46 chromosomes, which is the diploid chromosome number. *Mitosis* is the process by which somatic cells divide, forming daughter cells that contain the same chromosome number as the parent cell.

■ Human **gametes**—sperm and egg cells—are haploid and have half the number of chromosomes as a diploid cell. Human gametes have 23 chromosomes. A special type of cell division called *meiosis* results in gametes.

■ When the chromosomes are replicated, each duplicated chromosome consists of two **sister chromatids** attached by a **centromere**. Figure 2.9 will help you visualize this arrangement.

■ The two sister chromatids have identical DNA sequences.

■ Later, in the process of cell division, the two sister chromatids will separate and move into two new cells. Once the sister chromatids separate, they are considered individual chromosomes.

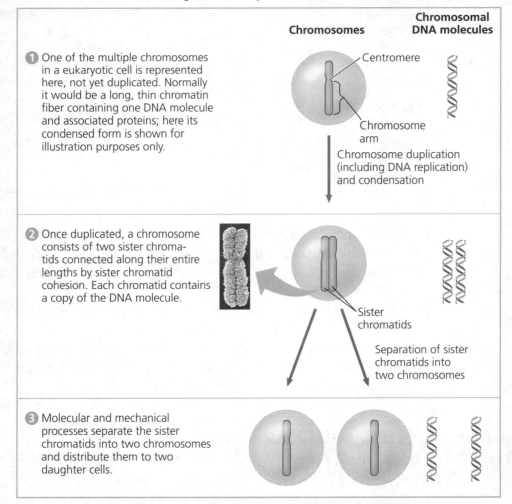

Figure 2.9 Chromosome duplication and distribution during cell division

■ **Mitosis** is the division of the cell's nucleus. It may be followed by **cytokinesis**, which is the division of the cell's cytoplasm. Where there was one cell, there are now two, each the genetic equivalent of the parent cell.

The mitotic phase alternates with interphase in the cell cycle (Biology, *11e: 12.2*; Focus, *2e: 9.2*)

■ The primary events of **interphase**, which is 90% of the cell cycle, follow:

■ In the **G₁ phase**, the cell grows while carrying out cell functions unique to its cell type.

■ In the **S phase**, the cell continues to carry out its unique functions but does one other important process—it duplicates its chromosomes. This means it faithfully makes a copy of the DNA that makes up the cell's chromosomes.

■ The **G₂ phase** is the period after the chromosomes have been duplicated and just before mitosis. The cell continues to grow and carry out its functions during this time. (See Figure 2.10)

> **WHAT'S IMPORTANT TO KNOW?**
> The Curriculum Framework says that you do not have to know the specific phases of mitosis. However, many students find it useful to organize their understanding of the process.

■ Mitosis can be broken down into five phases, not including cytokinesis. At each stage, find the specific references in Figure 2.10. We have provided the key features of each phase to simplify your studying. Focus on how each step contributes to the distribution of identical genetic information to two daughter cells.

■ **Prophase:**

1. The chromatin becomes more tightly coiled into discrete chromosomes.
2. The nucleoli disappear.
3. The mitotic spindle (consisting of microtubules extending from the two centrosomes) begins to form in the cytoplasm.

■ **Prometaphase:**

1. The nuclear envelope begins to fragment, allowing the microtubules to attach to the chromosomes.
2. The two chromatids of each chromosome are held together by the centromere. The centromere contains protein kinetochores on each chromatid, which is where the microtubules will attach.

■ **Metaphase:**

1. The microtubules move the chromosomes to the metaphase plate at the equator of the cell. The microtubule complex is referred to as the *spindle*.
2. The centrioles have migrated to opposite poles in the cell, riding along on the developing spindle.

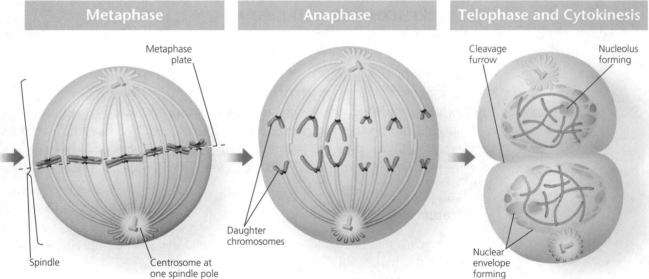

Figure 2.10 The mitotic division of an animal cell

- **Anaphase:**

  1. Sister chromatids begin to separate, pulled apart by motor molecules interacting with kinetochore microtubules, and the cell elongates.
  2. By the end of anaphase, the opposite ends of the cell both contain complete and equal sets of chromosomes.

- **Telophase:**

  1. The nuclear envelopes re-form around the sets of chromosomes located at opposite ends of the cell.
  2. The chromatin fiber of the chromosomes becomes less condensed.

3. **Cytokinesis** begins, during which the cytoplasm of the cell is divided. In animal cells, a **cleavage furrow** forms that eventually divides the cytoplasm; in plant cells, a **cell plate** forms that divides the cytoplasm.

▌ Prokaryotes replicate their genome by **binary fission** rather than mitosis.

The eukaryotic cell cycle is regulated by a molecular control system (Biology, *11e: 12.3;* Focus, *2e: 9.3*)

▌ The steps of the cycle are controlled by a **cell cycle control system**. This control system moves the cell through its stages by a series of **checkpoints**, during which molecular signals tell the cell either to continue dividing or to stop.

▌ The major cell cycle checkpoints include the **G_1 phase checkpoint, G_2 phase checkpoint**, and **M phase checkpoint**.

▌ The **G_1 phase checkpoint** seems to be most important. If the cell gets the go-ahead signal at this checkpoint, it usually completes the whole cell cycle and divides. If it does not receive the go-ahead signal, it enters a nondividing phase called the G_0 *phase*.

▌ Most mature human cells remain in G_0 and never receive the molecular signal to divide (pass through the G_1 checkpoint). Muscle and nerve cells never divide, but liver cells can respond to signals, moving from G_0 back to the cell cycle at G_1.

▌ **Kinases** are the enzymes that control the cell cycle. They exist in the cells at all times but are active only when they are connected to **cyclin** proteins. Thus, they are called **cyclin-dependent kinases (Cdks)**. Specific kinases give the go-ahead signals at the G_1 and G_2 checkpoints.

▌ As a specific example, cyclin molecules combine with Cdk molecules, producing enough molecules of **MPF** to pass the G_2 checkpoint and initiate the events of mitosis. (MPF promotes mitosis—think of it as **M**itosis **P**romoting **F**actor.)

▌ How does the cell stop cell division? During anaphase, MPF switches itself off by starting a process that leads to the destruction of cyclin molecules. Without cyclin molecules, Cdk molecules become inactive, bringing mitosis to a close.

▌ Normal cell division has two key characteristics:

  ▪ **Density-dependent inhibition**—the phenomenon in which crowded cells stop dividing
  ▪ **Anchorage dependency**—in which normal cells must be attached to a substratum, such as the extracellular matrix of a tissue, to divide

▌ Knowing the features of normal cell division is important because cancer cells exhibit neither density-dependent inhibition nor anchorage dependency. Cancer is covered in more depth in the section on molecular genetics, but here are several important points:

  ▪ **Transformation** is the process that converts a normal cell to a cancer cell.
  ▪ A **tumor** is a mass of abnormal cells within otherwise normal tissue. If the abnormal cells remain at the original site, the lump is called a **benign tumor**. A **malignant tumor** becomes invasive enough to impair the functions of one or more organs. An individual with a malignant tumor is said to have cancer.

■ **Metastasis** occurs when cells separate from a malignant tumor and enter blood or lymph vessels and travel to other parts of the body.

For Additional Review

Compare the process of meiosis with the process of mitosis. To do this, review the chromosome number in parent and daughter cells for each process and the purposes of meiosis and mitosis. Note: *The details of meiosis are covered in the first section of Topic 4.*

Level 1: Knowledge/Comprehension Questions

The Level 1, Knowledge/Comprehension, questions review essential content knowledge but don't represent the type of question you will see on the AP exam. The Level 2, Application/Synthesis, questions are similar to those you will see on the exam.

1. Salivary glands produce a large quantity of enzymes that are transported out of the secretory cells. Which of the following organelles would be in abundance in these cells?
   (A) nuclei
   (B) ribosomes
   (C) smooth ER
   (D) lysosomes

2. Prokaryotic and eukaryotic cells have all of the following structures in common EXCEPT
   (A) a plasma membrane.
   (B) cytoplasm.
   (C) linear chromosomes.
   (D) ribosomes.

Directions: Questions 3–6 consist of four lettered choices followed by a list of numbered phrases or sentences. For each numbered phrase or sentence, select the one choice that is most closely related to it. Each choice may be used once, more than once, or not at all in each group.

Questions 3–6
   (A) Mitochondria
   (B) Golgi apparatus
   (C) Lysosomes
   (D) Smooth endoplasmic reticulum

3. An organelle that is characterized by extensive, folded membranes and is abundant in cells that detoxify poisons, such as liver cells

4. An organelle with a *cis* and *trans* face, which acts as the packaging and secreting center of the cell

5. Organelles not found in red blood cells but present in large numbers in muscle cells

6. Large membrane-bound structures that contain hydrolytic enzymes and are found predominantly in animal cells

7. Cells of the pancreas will incorporate radioactively labeled amino acids into proteins. This "tagging" of newly synthesized proteins enables a researcher to track their location. In this case, we are tracking an enzyme secreted by pancreatic cells. What is its most likely pathway?
   (A) ER → lysosomes → vesicles that fuse with plasma membrane
   (B) Golgi apparatus → ER → lysosome
   (C) nucleus → ER → Golgi apparatus
   (D) ER → Golgi apparatus → vesicles that fuse with plasma membrane

8. Which of the following component molecules of the plasma membrane is most important in the reception phase of cell signaling?
   (A) protein
   (B) phospholipids
   (C) cholesterol
   (D) carbohydrates

9. Which of the following uses passive transport without the help of proteins to move materials across the cell membrane?
(A) the depolarization of a muscle cell
(B) the uptake of glucose by the microvilli of cells lining the stomach
(C) the movement of insulin across the cell membrane
(D) the movement of carbon dioxide across the cell membrane

10. Large molecules are moved out of the cell by which of the following processes?
(A) endocytosis
(B) exocytosis
(C) vesicles
(D) passive diffusion

11. In cell signaling, how is the flow of specific ions regulated?
(A) through opening and closing of ligand-gated ion channels
(B) through pores in the nuclear envelope
(C) by rearrangement of the cytoskeleton
(D) by endocytosis

12. Which of the following processes could result in the net movement of a substance into a cell if the substance is more concentrated in the cell than in the surroundings?
(A) active transport
(B) facilitated diffusion
(C) diffusion
(D) osmosis

13. What is a G protein?
(A) a specific type of membrane receptor protein
(B) a protein on the cytoplasmic side of a membrane that becomes activated by a receptor protein
(C) a membrane-bound enzyme that converts ATP to cAMP
(D) a guanine nucleotide that converts between GDP and GTP to activate and inactivate relay proteins

14. Which of the following can activate a protein by transferring a phosphate group to it?
(A) cAMP
(B) G protein
(C) protein phosphatase
(D) protein kinase

15. Many signal transduction pathways use second messengers to
(A) transport a signal through the lipid bilayer portion of the plasma membrane.
(B) relay a signal from the outside to the inside of the cell.
(C) relay the message from the inside of the membrane throughout the cytoplasm.
(D) diffuse directly into the nucleus, turning on genes.

16. Which of the following signal molecules pass through the plasma membrane and bind to intracellular receptors that move into the nucleus and function as transcription factors to regulate gene expression?
(A) epinephrine
(B) neurotransmitter released into synapse between nerve cells
(C) yeast mating factors alpha and **a**
(D) testosterone, a steroid hormone

Directions: Questions 17–20 consist of four lettered choices followed by a list of numbered phrases or sentences. For each numbered phrase or sentence, select the one choice that is most closely related to it. Each choice may be used once, more than once, or not at all in each group.

Questions 17–20
(A) Synthesis (S-phase)
(B) Gap 1
(C) Cytokinesis
(D) Gap 2

17. If this did not occur, daughter cells would have two complete sets of chromosomes.

18. The genetic material of the cell replicates to prepare for cell division.

19. The cell is carrying out its typical functions and is not engaged in producing molecules necessary for division.

20. Failure of this stage to occur prior to mitosis would result in daughter cells without sufficient DNA.

21. The fluid mosaic model describes the plasma membrane as consisting of
    (A) a phospholipid bilayer with embedded carbohydrates.
    (B) two layers of phospholipids with cholesterol sandwiched between them.
    (C) carbohydrates and phospholipids that can drift in the membrane.
    (D) diverse proteins embedded in a phospholipid bilayer.

22. Small, nonpolar, hydrophobic molecules
    (A) easily pass through a membrane's lipid bilayer.
    (B) very slowly diffuse through a membrane's lipid bilayer.
    (C) require transport proteins to pass through a membrane's lipid bilayer.
    (D) are actively transported across cell membranes.

23. Which of the following statements regarding the cell-cycle control system is *false*?
    (A) The cell-cycle control system receives messages from outside the cell that influence cell division.
    (B) The cell-cycle control system triggers and controls major events in the cell cycle.
    (C) The cell-cycle control system includes fluctuating levels of cyclins and cyclin-dependent kinases.
    (D) The cell-cycle control system operates independently of the growth factors.

Level 2: Application/Analysis/Synthesis Questions

Use the figure to answer questions 1 and 2.

1. Which figure depicts an animal cell placed in a solution hypotonic to the cell?
   (A) cell A
   (B) cell B
   (C) cell C
   (D) cell D

2. Which two figures show a cell that is hypertonic to its environment?
   (A) cells A and B
   (B) cells A and C
   (C) cells A and D
   (D) cells C and D

After reading the paragraph, answer the questions that follow.

Americans spend up to $100 billion annually for bottled water (41 billion gallons). The only beverages with higher sales are carbonated soft drinks. Recent news stories have highlighted the fact that most bottled water comes from municipal water supplies (the same source as your tap water), although it may undergo an extra purification step called reverse osmosis.

   Imagine two tanks separated by a membrane that is permeable to water but not to the dissolved minerals present in the water. Tank A contains tap water, and Tank B contains the purified water. Under normal conditions, the purified water would cross the membrane to dilute the more concentrated tap water solution. In the reverse osmosis process, pressure is applied to the tap water tank to force the water molecules across the membrane into the pure water tank.

3. After the reverse osmosis system has been operating for 30 minutes, the solution in Tank A would
   (A) be hypotonic to Tank B.
   (B) be isotonic to Tank B.
   (C) be hypertonic to Tank B.
   (D) move by passive transport to Tank B.

4. If you shut the system off and pressure was no longer applied to Tank A, you would expect
   (A) the water to flow from Tank A to Tank B.
   (B) the water to reverse flow from Tank B to Tank A.
   (C) the water to flow in equal amounts in both directions.
   (D) the water to flow against the concentration gradient.

5. Earl Sutherland received the Nobel Prize for his discovery of cAMP as a second messenger. Which observation suggested to Sutherland the involvement of a second messenger in epinephrine's effect on liver cells?
   (A) Enzymatic activity is proportional to the amount of calcium added to a cell-free extract.
   (B) Receptor studies indicate that epinephrine is a ligand.
   (C) Glycogen breakdown is observed only when epinephrine is administered to intact, living cells.
   (D) Glycogen breakdown is observed when epinephrine and glycogen phosphorylase are combined in living cells.

Use the figure to answer questions 6–8.

2.0 M sucrose
1.0 M glucose

1.0 M sucrose
2.0 M glucose

Selectively permeable membrane

U-Tube Setup

The diagram shows two different solutions of glucose and sucrose in a U-tube containing a semipermeable membrane. The membrane is permeable to both glucose and sucrose.

6. Which of the following is a reasonable hypothesis describing what will happen next?
   (A) No diffusion of sugars will occur because the total concentration of sugars on both sides of the membrane is equal.
   (B) Sucrose will diffuse from side B to side A.
   (C) Water will move from side B to side A.
   (D) Glucose will diffuse from side B to side A.

7. Look at the same figure, but assume the membrane is not freely permeable to both glucose ($C_6H_{12}O_6$) and sucrose ($C_{12}H_{22}O_{11}$) but only to the smaller of the two sugars. Now what results would you predict?
   (A) Glucose will diffuse from side A to side B.
   (B) Glucose will diffuse from side B to side A.
   (C) Sucrose will diffuse from side A to side B.
   (D) Sucrose will diffuse from side B to side A.

8. Using the same figure and assumption as for question 7, what effect will the movement of the sugar have on the water level in the tubes?
   (A) The water level will go up on side A.
   (B) The water level will go up on side B.
   (C) No net movement of water molecules will occur.
   (D) The membrane is not permeable to water—only to the sugar molecules.

Use the figure to answer questions 9 and 10.

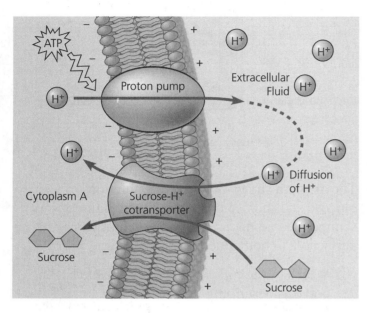

An ATP-powered pump that transports a specific solute can indirectly drive the active transport of another solute in a mechanism called cotransport, as illustrated in the figure. The cotransporter protein is able to use the diffusion of H^+ ions down their electrochemical gradient into the cell to drive the uptake of sucrose into the cell.

9. By what process are H^+ ions being moved from the cytoplasm to the extracellular fluid in this figure?
   (A) active transport
   (B) simple diffusion
   (C) facilitated diffusion
   (D) exocytosis

10. Based on the figure, how might the rate of sucrose into the cell be increased?
    (A) Decrease the extracellular sucrose concentration.
    (B) Decrease the extracellular pH.
    (C) Increase the cytoplasmic pH.
    (D) Make the membrane more permeable to hydrogen ions.

11. White blood cells (WBCs) are more resistant to lysis than are red blood cells (RBCs). When looking at a sample of blood for WBCs, what could you do to reduce interference from RBCs?
    (A) Mix the blood in a salty solution to cause the RBCs to lyse.
    (B) Mix the blood in an isotonic solution and allow the WBCs to float to the top.
    (C) Mix the blood in a hypotonic solution, which will cause the RBCs to lyse.
    (D) Mix the blood in a hypertonic solution, which will cause the RBCs to lyse.

After reading the paragraph, answer the questions that follow.

The skin is the body's largest organ. It's made up of many different types of cells. Oils, produced by the sebaceous glands, prevent the skin from drying and splitting. The protein melanin, produced by melanocytes in the epidermis, protects the skin from the harmful effects of ultraviolet radiation. Sweat, released through ducts to the skin surface, helps to cool the body. The types of cells that produce these compounds have different numbers of specific organelles, depending on their function.

12. Based on their function, you would expect melanocytes in the skin to have a higher than usual number of
    (A) lysosomes.
    (B) chloroplasts.
    (C) Golgi bodies.
    (D) microtubules.

13. If the melanin production were not sufficient to prevent UV damage to the DNA, which of the following would you expect?
    (A) decreased rate of melanin production
    (B) apoptosis and lysis of damaged cells
    (C) decreased cell divisions of the melanin-producing cells
    (D) dry, peeling skin due to DNA damage affecting the function of oil glands

14. The endosymbiont theory is supported by all of the following pieces of evidence *except* the fact that .
    (A) mitochondria have circular DNA like prokaryotes.
    (B) mitochondria use ATP like prokaryotes.
    (C) chloroplasts have ribosomes like prokaryotes.
    (D) chloroplasts reproduce through a splitting process like certain prokaryotes.

Use the figure and explanation to answer questions 15–19.

Yeast cells identify their mates by chemical signaling. There are two mating types, and each type produces a specific mating factor that binds to receptors only on the other type of cell. When a yeast cell binds mating factor molecules from a cell of the opposite mating type, a signaling pathway causes it to grow a projection toward the potential mate. The cell with the projection is called a "shmoo" (because it resembles a 1950s cartoon character by that name). The projections from the cells grow toward each other and fuse, forming a single cell with all the genetic material from both original cells.

Researchers sought to determine how mating factor signaling leads to growth of this cell projection on one side of the cell—in other words, to asymmetric cell growth. Previous work had shown that activation of Fus3, one of the kinases in the signaling cascade, caused it to move to the membrane near where the mating factor bound its receptor. The researchers' first experiment identified one of the phosphorylation targets of Fus3 kinase as formin, a protein that directs microfilament construction. Based on this information, the researchers developed the following working model for the signaling pathway that leads to the formation of shmoo projections in yeast cells.

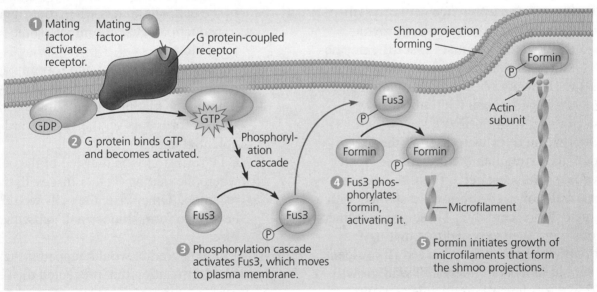

© Pearson Education, Inc.

To determine if Fus3 and formin were required for shmoo formation, the researchers generated two mutant yeast strains: one that lacked the gene for making Fus3 kinase (a strain called ΔFus3) and one that lacked the gene for making formin (Δformin). The researchers exposed the mutant strains to the mating factor and observed whether or not the cells formed shmoos.

15. A model, like the diagram, helps scientists form testable hypotheses. What hypothesis was being tested with the ΔFus3 strain?
    (A) Fus3 is required for the signal transduction pathway leading to shmoo formation.
    (B) A mating factor is required to start the signal transduction pathway leading to shmoo formation.
    (C) Fus3 is required for formin phosphorylation.
    (D) Fus3 causes shmoo formation in mating yeast.

16. In addition to testing shmoo formation in the two mutant strains of yeast, the scientists also tested shmoo formation in wild-type yeast. What is the purpose of including wild-type yeast cells in the experiment?
    (A) to show what happens to shmoo formation when both Fus3 kinase and formin are absent
    (B) to show the difference between symmetrical and asymmetrical growth
    (C) to allow the scientists to see the interaction between Fus3 kinase and formin
    (D) to show normal shmoo formation under the experimental conditions

17. Fluorescent dyes were used in the experiment to distinguish the old and new cell walls of the yeast cells. First, the existing cell walls of each strain were stained with a green fluorescent dye. These green-stained cells were then exposed to a mating factor and then stained with a red fluorescent dye that labels only new cell wall growth. Growth of the cell on all sides (symmetric growth) is indicated by a uniform yellow color, resulting from merged green and red stains. This occurs normally in wild-type cells that have *not* been exposed to a mating factor. One of their hypotheses was that Fus3 kinase is required for the signal transduction pathway leading to shmoo formation. If this hypothesis is correct, what result should be observed in the ΔFus3 strain?

    (A) The ΔFus3 strain should look the same as the wild type and form shmoos that stain red.
    (B) The ΔFus3 strain should form green-stained shmoos.
    (C) The ΔFus3 strain should *not* form shmoos, and the cells should *not* have a red zone in their walls.
    (D) The ΔFus3 strain should form multiple red-stained shmoos.

18. Fus3 kinase and formin proteins are generally distributed evenly throughout a yeast cell. Based on the model in the diagram, why does the shmoo projection emerge on the same side of the cell that bound the mating factor?
    (A) The only formin molecules that get phosphorylated and thus activated are those near the G protein-coupled receptor that binds the mating factor.
    (B) The G protein-coupled mating factor receptors are located on only one side of the cell, and that is where the signal transduction occurs to initiate shmoo formation.
    (C) All of the Fus3 kinase and formin molecules in the cell become activated by binding the mating factor, but the actin strands form only on the side toward the potential mate.
    (D) GTP forms only on the side of the cell where the mating factors fuse with the receptors. Otherwise, the cells would not be able to form shmoos and subsequently fuse.

19. What do you predict would happen if the yeast had a mutation that prevented the G protein from binding GTP?
    (A) Shmoos would form even in the absence of a mating factor.
    (B) Phosphorylated Fus3 kinase would accumulate in the cell in the presence of a mating factor.
    (C) No shmoo would form in response to a mating factor.
    (D) A mating factor would be unable to bind to the G protein-coupled receptor.

Grid-In Questions

The following questions require a numerical response.

1. Simple cuboidal epithelial cells line the ducts of certain human exocrine glands. Various materials are transported into or out of the cell by diffusion. (The formula for the surface area of a cube is $6 \times S^2$, and the formula for the volume of a cube is S^3, where S = the length of a side of the cube.) What would be the volume of the larger cell in μm^3?

   10 μm

   20 μm

2. How many of the small cells could fit inside the larger cell?

3. Sweet potato cores were placed in solutions of varying concentrations and were found to neither gain nor lose mass in a sucrose solution of 0.42M. Use this information to calculate the solute potential of the potato cores to the nearest hundredth. The temperature of the solution is 25°C. (Refer to Appendix A, AP Biology Equations and Formulas.)

Free-Response Question

1. *Prokaryotic and eukaryotic cells are physiologically different in many ways, but both represent functional, evolutionarily successful cells.*

   (a) It has been theorized that the organelles of eukaryotic cells evolved from prokaryotes living symbiotically within a larger cell. **Explain three** lines of evidence that support this theory.

   (b) **Create** a model to show the path of a protein in a eukaryotic cell from its formation to its secretion from the cell.

The Energy of Life

An Introduction to Metabolism
(Biology, *11e: Chapter 8;* Focus, *2e: Chapter 6*)

YOU MUST KNOW

- Exergonic reactions release free energy (ΔG is negative); endergonic reactions store free energy (ΔG is positive).
- ATP powers cellular work by coupling exergonic reactions to endergonic reactions.
- Enzymes work by lowering the energy of activation.
- The catalytic cycle of an enzyme that results in the production of a final product.
- Enzymes are specific in the reactions they catalyze because of the molecular shape of their active site.
- Factors that change the shape of the active site of enzymes and how they influence enzyme activity.
- How feedback inhibition is used to maintain appropriate levels of enzymes and enzyme products in a pathway.

An organism's metabolism transforms matter and energy, subject to the laws of thermodynamics (Biology, *11e: 8.1;* Focus, *2e: 6.1*)

▍ **Metabolism** is the totality of an organism's chemical reactions. Metabolism as a whole manages the material and energy resources of the cell.

▍ A **catabolic pathway** leads to the release of energy by the breakdown of complex molecules to simpler compounds. *Example*: Catabolic pathways occur when your digestive enzymes break down food and release energy.

▍ **Anabolic pathways** consume energy to build complicated molecules from simpler ones. *Example*: Anabolic pathways occur when your body links together amino acids to form muscle protein in response to physical exercise.

▍ **Energy** is defined as the capacity to do work. Anything that is moving is said to possess **kinetic energy**. An object at rest can possess **potential energy** if it has stored energy as a result of its position or structure. **Chemical energy**, a form of potential energy, is stored in molecules, and the amount of chemical energy a molecule possesses depends on its chemical bonds.

- **Thermodynamics** is the study of energy transformations that occur in matter.
  - The **first law of thermodynamics** states that the energy of the universe is constant and that energy *can* be transferred and transformed, but it *cannot* be created or destroyed.
  - The **second law of thermodynamics** states that every energy transfer or transformation increases the **entropy,** or the amount of disorder or randomness, in the universe.

The free-energy change of a reaction tells us whether or not the reaction occurs spontaneously (Biology, *11e: 8.2;* Focus, *2e: 6.2*)

- **Free energy** is defined as the part of a system's energy that is able to perform work when the temperature of a system is uniform.
- ΔG is a symbol for a change in free energy.
  - An **exergonic reaction** is one in which energy is released. Exergonic reactions occur spontaneously (which does not necessarily mean quickly) and release free energy to the system: $\Delta G < 0$.
  - An **endergonic reaction** is one that requires energy to proceed. Endergonic reactions absorb free energy; that is, they require free energy from the system: $\Delta G > 0$.
  - Is the breakdown of glucose in cellular respiration exergonic or endergonic? (ΔG is –686 kcal/mol.)

ATP powers cellular work by coupling exergonic reactions with endergonic reactions (Biology, *11e: 8.3;* Focus, *2e: 6.3*)

- A key feature in the way cells manage their energy resources to do cell work is **energy coupling**, the use of an exergonic process to drive an endergonic one.
- The primary source of energy for cells in energy coupling is **ATP (adenosine triphosphate)**. Study Figure 3.1 and note that ATP is made up of the nitrogenous

Adenosine triphosphate (ATP)

H_2O

$(P)_i$ + P—P

Inorganic phosphate

Adenosine diphosphate (ADP)

+ **Energy**

(b) The hydrolysis of ATP. The reaction of ATP and water yields inorganic phosphate ($(P)_i$) and ADP and releases energy.

Figure 3.1   The structure and hydrolysis of adenosine triphosphate (ATP)

base adenine, bonded to ribose and a chain of three phosphate groups. When a phosphate group is hydrolyzed, energy is released in an exergonic reaction.

▌ Work in the cell is done by the release of a phosphate group from ATP. The exergonic release of the phosphate group is used to do the endergonic work of the cell. When ATP transfers one phosphate group through hydrolysis, it becomes **ADP (adenosine diphosphate)**.

CONNECT TO THE CURRICULUM FRAMEWORK

Essential Knowledge 2.A.1 is about the constant input of free energy required by all living systems. The preceding section about entropy, ATP/ADP, and endergonic/exergonic reactions should be an important part of your study. Take time to understand this material well!

Enzymes speed up metabolic reactions by lowering energy barriers
(Biology, *11e: 8.4;* Focus, *2e: 6.4*)

▌ **Catalysts** are substances that can change the rate of a reaction without being altered in the process.

▌ **Enzymes** are macromolecules that are biological catalysts. In this topic, all enzymes considered are proteins; however, RNA may also have catalytic properties. RNA enzymes are termed *ribozymes*.

▌ The **activation energy** of a reaction is the amount of energy it takes to start a reaction—the amount of energy it takes to break the bonds of the reactant molecules. Enzymes speed up reactions *by lowering the activation energy* of the reaction—but without altering the free-energy change of the reaction. The reactant that the enzyme acts on is called a **substrate**. Figure 3.2 graphically depicts how enzymes function.

Figure 3.2   Effect of an enzyme on reaction rate

▌ The **active site** is the part of the enzyme that binds to the substrate. The enzyme and substrate form an **enzyme-substrate complex** that is generally

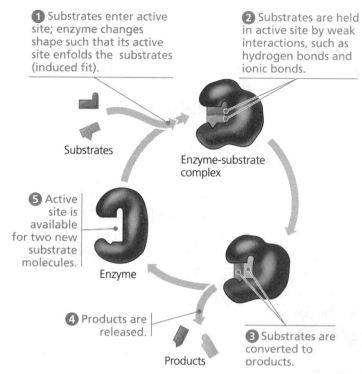

① Substrates enter active site; enzyme changes shape such that its active site enfolds the substrates (induced fit).

② Substrates are held in active site by weak interactions, such as hydrogen bonds and ionic bonds.

Substrates

Enzyme-substrate complex

⑤ Active site is available for two new substrate molecules.

Enzyme

④ Products are released.

Products

③ Substrates are converted to products.

Figure 3.3   The active site and catalytic cycle of an enzyme

held together by weak interactions. The substrate is then converted into **products**, and the products are released from the enzyme. Use Figure 3.3 to locate each step in the catalytic cycle of an enzyme.

▌ The activity of an enzyme can be affected by several factors:

- ▪ Protein enzymes have complicated three-dimensional shapes that are dramatically affected by changes in pH and temperature. Changes in the precise shape of an enzyme usually mean the enzyme will not be as effective. Note in the graphs (Figure 3.4) how the rate of the reaction is altered when temperature and pH are not optimal.

- ▪ Many enzymes require nonprotein helpers, termed **cofactors**, to function properly. Cofactors include metal ions such as zinc, iron, and copper and function in some crucial way to allow catalysis to occur. If the cofactor is organic, it is more properly referred to as a coenzyme. **Coenzymes** are organic cofactors; vitamins are examples of coenzymes.

- ▪ **Competitive inhibitors** are reversible inhibitors that *compete with the substrate for the active site* on the enzyme. Competitive inhibitors are often chemically very similar to the normal substrate molecule and reduce the efficiency of the enzyme as it competes for the active site.

- ▪ **Noncompetitive inhibitors** do not directly compete with the substrate molecule; instead, they impede enzyme activity by binding to another part of the enzyme. This causes the enzyme to change its shape, rendering the active site nonfunctional.

(a) Optimal temperature for two enzymes

(b) Optimal pH for two enzymes

Figure 3.4   Environmental factors affecting enzyme activity

Regulation of enzyme activity helps control metabolism
(Biology, *11e:* 8.5; Focus, *2e:* 6.5)

▌ Many enzyme regulators bind to an **allosteric** site on the enzyme, which is a specific binding site but not the active site. Once bound, the shape of the enzyme is changed, and this can either stimulate or inhibit enzyme activity.

▌ The end product on an enzymatic pathway can switch off its pathway by binding to the allosteric site of an enzyme in the pathway. This type of allosteric inhibition is termed **feedback inhibition**. Feedback inhibition increases the efficiency of the pathway by turning it off when the end product accumulates in the cell.

> **CONNECT WITH THE CURRICULUM FRAMEWORK**
>
> Big Idea 2 deals with energy and its transformations. Several learning objectives (LOs) address how changes in molecular concentrations will trigger feedback mechanisms. What is the effect of a change? How is homeostasis maintained? What predictions can you make? (LOs 2.15–2.18) The concept above on enzyme regulation is very important because it addresses all of these LOs.

Cellular Respiration and Fermentation

(Biology, *11e: Chapter 9;* Focus, *2e: Chapter 7*)

> **YOU MUST KNOW**
>
> - The summary equation of cellular respiration including the source and fate of the reactants and products.
> - The difference between fermentation and cellular respiration.
> - The role of glycolysis in oxidizing glucose to two molecules of pyruvate while releasing free energy to form ATP.
> - How pyruvate is moved from the cytosol into the mitochondria and introduced into the citric acid cycle.
> - How electrons from NADH and $FADH_2$ are passed to a series of electron acceptors to produce ATP by chemiosmosis.
> - The roles of the mitochondrial membrane, proton (H^+) gradient, and ATP synthase in generating ATP.

> ***TIP FROM THE READERS***
>
> Oxidation-reduction reactions, fermentation, cellular respiration, and photosynthesis are among the most technically challenging sections of the course. Here, we focus on the major steps of each of the processes as well as the results. Questions on the AP Biology Exam are likely to focus on the energy transfers of photosynthesis and respiration—not on the exact reactions that create the products. In addition, you are not expected to know the names of the enzymes involved in the process. As you work through these chapters, compare and contrast the two fundamental energy processes of photosynthesis and cellular respiration.

Catabolic pathways yield energy by oxidizing organic fuels
(Biology, *11e: 9.1;* Focus, *2e: 7.1*)

- **Catabolic pathways** occur when molecules are broken down and their energy is released. You should know these two catabolic pathways:

    - **Fermentation** is the partial degradation of sugars that occurs without the use of oxygen.
    - **Aerobic respiration** is the most prevalent and efficient catabolic pathway in which oxygen is consumed as a reactant along with the organic fuel.

- Carbohydrates, fats, and proteins can all be broken down to release energy in cellular respiration. However, glucose is the primary molecule used in cellular respiration. The standard way of representing the process of cellular respiration shows glucose being broken down in the following reaction:

$$C_6H_{12}O_6 + 6\,O_2 \rightarrow 6\,CO_2 + 6\,H_2O + \text{Energy (686 kcal/mol of glucose)}$$

▐ The exergonic release of energy from glucose is used to phosphorylate ADP to ATP. Life processes constantly consume ATP; cellular respiration burns fuels and uses the energy to regenerate ATP.

▐ The reactions of cellular respiration are of a type termed **oxidation-reduction (redox)** reactions. In redox reactions, electrons are transferred from one reactant to another.

    ▪ The loss of one or more electrons from a reactant is called **oxidation**. When a reactant is *oxidized*, it loses electrons and, consequently, energy.

    ▪ The gain of one or more electrons is **reduction**. When a reactant is *reduced*, it gains electrons and, therefore, energy.

▐ At key steps in cellular respiration, electrons are stripped from glucose. Each electron travels with a proton, thereby forming a hydrogen atom. The hydrogen atoms are not transferred directly to oxygen, as the formula might suggest, but instead are usually passed to an electron carrier, the coenzyme **NAD$^+$** (a derivative of the B vitamin niacin).

▐ Within the cell, **NAD$^+$** accepts two electrons, plus the stabilizing hydrogen ion, to form **NADH**. Note that NADH has been reduced and therefore has gained energy.

▐ Figure 3.5 shows the three stages of cellular respiration: glycolysis, pyruvate oxidation/citric acid cycle, and oxidative phosphorylation. Each stage is featured separately in the next three concepts. Use this figure to begin to develop an overall concept of the process of cellular respiration.

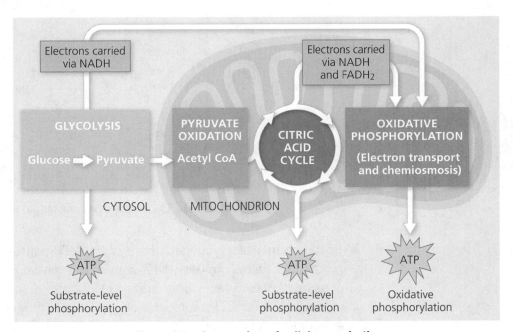

Figure 3.5 An overview of cellular respiration

Glycolysis harvests chemical energy by oxidizing glucose to pyruvate (Biology, *11e: 9.2*; Focus, *2e: 7.2*)

▌ In **glycolysis** (which occurs in the cytosol), the degradation of glucose begins as it is broken down into two pyruvate molecules. The six-carbon glucose molecule is split into two three-carbon sugars through a long series of steps.

> **STUDY TIP** Use Figure 3.6 as a guide to the important features of glycolysis. It is not necessary to know the enzymes and reactions for each step in glycolysis.

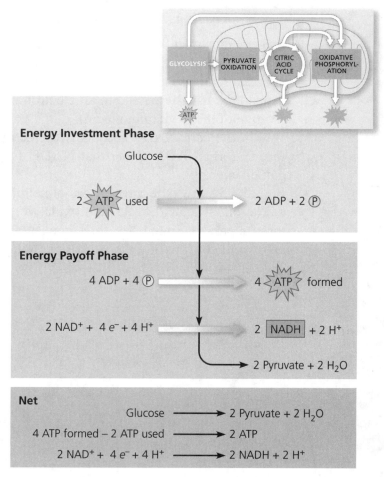

Figure 3.6   The energy input and output of glycolysis

▌ In the course of glycolysis, there is an ATP-consuming phase and an ATP-producing phase. In the ATP-consuming phase, two ATP molecules are consumed, which helps destabilize glucose and make it more reactive. Later in glycolysis, four ATP molecules are produced; thus, glycolysis results in a net gain of two ATP molecules. Two NADH molecules also are produced, and they will be used in the electron transport system (which requires oxygen) to produce ATP (see Figure 3.5).

■ Notice the *net* energy gain in glycolysis as indicated in Figure 3.6—two ATP molecules and two NADH molecules. Most of the potential energy of the glucose molecule still resides in the two remaining pyruvates, which will now feed into the citric acid cycle, as the next concept describes.

After pyruvate is oxidized, the citric acid cycle completes the energy-yielding oxidation of organic molecules (Biology, *11e: 9.3;* Focus, *2e: 7.3*)

■ After glycolysis, **pyruvate is oxidized to acetyl CoA**. This junction between glycolysis and the citric acid cycle is shown in Figure 3.7. Note the following steps in this figure:

- ■ A transport protein moves pyruvate from the cytosol into the matrix of the mitochondria.
- ■ In the matrix, an enzyme complex catalyzes three reactions: a CO_2 molecule is removed, electrons are stripped from pyruvate to convert NAD^+ to NADH, and coenzyme A joins with the remaining two-carbon fragment to form acetyl CoA.

Figure 3.7   An overview of pyruvate oxidation and the citric acid cycle

- Two acetyl CoA molecules are produced per glucose molecule. Acetyl CoA now enters the enzymatic pathway termed the "citric acid cycle."

■ In the **citric acid cycle** (which occurs in the mitochondrial matrix), the job of breaking down glucose is completed with CO_2 released as a waste product. Each turn of the citric acid cycle requires the input of one acetyl CoA. The citric acid cycle must make two turns before the glucose is completely oxidized.

■ Study Figure 3.7 and note that the citric acid cycle results in the following:

- Each turn of the citric acid cycle produces **2 CO_2, 3 NADH, 1 $FADH_2$,** and **1 ATP**.
- Because each glucose yields *two* pyruvates, the *total* products of the citric acid cycle are usually listed as the result of two cycles:

4 CO_2, 6 NADH, 2 $FADH_2$, and 2 ATP

■ Note that at the end of the citric acid cycle, the six original carbons in glucose have been released as CO_2. (You are exhaling this gas as you study.) Only two ATP molecules, however, have been produced. Where is all the energy? The energy is held in the electrons in the electron carriers, NADH and $FADH_2$. These electrons will be used by the electron transport system, which the next concept explains.

During oxidative phosphorylation, chemiosmosis couples electron transport to ATP synthesis (Biology, *11e: 9.4;* Focus, *2e: 7.4*)

■ Use Figure 3.8 as a map to understand the process of electron transport.

1. The electron transport chain is embedded in the inner membrane of the mitochondria. Notice that it is composed of three transmembrane proteins that work as hydrogen pumps and two carrier molecules that transport electrons between hydrogen pumps. There are thousands of such electron transport chains in the inner mitochondrial membrane.
2. The electron transport chain is powered by electrons from the electron carrier molecules NADH and $FADH_2$ ($FADH_2$ is also a B vitamin coenzyme that functions as an electron acceptor in the citric acid cycle). As the electrons flow through the electron chain, the loss of energy by the electrons is used to power the pumping of protons across the inner membrane. At the end of the electron chain, the electrons combine with two hydrogen ions and oxygen to form water. Notice that O_2 is the final electron acceptor, and when it is not available, the transport of electrons comes to a screeching halt! No hydrogen ions are pumped and no ATP is produced.
3. The hydrogen ions flow back down their gradient through a channel in the transmembrane protein known as ATP synthase. **ATP synthase** harnesses the **proton-motive force**—the gradient of hydrogen ions—to phosphorylate ADP, forming ATP. The proton-motive force is in place because the inner membrane of the mitochondria is impermeable to hydrogen ions. Like water behind a dam with its only exit being a spillway, electrons are held behind the inner membrane with their only exit, ATP synthase.

Figure 3.8   ATP production by chemiosmosis

4. This process is referred to as chemiosmosis. **Chemiosmosis** is an energy-coupling mechanism that uses energy stored in the form of an H^+ gradient across a membrane to drive cellular work (ATP synthesis, in our example). The electron transport chain and chemiosmosis compose **oxidative phosphorylation**. This specific term is used because ADP is phosphorylated, and oxygen is necessary to keep the electrons flowing.

5. The ATP yield per molecule of glucose is 30 to 32 ATP. Oxidative phosphorylation produces 26 to 28 of the total molecules. (You may notice that this number is less than you might have learned from another textbook, but it more accurately reflects the current biochemical analysis.)

> ***STUDY TIP*** Construct a model of the electron transport chain and ATP synthase to show the flow of electrons and production of ATP in aerobic respiration. Indicate the mitochondrial features that are important to establishing a proton gradient. This is a fundamental process that you should be able to diagram and explain, so practice!

Fermentation and anaerobic respiration enable cells to produce ATP without the use of oxygen (Biology, *11e: 9.5;* Focus, *2e: 7.5*)

▐ **Anaerobic respiration** by certain prokaryotes generates ATP without oxygen, using an electron transport chain.

▐ **Fermentation** is an expansion of glycolysis in which ATP is generated by substrate-level phosphorylation.

■ Fermentation consists of glycolysis (recall that glycolysis produces two net ATP molecules) and reactions that regenerate NAD^+. In glycolysis, oxygen is not needed to accept electrons; NAD^+ is the electron acceptor. Therefore, the pathways of fermentation must regenerate NAD^+.

■ In **alcohol fermentation**, pyruvate is converted to ethanol, releasing CO_2 and oxidizing NADH in the process to create more NAD^+.

■ In **lactic acid fermentation**, pyruvate is reduced by NADH (NAD^+ is formed in the process), and lactate is formed as a waste product.

■ **Facultative anaerobes** can make ATP by aerobic respiration if oxygen is present, but can switch to fermentation under anaerobic conditions. On a cellular level, your muscle cells operate as facultative anaerobes. **Obligate anaerobes** cannot survive in the presence of oxygen.

Glycolysis and the citric acid cycle connect to many other metabolic pathways (Biology, *11e: 9.6;* Focus, *2e: 7.6*)

■ In addition to glucose and other sugars, proteins and fats are often used to generate ATP through cellular respiration. Because the equation for aerobic respiration is always based on glucose, it is important for you to know that there are other molecules that enter the pathway.

■ **Phosphofructokinase** (PFK) is an allosteric enzyme that functions early in the pathway of glycolysis and acts as a regulator of respiration. It is inhibited by high levels of ATP, which slows the catalytic pathway of glycolysis. When there is adequate ATP, the breakdown of glucose to pyruvate is not required. When ATP is needed in higher concentrations, a product of ADP acts as an allosteric activator on PFK and increases ATP production.

■ By controlling the rate of the entire process of cellular respiration, PFK is considered the pacemaker of respiration. This is an excellent example of the regulation of a process by negative feedback.

Photosynthesis
(Biology, *11e: Chapter 10;* Focus, *2e: Chapter 8*)

YOU MUST KNOW

• The summary equation of photosynthesis, including the source and fate of the reactants and products.
• How leaf and chloroplast anatomy relate to photosynthesis.
• How photosystems convert solar energy to chemical energy.
• How linear electron flow in light reactions results in the formation of ATP, NADPH, and O_2.
• How the formation of a proton gradient in light reactions is used to form ATP from ADP plus inorganic phosphate by ATP synthase.
• How the Calvin cycle uses the energy molecules of the light reactions (ATP and NADPH) to produce carbohydrates (G3P) from CO_2.

Photosynthesis converts light energy to the chemical energy of food (Biology, *11e: 10.1*; Focus, *2e: 8.1*)

▌ Before you look at the molecular details of photosynthesis, it is important to think of photosynthesis in an ecological context.

- ▪ Life on Earth is solar powered by autotrophs. **Autotrophs** are "self-feeders"; they sustain themselves without eating anything derived from other organisms. Autotrophs are the ultimate source of organic compounds and are therefore known as *producers*.

- ▪ **Heterotrophs** live on compounds produced by other organisms and are thus known as *consumers*. Animals immediately come to mind as heterotrophs, but remember that decomposers such as fungi and many prokaryotes are also heterotrophs. Heterotrophs are dependent on the process of photosynthesis for both food and oxygen.

▌ **Chloroplasts** are the specific sites of photosynthesis in plant cells.

- ▪ Use Figure 3.9 to become familiar with the structure of chloroplasts. An envelope of two membranes encloses the **stroma**, which is a dense fluid-filled area. Within the stroma is a vast network of interconnected membranous sacs called **thylakoids**. The thylakoids segregate the stroma from another compartment, the **thylakoid space**.

- ▪ Note that the thylakoids set up compartments separate from the stroma. This arrangement will allow a proton gradient to be established.

- ▪ **Chlorophyll** is located in the thylakoid membranes and is the light-absorbing pigment that drives photosynthesis and gives plants their green color.

▌ The exterior of the lower epidermis of a leaf contains many tiny pores called **stomata**, through which carbon dioxide enters and oxygen and water vapor exit the leaf. The loss of water through open stomata is *transpiration*.

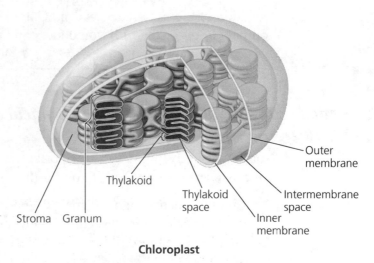

Chloroplast

Figure 3.9   Chloroplast structure

■ The overall reaction of photosynthesis looks like this:

$$6 \text{ CO}_2 + 6 \text{ H}_2\text{O} + \textbf{Light energy} \rightarrow \text{C}_6\text{H}_{12}\text{O}_6 + 6 \text{ O}_2$$

- Notice that the overall chemical change during photosynthesis is the reverse of the one that occurs during cellular respiration.
- All the oxygen you breathe was formed in the process of photosynthesis when a water molecule was split! Water is split for its electrons, which are transferred along with hydrogen ions from water to carbon dioxide, reducing it to sugar. This process requires energy (an endergonic process), which is provided by the sun.

■ Photosynthesis is a chemical process that requires two stages to complete. Refer to Figure 3.10 as you read this summary of photosynthesis.

- The **light reactions** occur in the thylakoid membranes where solar energy is converted to chemical energy. The net products of the light reactions are **NADPH** (which stores electrons), **ATP**, and **oxygen**. Here are the primary events:

  1. Light energy is absorbed by chlorophyll, which drives the transfer of electrons from water to $NADP^+$, forming **NADPH**.
  2. Water is split during these reactions, and O_2 is released.
  3. **ATP** is generated, using chemiosmosis to power the addition of a phosphate group to ADP, a process called **photophosphorylation**.

- The **Calvin cycle** occurs in the stroma, where CO_2 from the air is incorporated into organic molecules in **carbon fixation**. The Calvin cycle uses the fixed carbon plus NADPH and ATP from the light reactions in the formation of new sugars.

> *STUDY TIP* Construct a model to explain the two stages of photosynthesis. Include in your model the locations in the chloroplast where each stage occurs. (Sometimes the language of the AP course is confusing! You are being asked to make a diagram similar to Figure 3.10, which shows the location of the light reactions and Calvin cycle and summarizes the inputs/outputs of each stage.) If you understand the big picture, the details will be easier to comprehend.

The light reactions convert solar energy to the chemical energy of ATP and NADPH (Biology, *11e: 10.2;* Focus, *2e: 8.2*)

■ Not surprisingly, light is an important concept in photosynthesis. It is the primary energy source for life on Earth.

- Light is electromagnetic energy, and it behaves as though it is made up of discrete particles, called **photons**—each of which has a fixed quantity of energy.

Figure 3.10 Overview of photosynthesis

- Substances that absorb light are called **pigments**, and different pigments absorb light of different wavelengths. Chlorophyll is a pigment that absorbs violet-blue and red light while transmitting and reflecting green light, which is why we see summer leaves as green.
- A graph plotting a pigment's light absorption as a function of wavelength is called an **absorption spectrum**. The absorption spectrum of chlorophyll provides clues to the effectiveness of different wavelengths for driving photosynthesis. This is confirmed by an action spectrum.
- An **action spectrum** for photosynthesis graphs the effectiveness of different wavelengths of light in driving the process of photosynthesis. Notice examples of both of these graphs in your text, Figure 10.10 in *Campbell Biology,* 11e, and Figure 8.9 in *Campbell Biology in Focus,* 2e.
- The action spectrum confirms that plants use energy from red and blue light (which is absorbed) and very little energy from green light (which is reflected).

■ Photons of light are absorbed by certain groups of pigment molecules in the thylakoid membrane of chloroplasts. These groups are called **photosystems** and consist of two parts: a light-harvesting complex and a reaction center.

- The **light-harvesting complex** is made up of many chlorophyll and carotenoid molecules (accessory pigments in the thylakoid membrane). This arrangement allows the complex to gather light effectively. When chlorophyll absorbs light energy in the form of photons, one of the molecule's electrons is raised to an orbital of higher potential energy. The chlorophyll is then said to be in an "excited" state.

■ Like a human "wave" at a sports arena, the energy is transferred to the **reaction center** of the photosystem. The reaction center consists of two chlorophyll *a* molecules, which donate the electrons to the second member of the reaction center, the **primary electron acceptor**. The solar-powered transfer of an electron from the reaction-center chlorophyll *a* pair to the primary electron acceptor is the first step of the light reactions. This is the conversion of light energy to chemical energy and what makes photoautotrophs the producers of the natural world.

■ Thylakoid membranes contain two photosystems that are important to photosynthesis—**photosystem I (PS I)** and **photosystem II (PS II)**. PS I is sometimes designated P700 because the chlorophyll *a* in the reaction center of this photosystem absorbs red light of this wavelength the best; PS II is sometimes referred to as P680 for the same reason. Don't let switches in designation be confusing.

■ Following are the major steps of the light reactions of photosynthesis. The key to the light reactions is a flow of electrons through the photosystems in the thylakoid membrane, a process called **linear electron flow**. Find each step in Figure 3.11 as you read the following summary:

Figure 3.11   Linear electron flow

1. PS II absorbs light energy, allowing the P680 reaction center of two chlorophyll *a* molecules to donate an electron to the primary electron acceptor. The reaction-center chlorophyll is oxidized and now requires an electron.
2. An enzyme splits a water molecule into two hydrogen ions, two electrons, and an oxygen atom. The electrons are supplied to the P680 chlorophyll *a* molecules. The oxygen combines with another oxygen atom, forming the O_2 molecule that will be released into the atmosphere.
3. The original excited electron passes from the primary electron acceptor of PS II to PS I through an electron transport chain (similar to the electron chain in cellular respiration).
4. The energy from the transfer of electrons down the electron transport chain is used to pump protons, creating a gradient that is used in chemiosmosis to phosphorylate ADP to ATP. ATP will be used as energy in the formation of carbohydrates in the Calvin cycle.
5. Meanwhile, light energy has also activated PS I, resulting in the donation of an electron to its primary electron acceptor. The electrons just donated by PS I are replaced by the electrons from PS II. (Keep in mind that the ultimate source of electrons is water.)
6. The primary electron acceptor of PS I passes the excited electrons along to another electron transport chain, which transmits them to $NADP^+$, which is reduced to NADPH—the second of the two important light-reaction products. The high-energy electrons of NADPH are now available for use in the Calvin cycle.

▌ Chloroplasts and mitochondria generate ATP by the same basic mechanism: chemiosmosis. Examining Figure 3.12 will quickly demonstrate the same basic chemiosmotic plan as cellular respiration. Use Figure 3.12 to illustrate the following:

 ▪ An electron transport chain uses the flow of electrons to pump protons across the thylakoid membrane from the stroma into the thylakoid space.
 ▪ A proton-motive force is created within the thylakoid space that can be used by ATP synthase to phosphorylate ADP to ATP. This occurs when protons (H^+) flow out of the thylakoid space, down their electrochemical gradient, through ATP synthase, and into the stroma. Notice that the proton-motive force is generated in three places: (1) hydrogen ions from the splitting of water; (2) hydrogen ions pumped across the membrane by the cytochrome complex; (3) the removal of hydrogen ions from the stroma when $NADP^+$ is reduced to NADPH.
 ▪ Although similar, chemiosmosis in cellular respiration and photosynthesis are not identical. In addition to some spatial differences, the key conceptual difference is that mitochondria use chemiosmosis to transfer chemical energy from food molecules to ATP, whereas chloroplasts transform light energy into the chemical energy of ATP. This is the essence of the difference between a consumer and a producer.

Figure 3.12   Light reactions and chemiosmosis

CONNECT WITH THE CURRICULUM FRAMEWORK

Create a model that shows electron transport establishing an H$^+$ gradient across either the inner membrane of the mitochondria or a thylakoid membrane, and use it to explain the production of ATP. Be able to predict how changes in the model would affect the output of ATP. For example, what would happen if the thylakoid membrane were "leaky" and allowed H$^+$ to freely pass through? What if O$_2$ is not available in oxidative phosphorylation?

The Calvin cycle uses the chemical energy of ATP and NADPH to convert CO$_2$ to sugar (Biology, *11e: 10.3;* Focus, *2e: 8.3*)

▌ In the course of the **Calvin cycle**, carbon enters in the form of CO$_2$ and leaves in the form of a sugar. The cycle spends ATP as an energy source and consumes NADPH as reducing power for adding high-energy electrons to make the sugar. Use Figure 3.13 to chart each step summarized in the outline that follows. Note that to net one molecule of G3P, the cycle must go through three rotations and fix three molecules of CO_2.

▌ These are the major steps of the Calvin cycle. It is not necessary for you to memorize the intermediate organic molecules, but it is important to understand the conceptual scheme of reducing CO_2 to a sugar.

1. Three CO_2 molecules are attached to three molecules of the five-carbon sugar **ribulose bisphosphate (RuBP)**. These reactions are catalyzed by the enzyme **rubisco** (probably the most common protein in the biosphere) and produce an unstable product that immediately splits into two three-carbon compounds called 3-phosphoglycerate.

Figure 3.13   The Calvin cycle

At this point, carbon has been fixed—CO_2 incorporated into an organic compound.

2. The 3-phosphoglycerate molecules are phosphorylated (using ATP from the light reactions) to become 1, 3-bisphosphoglycerate.

3. Next, six NADPH molecules (from the light reactions) reduce the six 1, 3-bisphosphoglycerate molecules to six **glyceraldehyde 3-phosphate (G3P)** molecules.

4. *One* G3P molecule leaves the cycle to be used by the plant cell. (Two G3P molecules can combine to form glucose, which is generally listed as the final product of photosynthesis.)

5. Finally, the five remaining G3P molecules are rearranged to generate 3 RuBP molecules. . . . With the generation of new RuBP molecules, the Calvin cycle begins again.

▌ In the Calvin cycle, there is a net gain of one molecule of G3P which will be used for biosynthesis or the energy needs of the cell.

■ **Production of one G3P consumes** *nine molecules of ATP* along with *six molecules of NADPH*, which are both replenished by the light reactions.

WHAT'S IMPORTANT TO KNOW?

Knowledge of C_4/CAM photosynthesis is not required for the AP exam, but your teacher may teach this topic because it is an excellent example of evolutionary adaptations to arid conditions. C4 and CAM photosynthesis are evolutionary adaptations for photosynthesis by plants living in arid conditions, and are explained in this concept. This knowledge is not required for the AP exam, but serves as an excellent example of evolutionary adaptations.

Alternative mechanisms of carbon fixation have evolved in hot, arid climates (Biology, *11e: 10.4*; Focus, *2e: 8.3*)

▌ Because CO_2 enters the leaf through stomata, the same pores through which water exits the leaf in transpiration, having open stomata quickly leads to dehydration in arid habitats.

▌ The specific problem for C_3 plants is as follows:

■ On hot, dry days C_3 plants must keep their stomata closed to conserve water—thus, no CO_2 uptake. Therefore, they produce less sugar because the declining levels of CO_2 in the leaf starve the Calvin cycle.

■ In addition, the enzyme rubisco can bind O_2 in place of CO_2. This causes the oxidation or breakdown of RuBP, resulting in a loss of energy and carbon for the plant—a metabolic process called **photorespiration**. Photorespiration can drain away as much as 50% of the carbon fixed by the Calvin cycle!

■ How can hot, arid regions have any plants? The plants have structural adaptations such as reduced leaves or sunken stomata to reduce transpiration, as well as metabolic adaptations that reduce photorespiration. The two most important of these adaptations are C_4 and CAM plants.

■ C_4 plants have two strategies for reducing photorespiration.

1. **Structural strategy.** In C_3 photosynthesis, the light reactions and the Calvin cycle occur in the same cell. This puts the production of O_2 in close proximity to rubisco, leading to photorespiration. In C_4 plants, the two stages of photosynthesis are separated spatially into different kinds of cells. One type of cell specializes in the light reactions, whereas the other type of cell specializes in the Calvin cycle. This spatially separates the two phases of photosynthesis, thus reducing photorespiration.

2. **Biochemical strategy.** C_4 plants have an extra enzyme, PEP carboxylase, to fix carbon. PEP carboxylase does not combine with O_2, so it helps further reduce photorespiration. PEP carboxylase acts as a CO_2 pump, helping keep the concentration of CO_2 higher in the cells specializing in the Calvin cycle, again reducing photorespiration. Notice that C_4 plants still do the Calvin cycle and still use rubisco but have structural and biochemical adaptations that allow photosynthesis to occur, even on hot, dry days.

■ **CAM photosynthesis** is another adaptation to hot, dry climates.

■ CAM stands for *crassulacean acid metabolism,* referring to the family Crassulaceae, in which the process was first discovered. (This is a family with succulent leaves such as jade plants.)

■ These plants keep their stomata closed during the day to prevent excessive water loss. Of course, this also prevents gas exchange. At night, the stomata open and CO_2 is fixed in organic acids and stored in vacuoles. In the morning, when the stomata close, the plant cells release the stored CO_2 from the acids and proceed with photosynthesis.

■ In CAM plants, the two stages of photosynthesis are separated temporally.

■ In both C_4 and CAM photosynthesis, CO_2 is first transformed into an organic intermediate before it enters the Calvin cycle. All of the processes—C_3, C_4, and CAM photosynthesis—use the Calvin cycle; they just have different methods for getting there.

> *TIP FROM THE READERS*
> Be able to *compare* the process of chemiosmosis in the mitochondrion and the chloroplast. *Explain* how the H^+ gradient is established and *describe* the orientation of the ATP synthase molecules.

Level 1: Knowledge/Comprehension Questions

The Level 1, Knowledge/Comprehension, questions review essential content knowledge but don't represent the type of question you will see on the AP exam. The Level 2, Application/Synthesis, questions are similar to those you will see on the exam.

1. The graph most accurately depicts the energy changes that take place in which of the following types of reactions?

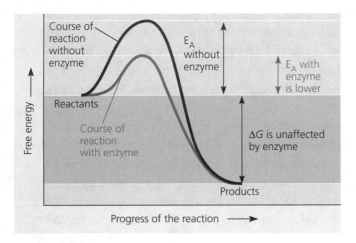

    (A) hypothermic
    (B) hyperthermic
    (C) endergonic
    (D) exergonic

2. Enzymes are organic catalysts. How do they increase the rate of chemical reactions?
    (A) by decreasing the free-energy change of the reaction
    (B) by increasing the free-energy change of the reaction
    (C) by raising the activation energy of the reaction
    (D) by lowering the activation energy of the reaction

Directions: Questions 3–6 consist of four lettered choices followed by a list of numbered phrases or sentences. For each numbered phrase or sentence, select the one choice that is most closely related to it. Each choice may be used once, more than once, or not at all.

Questions 3–6
    (A) Allosteric interactions
    (B) Feedback inhibition

    (C) Competitive inhibitor
    (D) Noncompetitive inhibitor

3. Describes a process by which an enzyme's function at the active site may be either activated or inhibited by the binding of a regulatory molecule at a separate site

4. A molecule that is so similar to the normal substrate that it competes for the active site of the enzyme

5. The process by which a metabolic pathway is shut off by the product it produces

6. A molecule that binds to the enzyme at a site other than the active site, causing the enzyme to change shape and be unable to bind substrate

7. The purpose of cellular respiration in a eukaryotic cell is to
    (A) synthesize carbohydrates from CO_2.
    (B) synthesize fats and proteins from CO_2.
    (C) break down carbohydrates to provide energy for the cell in the form of ATP.
    (D) provide oxygen to the cell.

8. One glucose molecule provides enough carbons for two trips through the citric acid cycle. How many molecules of ATP are directly produced in two trips through the citric acid cycle?
    (A) one
    (B) two
    (C) three
    (D) four

9. Groups of photosynthetic pigment molecules organized in the thylakoid membrane are called
    (A) photosystems.
    (B) carotenoids.
    (C) chlorophyll.
    (D) grana.

10. The main products of the light reactions of photosynthesis are
    (A) NADPH and FADH$_2$.
    (B) NADPH and ATP.
    (C) ATP and FADH$_2$.
    (D) ATP and CO$_2$.

11. The major product of the Calvin cycle is
    rubisco.
    ribulose bisphosphate.
    pyruvate.
    glyceraldehyde 3-phosphate.

12. Which of the following statements correctly links a process to its result?
    (A) The light reactions convert solar energy to chemical energy in the form of ATP and glucose.
    (B) The Calvin cycle uses ATP and NADPH to convert CO$_2$ to sugar.
    (C) The Calvin cycle occurs in the thylakoid membrane and results in the capture of light energy.
    (D) In chemiosmosis, electron transport chains pump protons (H$^+$) across a membrane from a region of high H$^+$ concentration to a region of low H$^+$ concentration.

13. Which of the following is mismatched with its location?
    (A) photosystems—thylakoid membrane
    (B) electron transport chain—thylakoid membrane
    (C) Calvin cycle—stroma
    (D) ATP synthesis—double membrane surrounding chloroplast

14. When light energy boosts electrons from the chlorophyll known as P680 in photosystem II to the primary electron acceptor, P680 has its electron "holes" filled by electrons from
    (A) photosystem I.
    (B) photosystem II.
    (C) water.
    (D) CO$_2$.

15. How many "turns" of the Calvin cycle are required to produce one molecule of glucose?
    (A) 1
    (B) 2
    (C) 3
    (D) 6

16. What are the final electron acceptors for the electron transport chains in the light reactions of photosynthesis and in cellular respiration?
    (A) oxygen in both
    (B) CO$_2$ in both
    (C) NADP$^+$ in the light reactions and oxygen in respiration
    (D) H$_2$O in the light reactions and oxygen in respiration

Level 2: Application/Analysis/Synthesis Questions

Use the following information to answer questions 1 and 2.

You're conducting an experiment to determine the effect of different wavelengths of light on the absorption of carbon dioxide as an indicator of the rate of photosynthesis in aquatic ecosystems. If the rate of photosynthesis increases, the amount of carbon dioxide in the environment will decrease and vice versa. You've added an indicator to each solution. When the carbon dioxide concentration decreases, the color of the indicator solution also changes.

You place small aquatic plants into three containers of water mixed with carbon dioxide and indicator solution. You place container A under normal sunlight, B under green light, and C under red light. You observe the containers for a 24-hour period.

1. Based on your knowledge of the process of photosynthesis, the plant in the container placed under red light would probably
   (A) absorb no CO_2.
   (B) absorb the same amount of CO_2 as the plants under both the green light and normal sunlight.
   (C) absorb more CO_2 than the plants under normal sunlight.
   (D) absorb more CO_2 than the plants under the green light.

2. Carbon dioxide absorption is an appropriate indicator of photosynthesis because
   (A) CO_2 is needed to produce sugars in the Calvin cycle.
   (B) CO_2 is needed to complete the light reactions.
   (C) plants produce oxygen gas by splitting CO_2.
   (D) the energy in CO_2 is used to produce ATP and NADPH.

After reading the paragraph, answer question 3.

As a scientist employed by the FDA, you've been asked to sit on a panel to evaluate a pharmaceutical company's application for approval of a new weight-loss drug called Fat Away. The company has submitted a report summarizing the results of its animal and human testing. In the report, it was noted that Fat Away works by affecting the electron transport chain. It decreases the synthesis of ATP by making the mitochondrial membrane permeable to H^+, which allows H^+ to leak from the intermembrane space to the mitochondrial matrix. This effect leads to weight loss.

3. Fat Away prevents ATP from being made by
   (A) destroying the H^+ gradient that allows ATP synthase to work.
   (B) preventing glycolysis from occurring.
   (C) preventing the conversion of NADH to NAD^+.
   (D) slowing down the citric acid cycle.

4. Catabolic and anabolic pathways are often coupled in a cell because
   (A) the intermediates of a catabolic pathway are used in the anabolic pathway.
   (B) both pathways use the same enzymes.
   (C) the free energy released from one pathway is used to drive the other pathway.
   (D) their enzymes are controlled by the same activators and inhibitors.

5. When a cell breaks down glucose, only about 34% of the energy is captured in ATP molecules. What happens to most of the remaining 66% of the energy?
   (A) It is used to increase the order necessary for life to exist.
   (B) It is lost as heat, in accordance with the second law of thermodynamics.
   (C) It is stored in starch or glycogen for later use by the cell.
   (D) It is released when the ATP molecules are hydrolyzed.

6. In an experiment, changing the pH from 7 to 6 resulted in an increase in product formation. From this we could conclude that
   (A) the enzyme's optimal pH is 6.
   (B) this enzyme works best at a neutral pH.
   (C) the temperature must have increased when the pH was changed to 6.
   (D) the enzyme was in a more active shape at pH 6.

7. When substance A was added to an enzyme reaction, product formation decreased. The addition of more substrate did not increase product formation. From this we conclude that substance A could be
   (A) product molecules.
   (B) an allosteric enzyme.
   (C) a competitive inhibitor.
   (D) a noncompetitive inhibitor.

8. The process in photosynthesis that bears the most resemblance to chemiosmosis and oxidative phosphorylation in cell respiration is called
(A) glycolysis.
(B) linear electron flow.
(C) ATP synthase coupling.
(D) substrate-level phosphorylation.

9. Which of the following statements correctly describes a metabolic effect of cyanide, a poison that blocks the passage of electrons along the electron transport chain?
(A) The pH of the intermembrane space becomes much lower than normal.
(B) Alcohol would build up in the mitochondria.
(C) NADH supplies would be exhausted, and ATP synthesis would cease.
(D) No proton gradient would be produced, and ATP synthesis would cease.

10. Glycolysis releases free energy held in the bonds of glucose, and this energy is held in these molecules:
(A) ATP, NADH, and CO_2
(B) ATP, NADH, and pyruvate
(C) ATP, NADPH, and RUBP
(D) ATP, CO_2, and H_2O

11. Which of the following provides evidence that glycolysis is one of the first metabolic pathways to have evolved?
(A) It relies on fermentation, which is characteristic of archaea and bacteria.
(B) It is found only in prokaryotes, whereas eukaryotes use mitochondria to produce ATP.
(C) It produces ATP only by oxidative phosphorylation and does not involve redox reactions.
(D) It is nearly universal, occurs in the cytosol, and does not involve O_2.

12. Bacterial production of the enzymes needed for the synthesis of the amino acid tryptophan declines with increasing levels of tryptophan

and increases as tryptophan levels decline. This is an example of
(A) competitive inhibition.
(B) noncompetitive inhibition.
(C) feedback inhibition.
(D) irreversible inhibition.

13. Brown fat, which is found in newborn infants and hibernating mammals, has uncoupler proteins that, when activated, make the inner mitochondrial membrane leaky to H^+. What is the function of brown fat?
(A) It produces more ATP than does regular fat and is also found in the flight muscles of ducks and geese, providing more energy for long-distance migrations.
(B) It lowers the pH of the intermembrane space, which results in the production of more ATP per gram than is produced by the oxidation of glucose or regular fat tissue.
(C) Because it dissipates the proton gradient, it generates heat through cellular respiration without producing ATP, thereby raising the body temperature of hibernating mammals or newborn infants.
(D) Its main function is insulation in endothermic animals, in which brown fat is common.

14. The release of the energy stored in glucose involves a series of reactions and processes. Which of the following correctly states the location and function of the process named?
(A) The citric acid cycle releases carbon dioxide from organic intermediates and synthesizes ATP from ADP via substrate-level phosphorylation.
(B) Glycolysis releases free energy from glucose to produce ATP by oxidative phosphorylation.
(C) Electron transport occurs in the cytoplasm and harvests the electrons from NADH and $FADH_2$ to establish the proton gradient.
(D) Chemiosmosis occurs when an enzyme in the inner mitochondrial membrane produces carbon dioxide and water from NADH and ATP.

After reading the paragraph and examining the graphs, answer questions 15 and 16.

Theodor Engelmann was one of the first scientists to use the microscope as an experimental tool rather than as simply an observational tool. He was also the first scientist to describe chemotaxis—the movement of bacteria toward regions where specific compounds are most concentrated.

Engelmann counted the number of oxygen-seeking bacteria that were attracted to the algal filament associated with each color of light. As shown in the following image, most of the bacteria were attracted to the regions of the alga illuminated by red or violet-blue light. This distribution of bacteria shows that red and violet-blue wavelengths are most effective in driving photosynthesis.

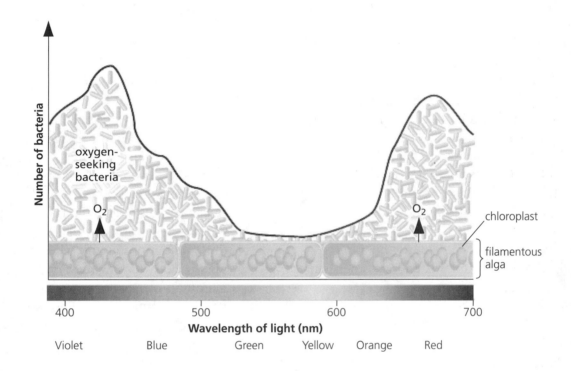

By measuring oxygen production with bacteria that were sensitive to oxygen and would migrate toward it, Engelmann described an action spectrum for photosynthesis. The action spectrum (indicated by the black line plot in the image above) shows the relative effectiveness of each color of light in driving photosynthesis.

15. What assumption did Engelmann make to conclude that red and violet-blue light were more effective than green light in driving photosynthesis?
    (A) Every photon absorbed by the alga was used to drive oxygen production by the alga.
    (B) The number of bacteria clustered at each wavelength (color) was approximately

proportional to the amount of oxygen being produced by that portion of the alga.
    (C) The distribution of chloroplasts within each algal cell differed significantly.
    (D) The alga absorbed the same number of photons at each wavelength (color).

A second assumption Engelmann made was that the sun (his light source) emits equal numbers of photons at each wavelength in the visible spectrum. In reality, the sun's emission peaks in the yellow region of the spectrum, with relatively fewer photons emitted in the red and violet-blue regions.

Recall that the action spectrum from Engelmann's experiment plotted the rate of photosynthesis (as measured by oxygen production) versus wavelength.

16. In each of the following graphs, the solid black line shows Engelmann's original action spectrum, which he deduced from the distribution of oxygen-sensitive bacteria around the alga. Which dotted line shows Engelmann's action spectrum corrected for the unequal number of photons emitted across the visible spectrum?

(A)

(B)

(C)

(D)

Use the following information to answer questions 17 and 18.

Exposing inner mitochondrial membranes to ultrasonic vibrations will disrupt the membranes. However, the fragments will reseal "inside out." The little vesicles that result can still transfer electrons from NADH to oxygen and synthesize ATP.

17. After the disruption, when electron transfer and ATP synthesis still occur, what must be present?
    (A) all of the electron transport proteins and ATP synthase
    (B) all of the electron transport system and the ability to add CoA to pyruvate
    (C) only the ATP synthase system, needed for oxygen and ATP production
    (D) plasma membrane proteins like those used by bacteria for respiration

18. These inside-out membrane vesicles will
    (A) become more acidic inside the vesicles when NADH is added.
    (B) reverse electron flow to generate NADH from NAD⁺ in the absence of oxygen.
    (C) become less acidic inside the vesicles when NADH is added.
    (D) use ATP to pump protons out of the interior of the vesicle.

Use the figure to answer questions 19 and 20.

(C) C, D, and E

(D) B, C, D, and E

19. If the carbon atom of each of the incoming CO_2 molecules is labeled with a radioactive isotope of carbon, which organic molecules could be radioactively labeled after one cycle?

(A) C

(B) C and B

To identify the molecule that accepts CO_2, researchers manipulated the carbon-fixation cycle either by cutting off CO_2 or cutting off the light from cultures of photosynthetic algae. They then measured the concentrations of the various members of the Calvin cycle.

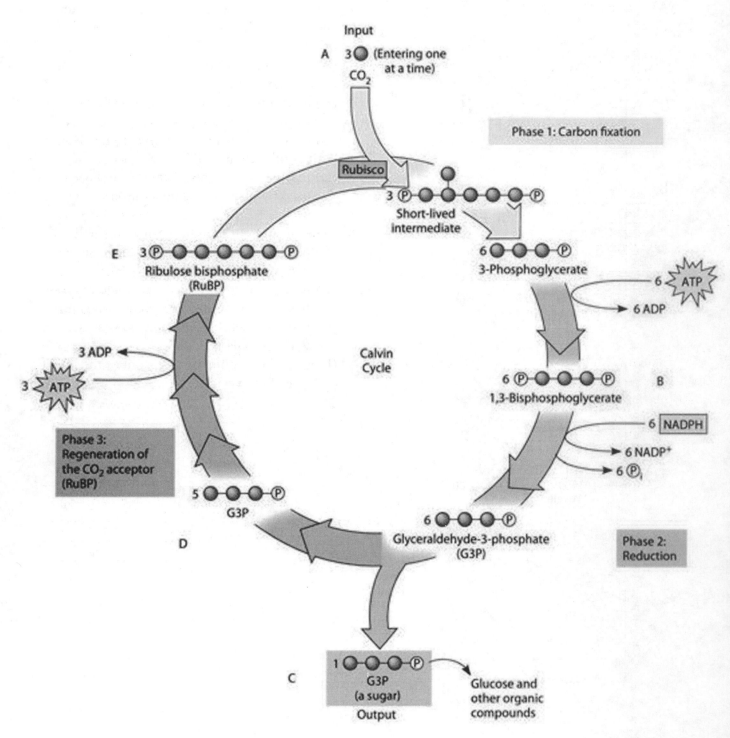

20. How could this experimental protocol be used to identify the member of the Calvin cycle that functions as the CO_2 acceptor?
    (A) The CO_2 acceptor concentration would decrease when either the CO_2 or light is cut off.
    (B) The CO_2 acceptor concentration would increase when either the CO_2 or light is cut off.
    (C) The CO_2 acceptor concentration would increase when the CO_2 is cut off but decrease when the light is cut off.
    (D) The CO_2 acceptor concentration would decrease when the CO_2 is cut off but increase when the light is cut off.

Grid-In Questions

The following questions require a numerical response.

1. The following chart shows the energy products produced in various stages of the breakdown of glucose.

Process	ATP Produced	NADH/FADH$_2$ Produced
Glycolysis	2	2 NADH
Pyruvate Oxidation (per molecule of pyruvate)		1 NADH
Citric Acid (Krebs) Cycle (per molecule of pyruvate)	1	3 NADH 1 FADH$_2$

Each molecule of NADH results in approximately 2.5 molecules of ATP, whereas each molecule of FADH$_2$ results in approximately 1.5 molecules of ATP when these molecules are fed into the electron transport chain.

1. What is the difference in the total number of ATP molecules produced between three molecules of glucose that undergo fermentation compared with three molecules of glucose that undergo aerobic respiration?
2. Glutamine is formed from glutamic acid by adding an ammonium molecule to glutamine. The overall reaction is endergonic, requiring 3.4 kcal/mole. The energy for the reaction comes from the exergonic splitting of a phosphate from ATP to form ADP, which releases 7.3 kcal/mole. What is the free energy change for this coupled reaction?
3. An enzyme in the liver removes a phosphate group from glucose so the glucose molecule can enter the bloodstream, providing energy for cellular respiration to the cells of the body. The rate of enzyme activity can be monitored by measuring the phosphate concentration over time. In this experiment, liver cells were placed in a phosphate solution. Every 5 minutes, cells were removed, and the intracellular concentration of phosphate was measured. What is the rate of phosphate formation per minute from 15 to 20 minutes?

Time (min.)	Phosphate Concentration in Liver Cells (μmol/mL)
0	0
5	10
10	90
15	180
20	270

Free-Response Question

1. *Organisms capture and store free energy for use in biological processes. Each of the following parts plays a role in the transfer of energy.*

    (a) Describe how a photosystem converts light energy to chemical energy.

    (b) Explain how glycolysis releases free energy from glucose.

    (c) Describe the role of water in both cellular respiration and photosynthesis.

PRACTICE THE PRACTICE: Making Predictions and Interpreting Data

1. The graph shows the pH difference across the inner mitochondrial membrane over time in an actively respiring cell. At the time indicated by the vertical arrow, a metabolic poison is added that specifically and completely inhibits all function of mitochondrial ATP synthase. Draw what you would expect to see for the rest of the graphed line, and explain your graph.

2. Phosphofructokinase (PFK) is an enzyme that acts on fructose 6-phosphate at an early step in glucose breakdown. Negative regulation of this enzyme by ATP and positive regulation by AMP control whether the sugar will continue on in the glycolytic pathway. Considering this graph, under which condition is PFK more active?

3. What is the likely mechanism by which PFK activity differs depending on ATP concentration?

4. Explain why accumulation of ATP has the effect seen in the graph.

You can find answers in Part V, Answers and Explanations, page 406.

STUDY TIP Enzymes are a key topic in biology. It is likely that you will do an investigation with enzymes. Know why certain factors such as pH and temperature affect enzyme action. Be able to pose a question about enzyme function, design an experiment to test this question, predict results, and analyze data from an enzyme experiment.

Mendelian Genetics

Meiosis and Sexual Life Cycles

(Biology, *11e: Chapter 13;* Focus, *2e: Chapter 10*)

YOU MUST KNOW

- The differences between asexual and sexual reproduction.
- The role of meiosis and fertilization in passing traits from parents to offspring. (LO 3.12)
- The importance of homologous chromosomes to meiosis.
- How the chromosome number is reduced from diploid to haploid in meiosis.
- Three events that occur in meiosis but not mitosis.
- The importance of crossing over, independent assortment, and random fertilization to increasing genetic diversity. (LO 3.10)

Offspring acquire genes from parents by inheriting chromosomes (Biology, *11e, 13.1;* Focus, *2e: 10.1*)

▍ **Genes** are segments of DNA that code for the basic units of heredity and are transmitted from one generation to the next. In animals and plants, reproductive cells that transmit genes from one generation to the next are called **gametes**.

▍ A **locus** (plural, *loci*) is the location of a gene on a chromosome. See Figure 4.1a.

▫ In **asexual reproduction**, a single parent passes copies of all its genes to its offspring. The new offspring arise by mitosis and have virtually exact copies of the parent's genome. An individual that reproduces asexually gives rise to a **clone**, a group of genetically identical individuals.

▫ In **sexual reproduction**, two individuals (parents) contribute genes to the offspring. This form of reproduction results in greater genetic variation in the offspring than asexual reproduction.

Fertilization and meiosis alternate in sexual life cycles (Biology, *11e: 13.2;* Focus, *2e: 10.2*)

▍ A **life cycle** is the generation-to-generation sequence of stages in the reproductive history of an organism, from conception to production of its own offspring.

▍ **Somatic cells** are all cells in the body that are not gametes. Each somatic cell in humans has 46 chromosomes. Liver cells and neurons are somatic cells.

Figure 4.1   Metaphase chromosome (a) and human karyotype (b)

▮ The **karyotype** of an organism refers to a picture of its complete set of chromosomes, arranged in pairs of homologous chromosomes from the largest pair to the smallest pair. Figure 4.1b shows a karyotype made from a human somatic cell. Notice that the 46 chromosomes are paired into 23 homologous chromosomes.

▮ **Homologous chromosomes** are pairs of similar (not identical) chromosomes. One homologous chromosome from each pair is inherited from each parent; in other words, half of the set of 46 chromosomes in your somatic cells was inherited from your mother, and the other half was inherited from your father.

  ▪ Both chromosomes of each pair carry genes that control the same inherited characteristics. If a gene for eye color is found at a specific locus on one chromosome, its homolog will have the same gene at the same locus.

  ▪ Homologous chromosomes are similar in length and centromere position, and they have the same staining pattern.

▮ An exception to the rule that all chromosomes are part of a homologous pair may be found with the **sex chromosomes**—in humans, it is the **X** and **Y**. Human females have a homologous pair of chromosomes, XX, but males have one X chromosome and one Y chromosome. Nonsex chromosomes—that is, all the chromosomes except the X and Y—are called **autosomes**.

▮ *What sex did the somatic cell come from that was used to make the karyotype in Figure 4.1?* (You can find the answer at the end of this topic on page 122.)

▮ **Gametes**—meaning sperm and ova (eggs)—are haploid cells. Haploid cells contain half the number of chromosomes of somatic cells, one chromosome of each homologous pair. In humans, gametes contain 22 autosomes plus a single sex chromosome (X in female, either X or Y in male), giving them a haploid number of 23. The haploid number of chromosomes is symbolized by *n*.

- **Meiosis** and **fertilization** are the key events in sexually reproducing life cycles.
- During **fertilization** (the combination of a sperm cell and an egg cell), one haploid gamete from the father fuses with one haploid gamete from the mother. The result is a fertilized egg called a **zygote**. It is **diploid** (has two sets of chromosomes) and may be symbolized by 2*n*.
- **Meiosis** is the type of cell division that reduces the numbers of sets of chromosomes from two to one. Fertilization restores the diploid number as the gametes are combined. *Fertilization and meiosis alternate in the life cycles of sexually reproducing organisms.*

Meiosis reduces the number of chromosome sets from diploid to haploid (Biology, *11e: 13.3*; Focus, *2e: 10.3*)

- Meiosis and mitosis have some features in common but very different outcomes. Both are preceded by the replication of the cell's DNA, for instance, but in meiosis this replication is followed by *two* stages of cell division: meiosis I and meiosis II while there is only one division in mitosis.
- The final result of meiosis is *four* **daughter cells**, each of which has *half* as many chromosomes as the parent cell—one chromosome from each homologous pair.

On the AP exam, you are not required to name specific phases of meiosis, but you must be able to describe the process and understand how it results in diversity in offspring. We will use the names of the phases to help you organize the processes. Carefully follow the stages in Figure 4.2 as they are explained:

- **Interphase:** Replication occurs, creating a copy of each chromosome. The replicated chromosome has two identical sister chromatids. This roughly doubles the amount of DNA in the cell.
- **Meiosis I:** The first cellular division in meiosis is referred to as meiosis I. Meiosis I begins with a diploid cell.
- **Prophase I:** *Understanding prophase I is critical to understanding meiosis. Study the unique events of prophase I carefully.*
  - The chromosomes condense. Sister chromatids are attached at their centromeres.
  - **Synapsis** occurs—that is, the joining of homologous chromosomes along their length. This newly formed structure is called a *tetrad* and precisely aligns the homologous chromosomes gene by gene. This perfect alignment is necessary for the next step—crossing over.
  - In **crossing over,** the DNA from one homolog is cut and exchanged with an exact portion of DNA from the other homolog. Essentially, a small part of the DNA from one parent is exchanged with the DNA from the other parent. *The result of crossing over is to increase genetic variation.* Where crossing over has occurred (two to three times per homologous pair), crisscrossed regions termed **chiasmata** form, which hold the homologs together until anaphase I.

MEIOSIS I: Separates homologous chromosomes

Prophase I

Centrosome
(with centriole pair)

Sister
chromatids   Chiasmata

Spindle

Homologous
chromosomes

Fragments
of nuclear
envelope

**Duplicated homologous
chromosomes (red and blue)
pair and exchange segments;
2n = 6 in this example.**

Metaphase I

Centromere
(with kinetochore)

Metaphase
plate

Microtubules
attached to
kinetochore

**Chromosomes line up
by homologous pairs.**

Anaphase I

Sister chromatids
remain attached

Homologous
chromosomes
separate

**Each pair of homologous
chromosomes separates.**

**Telophase I
and Cytokinesis**

Cleavage
furrow

**Two haploid cells
form; each chromosome
still consists of two
sister chromatids.**

Figure 4.2   Meiosis in an animal cell

■ After crossing over, the spindle poles move away from each other, the nuclear envelope disintegrates, and the spindle microtubules attach to the kinetochores forming on the chromosomes. The microtubules then begin to move the chromosomes to the metaphase plate of the cell.

> ### *ORGANIZE YOUR THOUGHTS*
>
> What are the important features of Prophase I?
>
> **1.** Synapsis of homologous chromosomes occurs, forming tetrads.
> **2.** Crossing over occurs between *homologous chromosomes* in the tetrads.
> **3.** Crossing over increases genetic variation.

▍**Metaphase I:** At this point in meiosis the homologous pairs of chromosomes are lined up at the metaphase plate. How many chromosomes and how many homologous pairs are found in the cell in Figure 4.2? (There are four chromosomes and two homologous pairs.)

▍**Anaphase I:** The spindle apparatus helps move the chromosomes toward opposite ends of the cell; sister chromatids stay connected and move together toward the poles.

▍**Telophase I** and **cytokinesis:** The homologous chromosomes move until they reach the opposite poles. Each pole, then, contains a haploid set of chromosomes, with each chromosome still consisting of two sister chromatids.

| Prophase II | Metaphase II | Anaphase II | Telophase II and Cytokinesis |

During another round of cell division, the sister chromatids finally separate; four haploid daughter cells result, containing unduplicated chromosomes.

Sister chromatids separate

Haploid daughter cells forming

- Cytokinesis is the division of the cytoplasm and occurs during telophase. The formation of a **cleavage furrow** occurs in animal cells, and the formation of **cell plates** (which become the cell wall) occurs in plant cells. *Note that the daughter cells are now haploid—although the sister chromatids are still attached to each other, the homologous pairs have separated.*

TIP FROM THE READERS
When does the cell go from diploid to haploid? Be sure you know and understand this! Refer again to Figure 4.2 and you should see that chromosome number is reduced during **meiosis I**. Each chromosome consists of two sister chromatids but the homologous pairs have separated.

STUDY TIP Be prepared to cite the following three examples when asked to explain differences between mitosis and meiosis.

- Three events occur during meiosis I that do not occur during mitosis.

  1. **Synapsis and crossing over:** Synapsis and crossing over do not occur during mitosis. *Synapsis increases genetic diversity.*

> 2. **Alignment of homologous pairs at the metaphase plate:** At metaphase I, paired homologous chromosomes (tetrads) are positioned on the metaphase plate, rather than individual replicated chromosomes, as in mitosis. *This allows the independent assortment of maternal and paternal chromosomes, which increases genetic diversity.*
> 3. **Separation of homologs.** At anaphase I, duplicated chromosomes of each homologous pair separate, but the sister chromatids of each duplicated chromosome stay attached. In anaphase of mitosis, sister chromatids separate.

Meiosis II: This is the second cellular division in meiosis. Meiosis II begins with a haploid cell.

- **Prophase II:** A spindle apparatus forms, and sister chromatids move toward the metaphase plate.
- **Metaphase II:** The haploid number of chromosomes is now arrayed on the metaphase plate. Because of crossing over, the sister chromatids are not genetically identical. The kinetochores of each sister chromatid are attached to microtubules from opposite poles.
- **Anaphase II:** The centromeres of the sister chromatids separate, and individual chromosomes move to opposite ends of the cell.
- **Telophase II** and **cytokinesis:** The chromosomes have moved all the way to opposite ends of the cell, nuclei reappear, and cytokinesis occurs. Each of the four daughter cells has the haploid number of chromosomes and is genetically different from the other daughter cells and from the parent cell.

Genetic variation produced in sexual life cycles contributes to evolution (Biology, *11e: 13.4;* Focus, *2e: 10.4*)

> *STUDY TIP* There are three important processes that contribute to variation and genetic diversity. We discuss them next. Be able to list and explain them.

- **Crossing over:** During prophase I, the exchange of genetic material on homologous chromosomes between nonsister chromatids occurs. Use Figure 4.2 to help make this unique feature of meiosis clear. Notice that all four chromatids that make up the tetrad are different because of crossing over. In metaphase II, when sister chromatids separate, each chromatid is unique, thus increasing variation.
- **Independent assortment of chromosomes:** In metaphase I, when the homologous chromosomes are lined up on the metaphase plate, they can pair up in any combination with any of the homologous pairs facing either pole. This means that there is a 50% chance that a particular daughter cell will get a maternal chromosome or a paternal chromosome from each of the homologous pairs. In humans, there are about 8.4 million (2^{23}) possible chromosome combinations resulting from independent assortment!

■ **Random fertilization:** Because each egg and sperm is different, as a result of independent assortment and crossing over, each combination of egg and sperm is unique. In humans, there are about 70 trillion ($2^{23} \times 2^{23}$) possible combinations—and this is all without considering crossing over!

Mendel and the Gene Idea

(Biology, *11e: Chapter 14*; Focus, *2e: Chapter 11*)

YOU MUST KNOW

- Terms associated with genetics problems: P, F_1, F_2, dominant, recessive, homozygous, heterozygous, phenotype, and genotype.
- How to derive the proper gametes when working a genetics problem.
- The difference between an allele and a gene.
- How to read a pedigree.
- How to use data sets to determine Mendelian patterns of inheritance. (LO 3.14)

Mendel used the scientific approach to identify two laws of inheritance
(Biology, *11e: 14.1*; Focus, *2e: 11.1*)

■ True-breeding parents in a genetic cross are called the **P (parental) generation**; their offspring are called the **F_1 (first filial) generation**. If the F_1 population is crossed, their offspring are called the **F_2 (second filial) generation**.

■ The following are four related concepts that make up Mendel's model, explaining the 3:1 inheritance pattern that he observed among F_2 offspring.

1. **Alternative versions of genes account for variations in inherited characteristics among offspring.** For example, consider flower color in peas. The gene for flower color in pea plants comes in two versions: white and purple. These alternative versions of the gene, called **alleles**, are the result of slightly different DNA sequences.
2. **For each character, every organism inherits one allele from each parent.**
3. **If the two alleles are different, then the *dominant allele* will be fully expressed in the offspring, whereas the *recessive allele* will have no noticeable effect on the offspring.**
4. **The two alleles for each character separate during gamete production.** If the parent has two of the same alleles, then the offspring will all get that version of the gene, but if the parent has two different alleles for a gene, each offspring has a 50% chance of getting one of the two alleles. This is Mendel's **law of segregation**.

> *STUDY TIP* Use Figure 4.3 to find each of the four basic concepts of Mendel's model illustrated in a monohybrid cross.

■ The **law of independent assortment** was Mendel's second law. It states that each pair of alleles will segregate (separate) independently during gamete

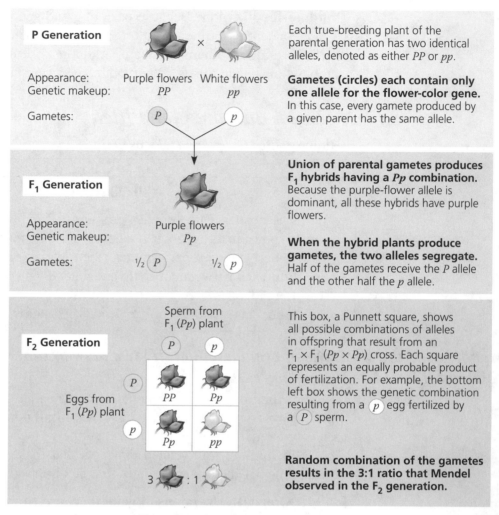

P Generation

Appearance: Purple flowers White flowers
Genetic makeup: PP pp

Gametes: P p

Each true-breeding plant of the parental generation has two identical alleles, denoted as either PP or pp.

Gametes (circles) each contain only one allele for the flower-color gene. In this case, every gamete produced by a given parent has the same allele.

F_1 Generation

Appearance: Purple flowers
Genetic makeup: Pp

Gametes: $\frac{1}{2}$ P $\frac{1}{2}$ p

Union of parental gametes produces **F_1 hybrids having a Pp combination.** Because the purple-flower allele is dominant, all these hybrids have purple flowers.

When the hybrid plants produce gametes, the two alleles segregate. Half of the gametes receive the P allele and the other half the p allele.

F_2 Generation

Sperm from F_1 (Pp) plant

P p

Eggs from F_1 (Pp) plant

P PP Pp
p Pp pp

3 : 1

This box, a Punnett square, shows all possible combinations of alleles in offspring that result from an $F_1 \times F_1$ ($Pp \times Pp$) cross. Each square represents an equally probable product of fertilization. For example, the bottom left box shows the genetic combination resulting from a p egg fertilized by a P sperm.

Random combination of the gametes results in the 3:1 ratio that Mendel observed in the F_2 generation.

Figure 4.3   Mendel's law of segregation

formation. In other words, Chromosomes 1, 2, and 4 from the mother and Chromosome 3 from the father may go to one daughter cell, while Chromosome 3 from the mother and Chromosomes 1, 2, and 4 from the father go to the other daughter cell. The maternal and paternal chromosomes *sort independently*. This occurs during anaphase I of meiosis.

▌ **Homozygous** organisms have two of the same alleles for a particular trait. If the dominant allele for a trait is designated as R (dominant traits are generally capitalized), and the recessive allele is designated r (recessive traits are generally not capitalized), then an individual could be homozygous for the dominant trait (RR) or homozygous for the recessive trait (rr).

▌ A **heterozygous** organism has two different alleles for a trait (Rr).

▌ **Phenotype** refers to an organism's expressed physical traits, and **genotype** refers to an organism's genetic makeup. For example, the phenotype of a seed might be round, and its genotype could be RR or Rr.

▌ A **testcross** is done to determine if an individual showing a dominant trait is homozygous or heterozygous. A testcross is always done between the unknown genotype and a *homozygous recessive* individual. If the unknown parent is homozygous dominant ($RR \times rr$), all the offspring will show the

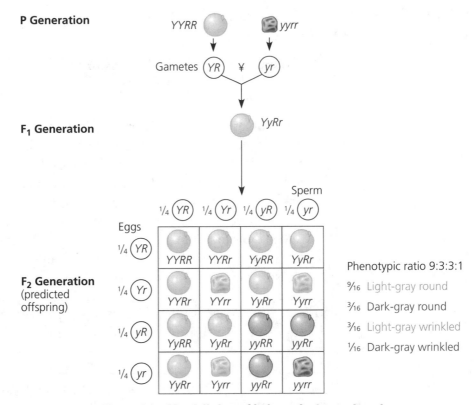

P Generation

YYRR   yyrr

Gametes YR ¥ yr

F₁ Generation

YyRr

Sperm

¼ YR   ¼ Yr   ¼ yR   ¼ yr

Eggs

¼ YR

YYRR   YYRr   YyRR   YyRr

F₂ Generation
(predicted
offspring)

¼ Yr

YYRr   YYrr   YyRr   Yyrr

¼ yR

YyRR   YyRr   yyRR   yyRr

¼ yr

YyRr   Yyrr   yyRr   yyrr

Phenotypic ratio 9:3:3:1

9/16 Light-gray round

3/16 Dark-gray round

3/16 Light-gray wrinkled

1/16 Dark-gray wrinkled

Figure 4.4   Mendel's law of independent assortment

dominant trait, but if the unknown parent is heterozygous (*Rr* × *rr*), some of the offspring will show the recessive trait.

▎A **monohybrid cross** is a cross intended to study only one character (for example, flower color), whereas a **dihybrid cross** is a cross intended to study two characters (for example, flower color and seed shape).

▎Figure 4.4 shows the results of a dihybrid cross. In this case, in the parental generation, two homozygous plants are crossed: one homozygous dominant for yellow and round seeds (*YYRR*) and one homozygous recessive for green and wrinkled seeds (*ppyy*). The only gamete type the first parent can produce is *YR*, and the only gamete the second parent can produce is *yr*. The F₁ generation, therefore, is composed of all heterozygous individuals with genotype *YyRr*. Crossing *YyRr* with a second *YyRr* gives an F₂ generation. Figure 4.4 shows the possible predicted offspring with their genotypes and phenotypic ratios.

STUDY TIP When working genetics problems, be sure you have written the genotypes of the parents correctly and derived the gametes correctly. Study Figure 4.4, paying special attention to how the gametes were obtained for the F₂ generation. For further help, refer to your text. Study **TIPS FOR GENETICS PROBLEMS** and do the problems in **TEST YOUR UNDERSTANDING**, found at the end of the chapter Mendel and the Gene Idea (*Biology*, 11e: Chapter 14; *Focus*, 2e: Chapter 11). Solutions for all end-of-chapter problems are found in Appendix A of your textbook.

Probability laws govern Mendelian inheritance (Biology, *11e: 14.2*; Focus, *2e: 11.2*)

▌ Understanding how to predict offspring of genetic crosses involves familiarity with the basic laws of probability. There are two laws that you will use directly in solving genetics problems:

- **The rule of multiplication:** When calculating the probability that two or more independent events will occur together in a specific combination, multiply the probabilities of each of the two events. Thus, the probability of a coin landing face up two times in two flips is $\frac{1}{2} \times \frac{1}{2} = \frac{1}{4}$.
- **The rule of addition:** When calculating the probability that any of two or more mutually exclusive events will occur, you need to add together their individual probabilities. For example, if you are tossing a die, what is the probability that it will land on *either* the side with four spots *or* the side with five spots? ($\frac{1}{6} + \frac{1}{6} = \frac{1}{3}$)

STUDY TIP What are the chances of event 1 *and* event 2? Multiply them. What are the chances of event 1 *or* event 2? Add them.

PRACTICE THE PRACTICE: Using Mathematical Routines to Solve Genetics Problems

1. If you cross two organisms with the genotypes AABb and AaBb, what is the probability of an offspring having the genotype AABB?

2. If you cross two organisms with the genotypes AABbCc and AaBbCc, what is the probability of an offspring having the genotype AaBbcc?

3. What is the probability that a couple would have three girls in a row *or* three boys in a row?

You can find answers at the end of the topic, on page 117.

Inheritance patterns are often more complex than predicted by simple Mendelian genetics (Biology, *11e: 14.3*; Focus, *2e: 11.3*)

▌ **Complete dominance** is dominance in which the heterozygote and the homozygote for the dominant allele are indistinguishable. A *Yy* yellow seed is just as yellow as a *YY* yellow seed.

▌ **Incomplete dominance** is a type of dominance in which the F$_1$ hybrids have an appearance that is in between that of the two parents. For example, if two plants, one with white flowers and one with red flowers, were crossed and all of the offspring had pink flowers, you could conclude that the trait for flower color exhibits incomplete dominance. Breeding two of the hybrids with incomplete dominance gives a flower ratio of 1 red:2 pink:1 white.

▌ **Codominance** occurs when two alleles are dominant and affect the phenotype in two different but equal ways. The traditional example for this type of dominance is human blood types. The alleles for A and B blood are dominant to the allele for type O blood, but A and B are codominant to each other. A person who has alleles for both A and B blood will have blood type AB because these alleles are each completely expressed.

- Most genes exist in more than two allelic forms. These traits are said to have **multiple alleles**. A good example of this is in human blood types. There are three alleles for human blood types: I^A, I^B, and I, but one person can receive any combination of two alleles.

- **Pleiotropy** is the property of a gene that causes it to have multiple phenotypic effects. For example, sickle-cell disease has multiple symptoms all caused by a single defective gene.

- In **epistasis**, a gene at one locus alters the effects of a gene at another locus. For example, an individual may have genes for heavy skin pigmentation, but if a separate gene that produces the pigment is defective, the genes for pigment deposition will not be expressed. This would lead to a condition known as albinism. (*If you read the Curriculum Framework closely, you will find that epistasis and pleiotropy are not required information—but we think it helps tell the complete story.*)

- In **polygenic inheritance**, two or more genes have an additive effect on a single character in the phenotype (such as height or skin color in humans). When several genes are involved, the phenotype usually is described by a bell-shaped curve, with fewer individuals at each extreme and most individuals clustered in the middle.

Many human traits follow Mendelian patterns of inheritance (Biology, *11e: 14.4*; Focus, *2e: 11.4*)

- A **pedigree** is a diagram that shows the relationship between parents and offspring across two or more generations. (See Figure 4.5.) In a typical pedigree, circles represent females, and squares represent males. White open circles or squares indicate that the individual did not or does not express a particular trait, whereas the shaded ones indicate that the individual expresses or expressed that trait. Through the patterns they reveal, pedigrees can help determine the genome of individuals that comprise them; pedigrees can also help predict the genome of future offspring.

- **Recessively inherited disorders** require two copies of the defective gene for the disorder to be expressed. Examples include the following:

  - **Cystic fibrosis** is caused by a mutation in an allele that codes for a cell membrane protein that functions in the transport of chloride ions into and out of cells. The resulting high extracellular levels of chloride cause mucus to be thicker and stickier, leading to organ malfunction and recurrent bacterial infections.
  - **Tay-Sachs** disease is caused by an allele that codes for a dysfunctional enzyme, which is unable to break down certain lipids in the brain. As these lipids accumulate in the brain cells, a child with the disease will suffer from blindness, seizures, and degeneration of brain function, leading to death.
  - **Sickle-cell disease** is caused by an allele that codes for a mutant hemoglobin molecule that forms long rods when the oxygen levels in the blood are low. These long rods cause the red blood cell to sickle, clogging small blood vessels and leading to pain, organ damage, and even paralysis.

PRACTICE THE PRACTICE: Using a Pedigree to Determine Inheritance Patterns

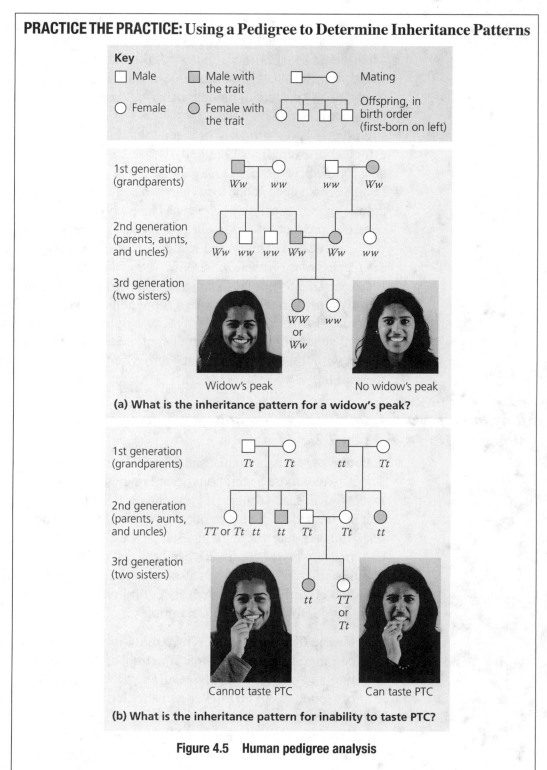

Key

☐ Male   ▨ Male with the trait   ☐—○ Mating

○ Female   ⬤ Female with the trait   Offspring, in birth order (first-born on left)

1st generation (grandparents)

Ww   ww   ww   Ww

2nd generation (parents, aunts, and uncles)

Ww   ww   ww   Ww   Ww   ww

3rd generation (two sisters)

WW or Ww   ww

Widow's peak   No widow's peak

(a) What is the inheritance pattern for a widow's peak?

1st generation (grandparents)

Tt   Tt   tt   Tt

2nd generation (parents, aunts, and uncles)

TT or Tt   tt   tt   Tt   Tt   tt

3rd generation (two sisters)

tt   TT or Tt

Cannot taste PTC   Can taste PTC

(b) What is the inheritance pattern for inability to taste PTC?

Figure 4.5   Human pedigree analysis

You can find answers at the end of the topic, on page 117.

- **Dominantly inherited disorders** require only one copy of the allele in order for the disorder to be expressed. *Achondroplasia* is a form of dwarfism that results from a relatively rare dominant allele. Some dominant alleles cause lethal diseases, but usually only lethal alleles that act late in life are passed on. **Huntington's disease** is caused by a lethal dominant allele. It is a degenerative disease of the nervous system that usually doesn't affect an individual until he or she is over 40 years old.

- A common misconception is that dominant alleles are more common than recessive alleles because dominant alleles are always expressed. Both of the disorders just described are examples of traits for which the frequency of the dominant allele is very low.

- Genetic testing of a fetus may detect certain genetic disorders. Two common tests are amniocentesis and chorionic villus sampling (CVS).

  - **Amniocentesis** occurs when the physician removes amniotic fluid from around the fetus. The amniotic fluid can be utilized to detect some genetic disorders, and the cells in the fluid can be cultured for a karyotype.
  - **Chorionic villus sampling** involves using a narrow tube inserted through the cervix to suction out a tiny sample of the placenta that contains only fetal cells. A karyotype can immediately be developed from these cells.
  - Fetal cells and fetal DNA can be isolated from its mother's blood and analyzed. This relatively new noninvasive technique is increasingly being used in fetal screening.

The Chromosomal Basis of Inheritance
(Biology, *11e: Chapter 15;* Focus, *2e: Chapter 12*)

YOU MUST KNOW

- How the chromosome theory of inheritance connects the physical movement of chromosomes in meiosis to Mendel's laws of inheritance.
- The unique pattern of inheritance in sex-linked genes.
- How alteration of chromosome number or structurally altered chromosomes (deletions, duplications, etc.) can cause genetic disorders.
- How genomic imprinting and inheritance of mitochondrial DNA are exceptions to standard Mendelian inheritance.

Morgan showed that Mendelian inheritance has its physical basis in the behavior of chromosomes (Biology, *11e: 15.1;* Focus, *2e: 12.1*)

- The **chromosome theory of inheritance** states that genes have specific locations (called *loci*) on chromosomes and that it is chromosomes that segregate and assort independently. It is important to connect this physical movement of chromosomes in meiosis to Mendel's laws of inheritance. If you are having trouble visualizing this connection, carefully work through Figure 15.2 in *Biology*, 11e, or Figure 12.2 in *Focus*, 2e. Pay particular attention to the explanations of the law of segregation and the law of independent assortment.

- A **sex-linked gene** is one located on a sex chromosome (X or Y in humans). After the chromosome theory of inheritance was formed, *Thomas Hunt Morgan* discovered the existence of sex-linked genes.

Sex-linked genes exhibit unique patterns of inheritance (Biology, *11e: 15.2;* Focus, *2e: 12.2*)

- In humans, there are two types of sex chromosomes, X and Y. A person who inherits two X chromosomes usually develops as a female, whereas a person who inherits one X and one Y chromosome normally develops as a male.
- Sex-linked genes may be either X-linked or Y-linked. Figure 4.6 shows the unique pattern of inheritance in an X-linked recessive trait. In addition to tracking the gene from one generation to the next, it is also necessary to track the sex of the offspring.

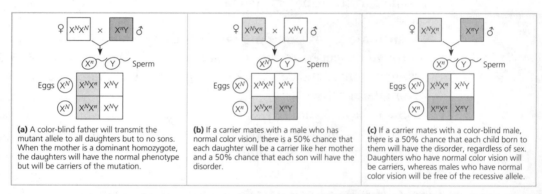

Figure 4.6 **The transmission of X-linked recessive traits. The superscript *N* represents the dominant allele for normal color vision carried on the X chromosome, while *n* represents the recessive allele, which has a mutation causing color blindness. White boxes indicate unaffected individuals, light gray boxes indicate carriers, and dark gray boxes indicate color-blind individuals.**

- As you study the previous three examples, notice that each of the following are demonstrated:

  - Each egg contains an X chromosome; there are two types of sperm: those with an X chromosome and those with a Y chromosome. In fertilization, there is a 50% chance that a sperm carrying an X or Y chromosome will reach and penetrate the egg first. Thus, gender is determined by chance and by the male sperm cell in humans.
  - Fathers pass X-linked genes on to their daughters but not to their sons; fathers pass the Y chromosome to all their sons.
  - Females will express an X-linked trait exactly like any other trait, but males—with only one X chromosome—will express the allele on the X chromosome they inherited from their mother. The terms *homozygous* and *heterozygous* do not apply to a male pattern of sex-linked genes.

- The vast majority of genes on the X chromosome are not related to sex.

■ Several X-linked disorders have medical significance:

  ■ **Duchenne muscular dystrophy** is an X-linked disorder characterized by a progressive weakening of the muscles and loss of coordination. Affected individuals rarely live past their early 20s.

  ■ **Hemophilia** is an X-linked disorder characterized by having blood with an inability to clot normally, caused by the absence of proteins required for blood clotting.

■ **X-inactivation** regulates gene dosage in females. Although female mammals inherit two X chromosomes, one of the X chromosomes (randomly chosen) in each cell of the body becomes inactivated during embryonic development by **methylation**. As a result, males and females have the same effective dose of genes with loci on the X chromosome.

■ The inactive chromosome condenses into a **Barr body**, which lies along the inside of the nuclear envelope. Still, females are not usually affected as heterozygote carriers of problematic alleles because half of their sex chromosomes are normal and produce the necessary proteins.

Linked genes tend to be inherited together because they are located near each other on the same chromosome (Biology, *11e: 15.3;* Focus, *2e: 12.3*)

■ **Linked genes** are located on the same chromosome and therefore tend to be inherited together during cell division.

■ **Genetic recombination** is the production of offspring with a new combination of genes inherited from the parents. This new combination results from crossing over during prophase I of meiosis. Many genetic crosses yield some offspring with the same phenotype as one of the parents (these offspring are referred to as **parental types**) and some offspring with phenotypes different from either parent (these offspring are referred to as **recombinants**).

■ **Crossing over** can explain why some linked genes get separated during meiosis. During meiosis, unlinked genes follow independent assortment because they are located on different chromosomes. Linked genes are located on the same chromosome and would not be predicted to follow independent assortment. However, sometimes genetic crosses give results that seem to indicate that some independent assortment has occurred, even when genes are on the same chromosome. These results are not caused by independent assortment but can be explained by crossing over.

■ Research indicates that the farther apart two genes are on a chromosome, the higher the probability that crossing over will occur between them. The likelihood of crossing over between different genes on the same chromosome is expressed as a percentage chance.

■ A **linkage map** is a genetic map that is based on the percentage of crossover events.

■ A **map unit** is equal to a 1% recombination frequency. Map units are used to express relative distances along the chromosome. Grid-in question 3 is a linkage map problem. Try this problem; then check in the Answers section to see how you did.

Alterations of chromosome number or structure cause some genetic disorders (Biology, *11e: 15.4;* Focus, *2e: 12.4*)

▎ **Nondisjunction** occurs when the members of a pair of homologous chromosomes do not separate properly during meiosis I or sister chromatids don't separate properly during meiosis II.

▎ As a result of nondisjunction, one gamete receives two copies of the chromosome, whereas the other gamete receives none. If the faulty gametes engage in fertilization, the offspring will have an incorrect chromosome number. This is known as **aneuploidy**.

▎ Fertilized eggs that have received three copies of the chromosome in question are said to be **trisomic**; those that have received just one copy of a chromosome are said to be **monosomic** for the chromosome.

▎ **Polyploidy** is the condition of having more than two complete sets of chromosomes, forming a $3n$ or $4n$ individual. Rare in animals, this condition is fairly frequent in plants.

▎ Errors in meiosis or damaging agents such as radiation can cause portions of a chromosome to be lost or rearranged, resulting in the following mutations:

  ▪ A **deletion** occurs when a chromosomal fragment is lost, resulting in a chromosome with missing genes. A large deletion may be lethal in the embryo.

  ▪ A **duplication** occurs when a chromosomal segment is repeated. This can alter gene dosage and be harmful.

  ▪ An **inversion** occurs when a chromosomal fragment breaks off and reattaches to its original position but backward, so that the part of the fragment that was originally at the attachment point is now at the end of the chromosome. If the gene's expression is influenced by its location among neighboring genes, inversion can have devastating effects.

  ▪ A **translocation** occurs when the deleted chromosome fragment joins a *nonhomologous* chromosome. If genes in the fragment have their expression altered by their location, the effects can be negative.

▎ Human disorders caused by nondisjunction in meiosis include the following:

  ▪ **Down syndrome:** an aneuploid condition that is the result of having an extra chromosome 21 (trisomy 21). Down syndrome includes characteristic facial features, short stature, heart defects, and developmental delays.

  ▪ **Klinefelter syndrome:** an aneuploid condition in which a male possesses the sex chromosomes XXY (an extra X). Klinefelter males have male sex organs but are sterile.

  ▪ **Turner syndrome:** a monosomic condition in which the female has just one sex chromosome, often designated XO. Turner syndrome females are sterile because the reproductive organs do not mature. Turner syndrome is the only known viable monosomy in humans.

Some inheritance patterns are exceptions to standard Mendelian inheritance (Biology, *11e: 15.5*)

▌ In mammals, geneticists have identified traits that differ, depending on which parent passed along the allele for those traits. This phenomenon is called **genomic imprinting**. The phenotypic effect of a gene may depend on which allele is inherited from which parent.

▪ Genomic imprinting occurs during gamete formation and results in the silencing of a particular allele of certain genes. The offspring expresses only one allele of an imprinted gene—hence the exception to Mendelian inheritance. Over 60 imprinted genes have been identified, with hundreds more suspected. Most of the known imprinted genes are critical for embryonic development.

▌ Genes that are present in mitochondria and plastids are inherited only from the mother because the zygote's cytoplasm comes only from the egg. You inherited your mitochondrial DNA only from your mother; your mother inherited her mitochondrial DNA only from her mother. Your mitochondrial DNA is your maternal grandmother's!

Answer to PRACTICE THE PRACTICE: Using Mathematical Routines to Solve Genetics Problems, p. 110

1. Probability of AABB = ½ (probability of AA) × ¼ (probability of BB) = **1/8**. Of course you could have created a 16-square Punnet square to arrive at this answer, but it is much easier and faster to use the multiplication rule.

2. Probability of AaBbcc = ½ (probability of Aa) × ½ (probability of Bb) × ¼ (probability of cc) = **1/16**. You would need to create a 64-square Punnet square to solve this without using the multiplication rule!

3. Probability of three girls in a row = 1/8 (½ × ½ × ½) + Probability of three boys in a row = 1/8 (½ × ½ × ½) = ¼. Recall that when it is either/or, you *add* both probabilities.

Answer to PRACTICE THE PRACTICE: Using a Pedigree to Determine Inheritance Patterns, p. 112

1. **The trait is autosomal dominant.** Notice that the trait is inherited by both males and females, which suggests it is not sex linked but rather autosomal. Now, is it dominant or recessive? In the third generation, note that the second-born daughter lacks a widow's peak, although both of her parents had the trait. Such a pattern indicates that the trait is a result of a dominant allele. If it were a result of a *recessive* allele, and both parents had the recessive phenotype (straight hairline), all of their offspring would also have the recessive phenotype.

2. **The trait is autosomal recessive.** Again, you may eliminate sex-linked inheritance because of the presence of the trait in both males and females. Specifically, since the first-born daughter in the third generation has the trait (is unable to taste PTC), though her father did not, you may rule out sex linkage. Because both parents lack the trait (they

can taste PTC), this pattern is explained if the nontaster phenotype is a result of a recessive allele. If it were due to a *dominant* allele, then at least one parent would also have had the trait.

Level 2: Application/Analysis/Synthesis Questions (All questions for this topic are Level 2.)

1. A couple has six children—all daughters. If they have a seventh child, what is the probability that the seventh child will be a daughter?
   (A) $\frac{6}{7}$
   (B) $\frac{1}{7}$
   (C) $\frac{1}{36}$
   (D) $\frac{1}{2}$

2. If genes *R* and *S* are on two different chromosomes and the probability of allele *R* segregating into a gamete is $\frac{1}{4}$, while the probability of allele *S* segregating into a gamete is $\frac{1}{2}$, what is the probability that both will segregate into the same gamete?
   (A) $\frac{1}{4} \times \frac{1}{2}$
   (B) $\frac{1}{4} \div \frac{1}{2}$
   (C) $\frac{1}{4} + \frac{1}{2}$
   (D) $\frac{1}{4} + \frac{1}{4}$

3. In llamas, coat color is controlled by a gene that exists in two allelic forms. If a homozygous yellow llama is crossed with a homozygous brown llama, the offspring have gray coats. If two of the gray-coated offspring were crossed, what percentage of their offspring would have brown coats?
   (A) 0%
   (B) 25%
   (C) 50%
   (D) 75%

4. Which of the following descriptions does not apply to meiosis?
   (A) During the first division, the sister chromatids travel to opposite ends of the cell.
   (B) The chromosome number of the daughter cells is half that of the parent cell.
   (C) The homologous chromosomes synapse and form tetrads before the first division.
   (D) The cytoplasm of the cell and all its organelles are divided approximately in half.

5. In rabbits, the gene for short hair (*S*) is dominant, and the gene for long hair (*s*) is recessive. The gene for green eyes (*G*) is dominant, and the gene for blue eyes (*g*) is recessive. A cross between two rabbits produces a litter of six short-haired rabbits with green eyes and two short-haired rabbits with blue eyes. What is the most likely genotype of the parent rabbits in this cross?
   (A) *ssgg* × *ssgg*
   (B) *SSGG* × *SSGG*
   (C) *SsGg* × *SsGg*
   (D) *SsGg* × *SSGg*

6. In humans, hemophilia is an X-linked recessive trait. If a man and a woman have a son who has hemophilia, which of the following is definitely *true*?
   (A) The mother carries an allele for hemophilia.
   (B) The father carries an allele for hemophilia.
   (C) The boy's paternal grandfather has hemophilia.
   (D) Both parents carry an allele for hemophilia.

7. Which of the following explains a significantly low rate of crossing over between two genes?
   (A) The genes are located very close together on homologous chromosomes.
   (B) The genes are located very close together on non-homologous chromosomes.
   (C) The genes code for proteins that have similar functions.
   (D) The genes code for proteins that have very different functions.

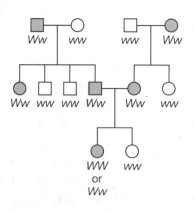

First generation (grandparents)

Second generation (parents plus aunts and uncles)

Third generation (two sisters)

8. In the given pedigree, circles represent females and squares represent males; those who express a particular trait are shaded, whereas those who do not are not shaded. Which pattern of inheritance best explains the pedigree for this trait?
   (A) X-linked recessive
   (B) codominant
   (C) autosomal recessive
   (D) autosomal dominant

9. If a woman has type A blood, and her child has type O blood, the father must have which of the following blood types?
   (A) A, B, or O
   (B) AB or A
   (C) AB or B
   (D) O only

10. If a person with type O blood were to have children with a person with type AB blood, which of the following represents the best prediction of the ratio of possible blood types for their offspring?
    (A) $3\ I^A i{:}1\ I^B i$
    (B) $1\ I^A i{:}1\ I^B i$
    (C) $1\ I^A i{:}2\ I^A I^B{:}1\ I^B i$
    (D) $9\ I^A I^B{:}3\ I^A Ii{:}3\ I^B i{:}1\ ii$

11. Two yellow mice with the genotype Yy mate. After many offspring, ⅔ are yellow and ⅓ are not yellow (a 2:1 ratio). Mendelian genetics dictates that this cross should produce offspring that were ¼ YY (yellow), ½ Yy (yellow), and ¼ yy (not yellow). What is the most likely conclusion from this experiment?
    (A) The mice did not bear enough offspring for the ratio calculation to be specific.
    (B) Y is lethal in the homozygous form and caused death early in development.
    (C) Nondisjunction occurred.
    (D) A mutation masked the effects of the Y allele.

12. All of the following contribute to genetic recombination or variation in offspring EXCEPT
    (A) random fertilization.
    (B) independent assortment.
    (C) crossing over.
    (D) gene linkage.

13. In cucumbers, warty (W) is dominant over dull (w), and green (G) is dominant over orange (g). A cucumber plant that is homozygous for warty and green is crossed with one that is homozygous for dull and orange. The F_1 generation is then crossed. If a total of 144 offspring are produced in the F_2 generation, which of the following is closest to the number of dull green cucumbers expected?
    (A) 3
    (B) 10
    (C) 28
    (D) 80

14. Chromosome number is reduced to haploid in meiosis. What event must occur to restore the diploid chromosome number?
    (A) synapsis during prophase
    (B) fertilization
    (C) mitosis
    (D) DNA replication

15. Which of the following events is typical of the second meiotic division?
    (A) Paternal and maternal chromosomes assort randomly.
    (B) The chromosome number becomes haploid.
    (C) Crossing over between nonsister chromatids occurs.
    (D) Sister chromatids migrate to separate poles.

16. A cell with a diploid number of six could produce gametes with how many different combinations of maternal and paternal chromosomes?
    (A) 6
    (B) 8
    (C) 12
    (D) 64

17. The DNA content of a diploid cell is measured in the G_1 phase. *After* meiosis I, the DNA content of one of the two cells produced would be
    (A) equal to that of the G_1 cell.
    (B) twice that of the G_1 cell.
    (C) one-half that of the G_1 cell.
    (D) one-fourth that of the G_1 cell.

18. Which of the following is true for both meiosis II and mitosis?
    (A) Sister chromatids separate.
    (B) Homologous chromosomes separate.
    (C) DNA replication precedes the division.
    (D) Haploid cells are produced.

19. Given the following recombination frequencies, what is the correct order of the genes on the chromosome? A-B, 8 map units; A-C, 28 map units; A-D, 25 map units; B-C, 20 map units; B-D, 33 map units
    (A) A-B-C-D
    (B) D-C-A-B
    (C) A-D-C-B
    (D) D-A-B-C

20. X-linked conditions are more common in men than in women because
    (A) the genes associated with the X-linked conditions are linked to the X chromosome, which determines maleness.
    (B) men need to inherit only one copy of the recessive allele for the condition to be fully expressed.
    (C) women simply do not develop the disease regardless of their genetic composition.
    (D) the sex chromosomes are more active in men than in women.

21. If these four cells resulted from cell division of a single cell with diploid chromosome number $2n = 4$, what best describes what just occurred?

Gametes

$n + 1$ $n - 1$ n n

Number of chromosomes

    (A) normal meiosis
    (B) translocation
    (C) inversion
    (D) nondisjunction

After reading the paragraph, answer questions 22 and 23.

A woman has been trying to conceive for several years unsuccessfully. Specialists at a fertility clinic discover that she has blocked fallopian tubes. Using modern technologies, some of her eggs are removed, fertilized with her husband's sperm, and implanted into her uterus. The procedure is successful, but the couple discovers that their new son is colorblind and has type O blood. The woman claims that the child can't be theirs because she has type A blood and her husband has type B. Also, neither parent is colorblind, although one grandparent (the woman's father) is also colorblind.

22. As a genetic counselor, you would explain to the parents that
    (A) the eggs must have been accidentally switched because the baby's blood type has to match one of his parents'.
    (B) each parent could have contributed one recessive allele, resulting in type O blood.
    (C) the eggs must have been accidentally switched because a type A parent and a type B parent can have any type children except O.
    (D) it is possible for the baby to have type O blood because type O is inherited through a dominant allele.

23. In regard to the baby's colorblindness, a sex-linked recessive trait, you explain that
    (A) colorblindness often appears randomly, even if neither parent is colorblind.
    (B) the baby's father must have a recessive allele for colorblindness.
    (C) because colorblindness is sex-linked, a son can inherit colorblindness if his mother has the recessive colorblindness allele.
    (D) the eggs must have been accidentally switched because males inherit sex-linked traits only from their fathers.

24. The independent orientation of chromosomes at metaphase I results in an increase in the number of
    (A) gametes.
    (B) homologous chromosomes.
    (C) possible combinations of characteristics.
    (D) sex chromosomes.

Additional Sample Problems

1. A black guinea pig crossed with an albino guinea pig produces 12 black offspring. When the albino guinea pig is crossed with a second black one, 7 blacks and 5 albinos are obtained. What is the best explanation for this genetic situation? Write genotypes for the parents, gametes, and offspring.

2. In pea plants, pod color may be green (*G*) or yellow (*g*), and the pod shape may be inflated (*I*) or constricted (*i*). Two pea plants heterozygous for the characters of pod color and pod shape are crossed. Determine the phenotypic ratios of the offspring.

3. In some plants, a true-breeding, red-flowered strain gives all pink flowers when crossed with a white-flowered strain: $C^R C^R$ (red) $\times$ $C^W C^W$ (white) $\rightarrow$ $C^R C^W$ (pink). The placement of the flower can be determined by the dominant allele for an axial flower (*A*) or the recessive allele (*a*) for a terminal flower. What will be the phenotypic ratio of the F_1 generation resulting from the following cross: axial-red (both genes are homozygous) $\times$ terminal white? What will the phenotypic ratio be in the F_2?

Grid-In Questions
These questions call for a numerical response.

1. A yeast cell in the early portion of interphase of meiotic cell division has 24 fg of DNA (fg = 1×10^{-15} grams). If the yeast cell completes meiotic division to form four haploid cells, how many fg of DNA would be expected in each haploid cell?
2. In pea plants T = Tall, t = dwarf, R = Round seeds, and r = wrinkled seeds. If a *TtRr* plant is crossed with a *Ttrr* plant, what fraction of the offspring will be tall and wrinkled?
3. In fruit flies a gray body is dominant to a black body, and normal wings are dominant to vestigial wings. Flies heterozygous for both gray bodies and normal wings were crossed with flies that had black bodies and vestigial wings. The following results were obtained:

Phenotype	Number of Flies
Gray body/normal wings	482
Black body/vestigial wings	472
Black body/vestigial wings	103
Black body/ normal wings	92

The results indicate that the genes for wings and body color are on the same chromosome. The recombinant offspring are a result of crossing over. How many map units (expressed as a percentage to the nearest whole number) apart are the two genes? The formula for calculating recombination frequency is:

Recombination Frequency = number of recombinants/total number of offspring $\times$ 100

Answer from page 102: The karyotype in Figure 4.1 is that of a male. Note the X and Y chromosomes in the bottom right corner of the karyotype.

Molecular Genetics

The Molecular Basis of Inheritance
(Biology, *11e: Chapter 16;* Focus, *2e: Chapter 13*)

YOU MUST KNOW

- The structure of DNA.
- The knowledge about DNA gained from the work of Griffith; Avery, MacLeod, and McCarty; Hershey and Chase; Wilkins and Franklin; and Watson and Crick. (LO 3.2)
- That replication is semiconservative and occurs 5′ to 3′.
- The roles of DNA polymerase, ligase, helicase, and topoisomerase in replication. (LO 3.3)
- The general differences between bacterial chromosomes and eukaryotic chromosomes.
- How DNA packaging can affect gene expression.

DNA is the genetic material (Biology, *11e: 16.1;* Focus, *2e: 13.1*)

▌ Once chromosomes were shown to carry genes, the next question had to do with which of the two organic compounds that make chromosomes, DNA or protein, was the genetic material. The path to demonstrating that DNA is the genetic material had several key steps, which we describe as follows.

   ▪ Fredrick Griffith studied two strains of the bacterium *Streptococcus pneumoniae*. In mice, bacteria of the smooth strain caused pneumonia, whereas the rough strain was nonpathogenic. However, when Griffith mixed heat-killed smooth-strain bacteria (nonpathogenic) and rough strains (nonpathogenic) and injected mice with the mixture, the mice developed pneumonia and died! Griffith concluded that the living rough strain had been transformed into the pathogenic smooth form by a heritable agent. The question remained: What was the heritable agent—protein or DNA?

   ▪ O. T. Avery, along with his colleagues McCarty and MacLeod, dedicated 14 years to identifying the "transforming agent" from Griffith's work. In 1944 they concluded that DNA was the transforming factor. Their results were greeted with interest but skepticism. Scientists had difficulty believing that a macromolecule as simple as DNA, rather than the much more complex protein molecule, could be the genetic material.

■ In 1952 **Alfred Hershey and Martha Chase** provided an unambiguous answer to the DNA or protein question utilizing *bacteriophages*—viruses that infect bacteria. Bacteriophages were excellent organisms for this study, in part because they are made of only two organic compounds: DNA and protein. Hershey and Chase used a radioactive isotope of phosphorus to tag the DNA in one culture of bacteriophages and radioactive sulfur to tag the protein in a second culture. Their results clearly showed that only the DNA entered bacteria infected by the virus; the protein never entered the cell. This research convinced scientists that DNA must be the genetic material.

■ Further evidence that DNA is the genetic material came from the laboratory of biochemist **Erwin Chargaff**. He noticed the proportion of the nucleotides making up DNA varied by species and also that the amount of adenine was approximately equal to the amount of thymine, and cytosine and guanine were equivalent. These two findings became known as *Chargaff's rules*. The basis for these rules remained unexplained until the discovery of the double helix.

■ The next big question centered on the structure of DNA. Would the structure of DNA give any clues as to how it functioned as the genetic material?

- **James Watson and Francis Crick** were the first to solve the puzzle of the structure of DNA. Critical to their success was the work of Rosalind Franklin and Maurice Wilkins, both working in the field of X-ray crystallography.
- **X-ray crystallography** is a process used to visualize molecules three dimensionally. X-rays are diffracted as they pass through the molecule, and they bounce back to produce patterns that can be interpreted through mathematical equations. Through this technique, a rough blueprint of DNA was formed and the helical structure was deduced.

■ Watson and Crick's model determined four major features of DNA. Find each major point by examining Figure 5.1 as we explain the model.

- DNA is a **double helix**, which can be described as a twisted ladder with rigid rungs. The side, or backbone, is made up of sugar-phosphate components, whereas the rungs are made up of pairs of nitrogenous bases.
- Notice the single nucleotide circled in Figure 5.1. It is composed of a sugar (deoxyribose) attached to a phosphate and a nitrogen base.
- The nitrogenous bases of DNA are adenine (A), thymine (T), guanine (G), and cytosine (C). In DNA, adenine pairs only with thymine, and guanine pairs only with cytosine. This model explains Chargaff's rules.
- Notice that the chain on the right side of the model runs in one direction, whereas the left side of the chain runs in the opposite, upside-down direction. The strands are termed **antiparallel**. The left side runs 5′ to 3′, and the opposite strand runs 3′ to 5′. (Recall that the carbons are numbered, and you will see that the number 5 carbon and number 3 carbon, and the resultant nucleotides, are flipped relative to each other.) Nucleic acid strands are always antiparallel, whether they are DNA/DNA or DNA/RNA or RNA/RNA interactions.

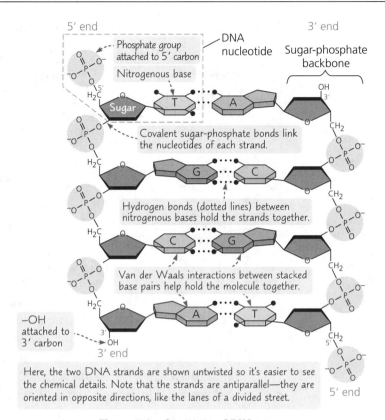

Figure 5.1   Structure of DNA

Many proteins work together in DNA replication and repair (Biology, *11e: 16.2;* Focus, *2e: 13.2*)

CONNECT WITH THE CURRICULUM FRAMEWORK

Big Idea 3

Be able to use a model to illustrate how genetic information is copied for transmission between generations. (LO 3.3) Know the roles of the enzymes involved in DNA replication.

■ **Replication** is the making of DNA from an existing DNA strand. DNA replication is *semiconservative*. This means that at the end of the first replication, each of the daughter molecules has one old strand (the dark one), derived from the parent strand of DNA, and one strand that is newly synthesized (the light one). Study Figure 5.2 to see the pattern of semiconservative replication.

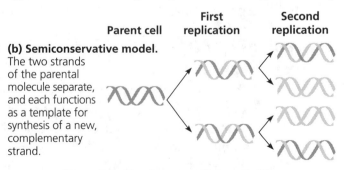

Figure 5.2   Semiconservative replication

- The replication of DNA includes six major points:
    1. The replication of DNA begins at sites called the *origins of replication.*
    2. Initiation proteins bind to the origin of replication and separate the two strands, forming a *replication bubble.* DNA replication then proceeds in both directions along the DNA strand until the molecule is copied.
    3. A group of enzymes called **DNA polymerases** catalyzes the elongation of new DNA at the replication fork.
    4. DNA polymerase adds nucleotides to the growing chain one by one, working in a 5′ to 3′ direction, matching adenine with thymine and guanine with cytosine.
    5. Recall that the strands of DNA are antiparallel. This means that DNA replication occurs continuously along the 5′ to 3′ strand, which is called the **leading strand**. The strand that runs 3′ to 5′ is copied in a series of segments and termed the **lagging strand**. Read steps 1–3 in Figure 5.3 to visualize this process.
    6. The lagging strand is synthesized in separate pieces called **Okazaki fragments**, which are then sealed together by **DNA ligase** (steps 4–7, Figure 5.3), forming a continuous DNA strand.

- There are several factors contributing to the accuracy of DNA replication:
    - The specificity of base pairing (A = T, G = C)
    - **Mismatch repair**, in which special repair enzymes fix incorrectly paired nucleotides
    - **Nucleotide excision repair**, in which incorrectly placed nucleotides are excised or removed by enzymes termed **nucleases**, and the gap left over is filled in with the correct nucleotides

- The fact that DNA polymerase can add nucleotides only to the 3′ end of a molecule means that it would have no way to complete the 5′ end of the DNA molecule at the end of the chromosome. Every time the chromosome is replicated for mitosis, a small portion of the tip of the chromosome is removed. To avoid losing the terminal genes, the linear ends of eukaryotic chromosomes are "capped" with **telomeres**—short, repetitive nucleotide sequences that do not contain genes. This means that any given cell has a finite number of times it can divide before essential information is lost. In tumor cells, such as HeLa cells, a mutation activates an enzyme called *telomerase*, which prevents this degradation and renders the cells "immortal."

A chromosome consists of a DNA molecule packed together with proteins (Biology, *11e: 16.3;* Focus, *2e: 13.3*)

- A bacterial chromosome is one double-stranded, circular DNA molecule associated with a small amount of protein.
- Eukaryotic chromosomes are linear DNA molecules associated with large amounts of protein.
- In eukaryotic cells, DNA and proteins are packed together as **chromatin**.

Overview

Lagging strand

Leading strand

Leading strand

Origin of replication

Leading strand

Lagging strand

Lagging strand

Overall directions of replication

3 The leading strand is synthesized continuously in the 5′ to 3′ direction by DNA pol III.

Leading strand template

Leading strand

2 Molecules of single-strand binding protein stabilize the unwound template strands.

DNA pol III

Primase

Primer

5′

3′

1 Helicase unwinds the parental double helix.

Parental DNA

4 Primase begins synthesis of the RNA primer for the fifth Okazaki fragment.

DNA pol III

3′ 5′

5′

5 DNA pol III is completing synthesis of fragment 4. When it reaches the RNA primer on fragment 3, it will detach and begin adding DNA nucleotides to the 3′ end of the fragment 5 primer in the replication fork.

Lagging strand

Lagging strand template

6 DNA pol I removes the primer from the 5′ end of fragment 2, replacing it with DNA nucleotides added one by one to the 3′ end of fragment 3. After the last addition, the backbone is left with a free 3′ end.

DNA pol I

3

2

DNA ligase

1

3′

5′

3′

5′

7 DNA ligase joins the 3′ end of fragment 2 to the 5′ end of fragment 1.

Figure 5.3 DNA replication

- As DNA becomes more highly packaged, it becomes less accessible to transcription enzymes, which reduces gene expression. In interphase cells, most chromatin is in the highly extended form (**euchromatin**) and is available for transcription. When the euchromatin condenses to chromosomes during mitotic division, the more condensed chromatin (**heterochromatin**) is no longer available for transcription. Heterochromatin is largely inaccessible to transcription enzymes and, thus, generally is not transcribed.
- Barr bodies (permanently condensed X chromosomes seen in the cells of females) are another example of heterochromatin. The condensing of one X chromosome means only one of the two X chromosomes will be available for transcription in each cell.

Gene Expression: From Gene to Protein
(Biology, *11e: Chapter 17*; Focus, *2e: Chapter 14*)

YOU MUST KNOW

- How RNA and DNA are similar and different and how this defines their roles.
- The differences between *replication, transcription*, and *translation* and the role of DNA and RNA in each process.
- How eukaryotic cells modify RNA after transcription.
- How genetic material is translated into polypeptides. (LO 3.4)
- How mutations can change the amino acid sequence of a protein and be able to predict how a mutation can result in changes in gene expression. (LO 3.6)

TIP FROM THE READERS

This is the central chapter for molecular genetics. It is one of the top five chapters you must know to perform well on the AP exam!

Be sure you know the difference between *replication* (DNA to DNA), *transcription* (DNA to RNA), and *translation* (RNA to protein). In essay questions that use these terms, often 20% of the students confuse the processes!

Genes specify proteins via transcription and translation
(Biology, *11e: 17.1*; Focus, *2e: 14.1*)

- **Gene expression** is the process by which DNA directs the synthesis of proteins (or, in some cases, RNAs). It has two stages: transcription and translation.
- The **one gene–one polypeptide hypothesis** states that each gene codes for a polypeptide, which can be—or can constitute a part of—a protein.
- **Transcription** is the synthesis of RNA using DNA as a template. It takes place in the nucleus of eukaryotic cells.
- **Messenger RNA**, or **mRNA**, is produced during transcription. It carries the genetic message of DNA to the protein-making machinery of the cell in the cytoplasm, the *ribosome*.
- In eukaryotes, transcription results in *pre-mRNA*, which undergoes **RNA processing** (also known as RNA editing) to yield the final mRNA.

- In prokaryotes, transcription produces mRNA which is not processed. Transcription and translation can occur simultaneously.
- **Translation** is the production of a polypeptide chain using the mRNA transcript and occurs at the ribosomes.
- The directional flow of genetic information is **DNA ⇒ RNA ⇒ Protein**. This has been dubbed the *central dogma of biology*.
- The instructions for building a polypeptide chain are written as a series of three-nucleotide groups; this is called a *triplet code*. The mRNA base triplets are called **codons**. *They are written in the 5′ to 3′ direction.*
- During transcription, only one strand of the DNA is transcribed, and it is called the **template strand**. The mRNA that is produced is said to be *complementary* to the original DNA strand.

> ### *TIP FROM THE READERS*
> On recent AP exams, we have noted that students can be confused by whether a DNA strand is designated as a *template strand* or as the *coding strand*. Think of it this way: One DNA strand is actually used by RNA polymerase as the scaffold upon which a strand of mRNA complementary to it is assembled. This is the *template strand* because it serves as the pattern or instructions for mRNA. The other DNA strand will have the same nucleotide sequence as the newly coded mRNA (except for the substitutions of thymine for uracil), so it is called the *coding strand*.

- The mRNA codons are read (translated into amino acids) based on a consistent *reading frame*—the groups of three must be read in the correct groupings in order for translation to be successful. If a single nucleotide is lost, the reading frame is shifted, and different amino acids are specified.
- A **codon** is an mRNA triplet. The 64 different codons include 3 stop codons and 61 codons that code for the 20 different amino acids. Most amino acids can therefore be designated by more than one codon.
- There are 64 codons. Because there are four different RNA nucleotides (A, U, C, and G), taking them three at a time results in 64 different codons ($4^3 = 64$). One of these triplets serves as a "start" codon, and 3 serve as "stop" signals. The remainder of the codons all code for specific amino acids. Because there are only 20 amino acids, the genetic code is *redundant*, meaning that some of the amino acids are coded for by more than one triplet codon.

Transcription is the DNA-directed synthesis of RNA: a closer look (Biology, *11e: 17.2; Focus, 2e: 14.2*)

- **RNA polymerase** is an enzyme that separates the two DNA strands and connects the RNA nucleotides as they base-pair along the DNA template strand.
- The RNA polymerases can add RNA nucleotides only to the 3′ end of the strand, so RNA elongates in the 5′ to 3′ direction. As RNA nucleotides are added, remember that uracil replaces thymine when base pairing to adenine.
- The DNA sequence at which RNA polymerase attaches is called the **promoter**, whereas the DNA sequence that signals the end of transcription is called the **terminator**.

- A **transcription unit** is the entire stretch of DNA that is transcribed into an RNA molecule. A transcription unit may code for a polypeptide or an RNA, such as transfer RNA or ribosomal RNA.
- There are three main stages of transcription:

1. **Initiation:** In bacteria, RNA polymerase recognizes and binds to the promoter. In eukaryotes, RNA polymerase II, the specific RNA polymerase that transcribes mRNA, cannot bind to the promoter without supporting help from proteins known as transcription factors. **Transcription factors** assist the binding of RNA polymerase to the promoter and, thus, the initiation of transcription. The whole complex of RNA polymerase II and transcription factors is called a **transcription initiation complex** (Figure 5.4).

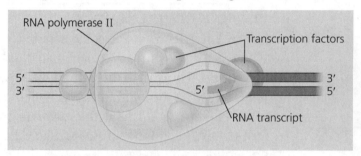

Figure 5.4 Transcription initiation complex

2. **Elongation:** RNA polymerase moves along the DNA, continuing to untwist the double helix. RNA nucleotides are continually added to the 3' end of the growing chain. As the complex moves down the DNA strand, the double helix reforms, with the new RNA molecule straggling away from the DNA template. Find these key steps in Figure 5.5.

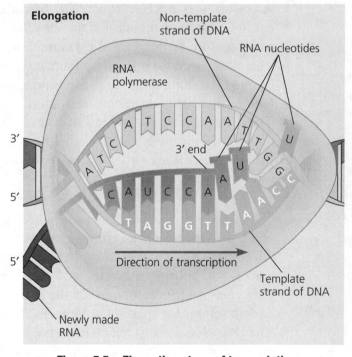

Figure 5.5 Elongation stage of transcription

3. **Termination:** After RNA polymerase transcribes a terminator sequence in the DNA, the RNA transcript is released, and the polymerase detaches.

Eukaryotic cells modify RNA after transcription (Biology, *11e: 17.3;* Focus, *2e: 14.3*)

▮ In eukaryotes, there are a couple of key posttranscriptional modifications to RNA—the addition of a **5′ cap** and the addition of a **poly-A tail**. The 5′ cap is a modified guanine nucleotide that is added onto the 5′ end of the mRNA. The poly-A tail is a group of 50 to 250 adenine nucleotides added to the 3′ end. What are their functions?

▮ The 5′ cap and the poly-A tail facilitate the export of mRNA from the nucleus, help protect the mRNA from degradation by enzymes, and facilitate the attachment of the mRNA to the ribosome.

▮ **RNA splicing** occurs in eukaryotic cells. In RNA splicing, large portions of the newly synthesized RNA strand are removed. The sections of the mRNA that are spliced out are called **introns**, and the sections that remain—and subsequently spliced together by a *spliceosome*—are called **exons**. The spliceosome is composed of small RNAs and proteins. Use Figure 5.6 to help you visualize how spliceosomes remove the introns and splice together the exons to produce functional mRNA.

Figure 5.6   Role of spliceosomes in pre-mRNA splicing

- One amazing thing about how spliceosomes work is the role of a special kind of RNA, termed **small nuclear RNA** (snRNA). The snRNA plays a major role in catalyzing the excision of the introns and joining of the exons. When RNA serves a catalytic role, the molecule is termed a **ribozyme**. For many years, it was thought that only proteins (functioning as enzymes) could be catalytic, but the discovery of ribozymes totally changed that idea!
- Another rethinking that has taken place came with the realization that we have only about 20,000 genes to make approximately 100,000 polypeptides. One gene can often make more than one polypeptide. An intron removed in the production of one polypeptide can be an exon in a second polypeptide made from the same gene! Alternative RNA splicing allows for different combinations of exons, resulting in more than one polypeptide per gene.

Translation is the RNA-directed synthesis of a polypeptide: a closer look (Biology, *11e: 17.4*; Focus, *2e: 14.4*)

- In addition to mRNA, two additional types of RNA play important roles in translation: transfer RNA (tRNA) and ribosomal RNA (rRNA).
- **tRNAs** transfer amino acids from the cytoplasm to the mRNA at the ribosome for assembling the polypeptide chain. Each type of **tRNA** is specific for a particular amino acid; at one end it loosely binds the amino acid, and at the other end it has a nucleotide triplet called an **anticodon**, which allows it to pair specifically with a complementary codon on the mRNA.
- A ribosome is composed of **rRNA** and protein and has 2 subunits. The large subunit of a ribosome has three binding sites for tRNA molecules. Locate each tRNA binding site in Figure 5.7 and Figure 5.8 as you read the descriptions that follow:

  - A **P site**, which holds the tRNA that carries the growing polypeptide chain
  - An **A site**, which holds the tRNA that carries the amino acid that will be added to the chain next
  - An **E site**, which is the exit site for each tRNA

- Translation, like transcription, can be divided into three stages:

  1. **Initiation:** Organize initiation into these three steps. Use Figure 5.7 to find each step.

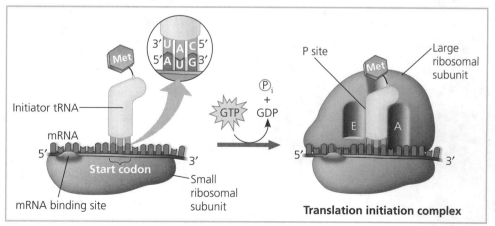

Figure 5.7   Initiation stage of translation

A. A small ribosomal subunit binds to mRNA in such a way that the first codon of the mRNA strand, which is always AUG, is placed in the proper position.

B. The tRNA with anticodon UAC, which carries the amino acid methionine, hydrogen bonds to the first codon (initiation factors are proteins that assist in holding all this together).

C. The large ribosomal subunit attaches, allowing the tRNA with methionine to attach to the P site. Notice that the A site is now available to the tRNA that will bring the second amino acid.

2. **Elongation:** Read about the three steps of elongation—codon recognition, peptide bond formation, and translocation—using Figure 5.8. This is an important idea; follow the explanations and the diagrams carefully.

3. **Termination:** A stop codon in the mRNA is reached, and translation stops. A protein called release factor binds to the stop codon, and the polypeptide is freed from the ribosome.

Polypeptides fold to assume their specific conformation, and they are almost always modified further to render them functional. The destination of a protein is often determined by the sequence of about 20 amino acids at the leading end of the polypeptide chain. The **signal peptide**, the sequence of the leading 20 or

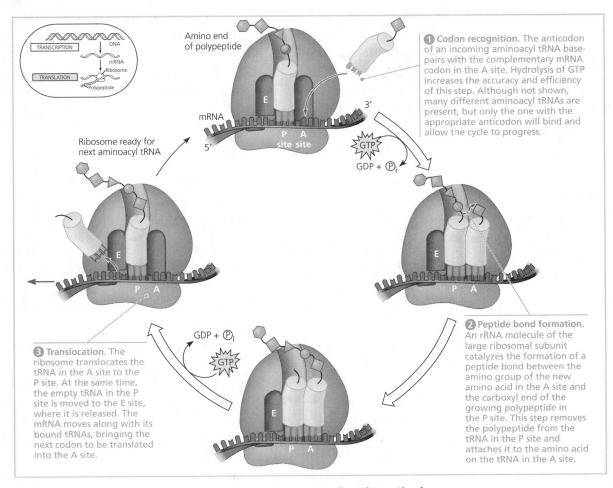

Figure 5.8 Protein synthesis

so amino acids, serves as a sort of cellular zip code, directing proteins to their final destination.

Mutations of one or a few nucleotides can affect protein structure and function (Biology, *11e: 17.5*; Focus, *2e: 14.5*)

▌ Mutations are alterations in the genetic material of the cell; **point mutations** are alterations of just one nucleotide base pair of a gene. One nucleotide and its partner are replaced with another pair of nucleotides. These are the basic types of point mutations:

- **Missense mutations** are those substitutions that enable the codon to still code for an amino acid, although it might not be the correct one.
- **Nonsense mutations** are those substitutions that change a regular amino acid codon into a stop codon, ceasing translation.
- **Silent mutations** are those where a base pair substitution does not alter the specified amino acid. Recall that several amino acids are coded for by several different triplet codons. Because the genetic code is redundant, it is possible for the codon to be changed without changing the amino acid that is specified.

▌ **Insertions** and **deletions** refer to the additions and losses of nucleotide pairs in a gene. If they interfere with the codon groupings (reading frame), they can cause a **frameshift mutation**, which causes the mRNA to be read incorrectly on each remaining codon.

▌ **Mutagens** are substances or forces that interact with DNA in ways that cause mutations. X-rays and other forms of radiation are known mutagens, as are certain chemicals such as asbestos and compounds in cigarette smoke.

Regulation of Gene Expression

(Biology, *11e: Chapter 18*; Focus, *2e: Chapter 15*)

YOU MUST KNOW

- That genes can be activated by *inducer* molecules or that they can be inhibited by the presence of a *repressor* as they interact with regulatory proteins or sequences. (EK 3.B.1)
- That a *regulatory gene* is a sequence of DNA that codes for a regulatory protein such as a repressor protein.
- How the components of an operon function to regulate gene expression in both repressible and inducible operons.
- How positive and negative control function in gene expression. (EK 3.B.1)
- The impact of DNA methylation and histone acetylation on gene expression.
- How timing and coordination of specific events are regulated in normal development, including pattern formation and induction. (EK 2.E.1)
- The role of microRNAs in control of cellular functions.
- The role of gene regulation in embryonic development and cancer.

Bacteria often respond to environmental change by regulating transcription (Biology, *11e: 18.1; Focus, 2e: 15.1*)

▌ Every cell in an organism has the same genome, yet not all genes are expressed in each cell type. Within a cell, certain genes are being activated or repressed while others are continuously expressed. Patterns of gene expression are altered in response to internal signals as well as changes in environmental conditions.

▌ Unraveling the secrets of gene expression began with bacteria, where only the genes whose products are needed by the cell are expressed. A look at how this is regulated in bacteria will provide insights into the basic elements of gene expression.

▌ In bacteria, genes are often clustered into groups called *operons*, which allows several related genes to be controlled as a unit. Figure 5.9 shows a repressible operon with an inactive repressor. Locate each part of the operon and the regulatory gene as you read the accompanying text.

▌ An **operon** consists of three parts:

▪ An **operator** that controls the access of RNA polymerase to the genes. The operator is found within the promoter site or between the promoter and the protein coding genes of the operon.

▪ The **promoter**, which is where RNA polymerase attaches.

▪ The **genes of the operon**. This is the entire stretch of DNA required for all the enzymes produced by the operon.

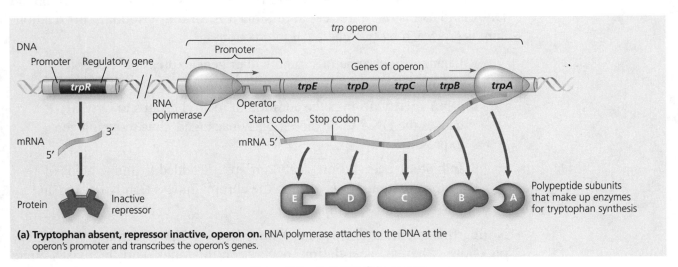

(a) Tryptophan absent, repressor inactive, operon on. RNA polymerase attaches to the DNA at the operon's promoter and transcribes the operon's genes.

Figure 5.9   A repressible operon

- Located some distance from the operon is a regulatory gene. **Regulatory genes** produce repressor proteins that may bind to the operator site. When a regulatory protein occupies the operator site, RNA polymerase is blocked from the genes of the operon. In this situation the operon is off.

- A **repressible operon** is normally *on* but can be inhibited. This type of operon is normally anabolic, building an essential organic molecule. The repressor protein produced by the regulatory gene is inactive. If the organic molecule being produced by the operon is provided to the cell, the molecule can act as a **corepressor** and bind to the repressor protein, activating it. The activated repressor protein binds to the operator site, shutting down the operon. This type of repressible operon is shown in Figure 5.9. Figure 18.3b in *Campbell Biology*, 11e, or Figure 15.3b in *Focus*, 2e, shows the corepressor turning off the operon.

- An **inducible operon** is normally *off* but can be activated. The *lac* operon is an example. Bacteria make only the enzymes to digest lactose when lactose is available in the environment, so the presence of lactose will *induce* the expression of these enzymes. This type of operon is normally catabolic, breaking down food molecules for energy. The repressor protein produced by the regulatory gene is active. To turn an inducible operon on, a specific small molecule, called an **inducer**, binds to and inactivates the repressor protein. With the repressor out of the operator site, RNA polymerase can access the genes of the operon. The *lac* operon is an example of an inducible operon and can be seen in Figure 18.4 in *Campbell Biology*, 11e, or Figure 15.4 in *Focus*, 2e.

Eukaryotic gene expression is regulated at many stages (Biology, *11e: 18.2;* Focus, *2e: 15.2*)

- Eukaryotic genes can be turned off and on at any point along the pathway from gene to functional protein. Further, the differences between cell types are not caused by different genes being present but by **differential gene expression**, the expression of different genes by cells with the same genome.

- Recall that the fundamental packaging unit of DNA, the nucleosome, consists of DNA bound to small proteins termed histones. The more tightly bound DNA is to its histones, the less accessible it is for transcription. This relationship is governed by two chemical interactions:

  - Changes in chromatin structure alter gene expression. Several examples follow:
  - **DNA methylation** is the addition of methyl groups to DNA. It causes the DNA to be more tightly packaged, thus reducing gene expression.

  - In **histone acetylation**, acetyl groups are added to amino acids of histone proteins, thus making the chromatin less tightly packed and encouraging transcription.

- Notice that methylation occurs primarily on DNA and reduces gene expression, whereas acetylation occurs on histones and increases gene expression.

- **Epigenetic inheritance** is the inheritance of traits transmitted by mechanisms not directly involving the nucleotide sequence. The DNA sequence is not changed; only its expression is changed. DNA methylation alters gene expression in this manner.
- *Transcription initiation* is another important control point in gene expression. At this stage, DNA control elements that bind transcription factors are involved in regulation.
- The **transcription initiation complex** greatly enhances gene expression. Study Figure 5.10 and note its essential elements. DNA sequences far from the gene, termed **enhancer regions**, are bound to the promoter region by proteins termed **activators**.
- The control of gene expression may also occur after transcription and just after translation, when proteins are processed.
- Coordinately controlled genes, such as the genes coding for the enzymes of a metabolic pathway, are expressed together. This is possible even though the genes in a given pathway may be scattered on different chromosomes. All of

Figure 5.10   Formation of transcription initiation complex plays a key role in gene expression

the genes that code for the enzymes of the pathway share the same control elements. In general, eukaryotes do not have operons.

STUDY TIP

To summarize how gene regulation results in differential gene expression, understand the following:

1. **Inducers** turn on specific genes.
2. **Repressors** inhibit expression of specific genes.
3. Inducers and repressors interact with regulatory proteins or regulatory sequences.
4. **Regulatory proteins** can stimulate gene expression by binding DNA and stimulating transcription (*positive control*) or blocking transcription (*negative control*).
5. **Transcription factors** can be general or specific and act as either activators or repressors. They will bind to the regulatory region of a gene and their combination determines how much, if any, of the gene product will be produced.

Noncoding RNAs play multiple roles in controlling gene expression (Biology, *11e: 18.3;* Focus, *2e: 15.3*)

▌ Recent research has indicated that large, diverse populations of RNA molecules in the cell play crucial roles in regulating gene expression. Small molecules of single-stranded RNA can complex with proteins and influence gene expression.

  ▪ Two types of RNA, *micro RNAs* (*miRNA*) and *small interfering RNAs* (*siRNAs*), can bind to mRNA and degrade the mRNA or bind to mRNA and block its translation. The blocking of gene expression in this manner is called RNA interference (RNAi).

  ▪ The existence of miRNAs was unknown 25 years ago, and yet it is estimated that at least one-half of all human genes may be regulated by them! Other noncoding RNAs (ncRNAs) including piRNAs and lncRNAs have been discovered and have the ability to regulate gene expression at multiple steps and in many ways. Watch for more information about their importance in future years.

A program of differential gene expression leads to the different cell types in a multicellular organism (Biology, *11e: 18.4;* Focus, *2e:16.1*)

▌ The zygote undergoes transformation through three interrelated processes:

  1. **Cell division** is the series of mitotic divisions that increases the number of cells. However, this would just result in a ball of cells.
  2. **Cell differentiation** is the process by which cells become specialized in structure and function. This is accomplished by differential gene expression resulting from different activators and repressors in the cells.
  3. **Morphogenesis** gives an organism its shape.

■ What controls differentiation and morphogenesis?

1. **Cytoplasmic determinants** are maternal substances in the egg that influence the course of early development. These are distributed unevenly in the early cells of the embryo and result in different effects by regulating gene expression during differentiation.

2. The environment around a particular cell also affects gene expression in embryonic cells. As the number of embryonic cells increases, **cell-cell signals** result from molecules, such as growth factors produced by one cell influencing neighboring cells, a process called **induction**. The target cells have cell-surface receptors, and the signaling molecules activate signaling pathways. This sends a cell down a specific developmental path and causes cells to differentiate.

■ **Determination** is the series of events that leads to observable differentiation of a cell. Differentiation is caused by cell-cell signals and is irreversible. During the time when most cells are differentiating, some cells are genetically programmed to die. This "programmed cell death" is called **apoptosis** and plays a crucial role in the developing embryo. This is how the digits of appendages are formed and how the tail of a tadpole disappears.

■ **Pattern formation** sets up the body plan and is a result of cytoplasmic determinants and inductive signals. This is what determines head and tail, left and right, back and front. An uneven distribution of substances called **morphogens** plays a role in establishing these axes.

■ **Homeotic genes** are master control genes that control pattern formation.

Cancer results from genetic changes that affect cell cycle control
(Biology, *11e: 18.5;* Focus, *2e: 16.3*)

■ **Oncogenes** are cancer-causing genes; **proto-oncogenes** are genes that code for proteins responsible for normal cell growth. Proto-oncogenes become oncogenes when a mutation occurs that causes an increase in the product of the proto-oncogene or an increase in the activity of each protein molecule produced by the gene.

■ **Cancer** can also be caused by a mutation in a gene whose products normally inhibit cell division. These genes are called **tumor-suppressor genes**.

■ An important tumor-suppressor gene is the **p53 gene**. The product of this gene is a protein that suppresses cancer in four ways:

1. The *p53* protein can activate the *p21* gene, whose product halts the cell cycle by binding to cyclin-dependent kinases. This allows time for DNA to be repaired before the resumption of cell division.

2. The *p53* protein activates a group of miRNAs, which inhibit the cell cycle.

3. The *p53* protein turns on genes directly involved in DNA repair.

4. When DNA damage is too great to repair, the *p53* protein activates "suicide" genes whose products cause cell death, a process termed **apoptosis**.

- The multistep model of cancer development is based on the idea that cancer results from the accumulation of mutations that occur throughout life. The longer we live, the more likely it is that mutations will accumulate and that cancer might develop.
- *Embryonic development* represents what happens when gene regulation proceeds correctly and *cancer* shows what can happen when gene regulation goes awry.

CONNECT WITH THE CURRICULUM FRAMEWORK

Big Idea 3

Intercellular and intracellular signals mediate gene expression, and this underlies many diverse processes including cancer, development in the embryo, seed germination and fruit ripening, and morphological changes such as those seen in yeast cells when mating pheromones are present. (EK 3.B. 2) The importance of this topic to your understanding of biology cannot be overstated.

Viruses

(Biology, *11e: Chapter 19;* Focus, *2e: Chapter 17*)

YOU MUST KNOW

- The components of a virus.
- The differences between lytic and lysogenic cycles.
- How viruses can introduce genetic variation into host organisms. (LO 3.29)
- Mechanisms that introduce genetic variation into viral populations. (LO 3.30)

A *virus consists of a nucleic acid surrounded by a protein coat* (Biology, *11e: 19.1;* Focus, *2e: 17.1*)

- Smaller than ribosomes, the tiniest viruses are about 20 nm across.
- The two essential components of a virus are a protein shell or **capsid** that surrounds **the genetic material** (either double- or single-stranded DNA *or* double- or single-stranded RNA).
- Many viruses found in animals have membranous **viral envelopes** that surround the capsid and aid the viruses in infecting their hosts. (See Figure 5.11.)
- **Bacteriophages**, or **phages**, are viruses that infect bacterial cells.

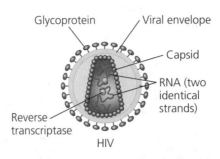

Figure 5.11   Structure of HIV. Note the components of a typical virus: nucleic acid, capsid. This virus also has an envelope, and reverse transcriptase

Viruses replicate only in host cells (Biology, *11e: 19.2;* Focus, *2e: 17.2*)

▌ Viruses have a limited **host range**. This means they can infect only a very limited variety of hosts. *Example:* The human cold virus infects only cells of the upper respiratory tract.

▌ Viral reproduction occurs only in host cells. Two variations have been studied in bacteriophages. Read the following; then study Figure 5.12.

1. The **lytic cycle** ends in the death of the host cell by rupturing it (lysis). In this cycle, a bacteriophage injects its DNA into a host cell and takes over the host cell's machinery to synthesize new copies of the viral DNA as well as protein coats. These new viral components self-assemble, and the bacterial cell is lysed, releasing multiple copies of the virus.

2. In the **lysogenic cycle**, the bacteriophage's DNA becomes incorporated into the host cell's DNA and is replicated along with the host cell's genome. The viral DNA is known as a **prophage**. Under certain conditions, the prophage will enter the lytic cycle, described earlier.

▌ Why haven't phages exterminated all bacteria? Lysogeny is one reason, but bacteria also have their own defenses against viruses.

1. **Natural selection** favors bacterial mutants with surface proteins that are no longer recognized as receptors by a particular type of phage.

2. **Restriction enzymes** destroy the foreign DNA of the phage by cutting it up. The bacterial DNA is methylated in a way that prevents attack by its own restriction enzymes.

3. The **CRISPR-Cas9 system** is a third bacterial defense against viral invasion. Repetitive DNA sequences (CRISPRs) correspond to DNA from a phage that had infected the cell. The CRISPr DNA interacts with nucleases, called Cas9 proteins. Nucleases are enzymes that identify and cut DNA so the viral DNA is rendered harmless.

▌ The CRISPR-Cas9 system is used in the laboratory to alter genes in cells of other organisms and is a major new DNA technology that you should spend time learning more about. See *Biology*, 11e, Concept 20.2, or *Focus*, 2e, Concept 13.4.

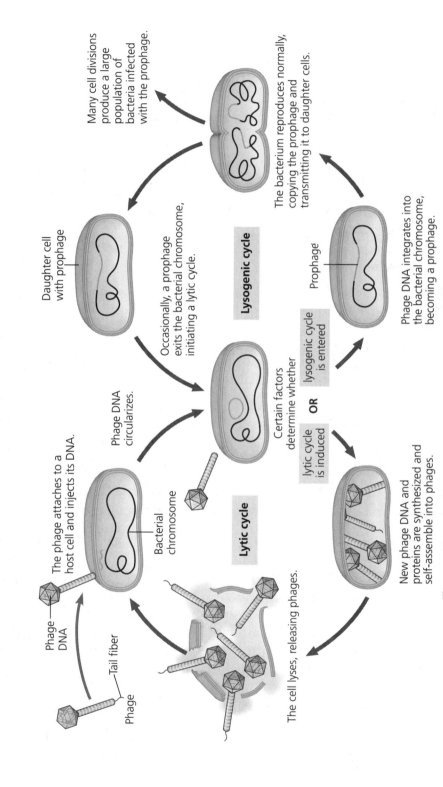

The phage attaches to a host cell and injects its DNA.

Phage DNA

Tail fiber

Phage

Phage DNA circularizes.

Bacterial chromosome

Lytic cycle

The cell lyses, releasing phages.

New phage DNA and proteins are synthesized and self-assemble into phages.

Certain factors determine whether

lytic cycle is induced **OR** lysogenic cycle is entered

Occasionally, a prophage exits the bacterial chromosome, initiating a lytic cycle.

Lysogenic cycle

Daughter cell with prophage

Many cell divisions produce a large population of bacteria infected with the prophage.

The bacterium reproduces normally, copying the prophage and transmitting it to daughter cells.

Phage DNA integrates into the bacterial chromosome, becoming a prophage.

Prophage

Figure 5.12   Infection of a bacterial cell by a bacteriophage. Note the two cycles

- **Retroviruses** are RNA viruses that use the enzyme **reverse transcriptase** to transcribe DNA from an RNA template. The new DNA then permanently integrates into a chromosome in the nucleus of an animal cell. The host transcribes the viral DNA into RNA that may be used to synthesize viral proteins or may be released from the host cell to infect more cells. *Example:* HIV is a retrovirus.

- Viruses have the ability to introduce genetic change into organisms as well as to undergo rapid genetic change themselves. Moving from one host to another, viruses may pick up pieces of the first host's DNA and carry it to the next cell to be infected. This is very common in bacteria infected by viruses, where the process is called **transduction**.

- RNA viruses lack replication error-checking mechanisms and thus have higher rates of mutation. Mutations may accumulate rapidly and give rise to diverse clones of the virus within one organism, as occurs in humans with AIDS, or may result in new genetic strains that could cause disease. This rapid mutation of viruses explains why there is no vaccine against the common cold.

Viruses and prions are formidable pathogens in animals and plants (Biology, *11e: 19.3; Focus, 2e: 17.3*)

- This concept is worth reading about thoroughly in your text! Many of the diseases that are in the news today are discussed—including their history, transmission, and treatment.

- Viral disease symptoms may be caused by direct viral harm to cells or by the action of the immune system. *Vaccines* stimulate the immune system to defend the host against specific viruses. However, RNA viruses in particular mutate frequently as RNA polymerase does not have a proofreading function and errors arise during replication of the RNA genome. Many viral diseases mutate so rapidly it is difficult to combat them. This is why persons with HIV infection may take a "cocktail" of antiviral drugs and why there is no vaccination against the common cold.

- **Emerging viral diseases** are usually not new but rather are caused by existing viruses. The H1N1 2009 flu virus was a new combination of pig, human, and avian viral genes that caused a *pandemic* (global epidemic). HIV, Ebola, West Nile, Zika, and Chikungunya are all examples of emerging viruses.

- How have these emerging viruses burst on the scene? One reason is the high mutation rate of RNA viruses, a second is the ability of people to travel globally with relative ease, and a third is the spread of existing viruses from other animals. The viruses that are transmitted by mosquitoes are expanding their distribution because of climate change.

- **Prions** are misfolded, infectious proteins that cause the misfolding of normal proteins in the brains of various animal species. Their damage to the brain accumulates over time and eventually leads to death. *Examples* of diseases caused by prions include mad cow disease and, in humans, Creutzfeldt-Jakob disease.

DNA Tools and Biotechnology

(Biology, *11e: Chapter 20; Focus, 2e: Concepts 13.4, 15.4, 16.2*)

WHAT'S IMPORTANT TO KNOW?

The Curriculum Framework expects you to be familiar with techniques of modern biotechnology as well as examples of products of genetic engineering. Your teacher may not cover all of the possibilities described in this chapter.

YOU MUST KNOW

- The terminology of biotechnology.
- How plasmids are used in bacterial transformation to clone genes.
- The key ideas that make polymerase chain reaction (PCR) possible and applications of this technology.
- How gel electrophoresis can be used to separate DNA fragments or protein molecules.
- Information that can be determined from DNA gel results, such as fragment sizes and RFLP analysis.

DNA sequencing and cloning are valuable tools in genetic engineering and biological inquiry (Biology, *11e: 20.1; Focus, 2e: 13.4*)

▌ The key to unlocking the concepts of biotechnology is to understand the terms. Know the following commonly used terms:

- **Genetic engineering** is the process of manipulating genes and genomes for practical purposes.
- **DNA sequencing** is used to determine the complete nucleotide sequence of a DNA molecule and uses the principle of complementary base pairing. The entire genome of numerous organisms, including humans, has been completed. The Human Genome Project was completed in 2003 and marked a turning point in biology because it sparked remarkable technological advances in DNA sequencing. The process continues to get faster and less expensive with each generation of technology.
- **Biotechnology** is the process of manipulating organisms or their components for the purpose of making useful products.
- **Recombinant DNA** is DNA that has been artificially made, using DNA from different sources—and often different species. An example is the introduction of a human gene into an *E. coli* bacterium in an engineered plasmid.
- **Gene cloning** is the process by which scientists can produce multiple copies of specific segments of DNA that they can then work with in the lab. Many bacteria have DNA outside the main circular chromosome

in plasmids. A **plasmid** is a small, circular extra-chromosomal loop of DNA. Plasmids are often used in biotechnology.

■ **Restriction enzymes** are used to cut strands of DNA at specific locations (called **restriction sites**). They are mostly derived from bacteria where they serve the important function of protection against invading viruses.

■ When a DNA molecule is cut by restriction enzymes, the result will always be a set of **restriction fragments**, which may have at least one single-stranded end, called a **sticky end**. Sticky ends can form hydrogen bonds with complementary single-stranded pieces of DNA. These unions can be sealed with the enzyme **DNA ligase**. Follow this important step in *Biology,* 11e, Figure 20.6, or *Focus,* 2e, Figure 13.25.

■ Follow the steps that may occur to clone a gene in Figure 5.13.

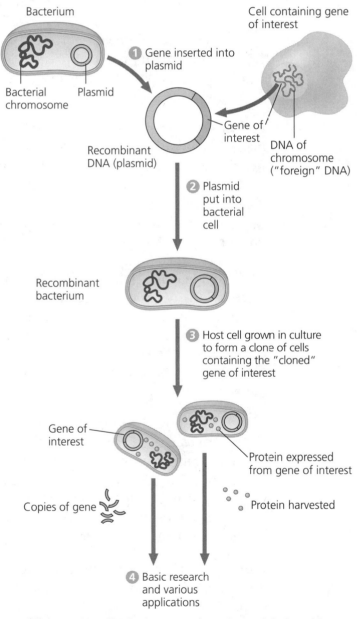

Figure 5.13   Cloning a gene using a bacterial plasmid

1. *Identify and isolate the gene of interest and a **cloning vector***. The vector will carry the DNA sequence to be cloned and is often a bacterial plasmid.
2. *Cut both the gene of interest and the vector with the same restriction enzyme*. This gives the plasmid and the human gene complementary sticky ends.
3. *Join the two pieces of DNA*. Form recombinant plasmids by mixing the plasmids with the DNA fragments. The human DNA fragments can be sealed into the plasmid using *DNA ligase*.
4. *Get the vector carrying the gene of interest into a host cell*. The plasmids are taken up by the bacterium by *transformation*. The process of transformation is a key part of Investigation 8.
5. *Select for cells that have been transformed*. The bacterial cells carrying the clones must be identified or selected. This can be done by linking the gene of interest to an antibiotic resistance gene or a *reporter gene* such as green fluorescent protein. In AP Investigation 8, we use an ampicillin-resistant plasmid. Any bacterial cells that do not pick up the plasmid by transformation will be killed when grown on agar with the antibiotic ampicillin.

▌ For certain applications, the next step is finding the gene of interest among the many colonies present after transformation. A process known as **nucleic acid hybridization** can be used to find the gene. If we know at least part of the nucleotide sequence of the gene of interest, we can synthesize a **probe** complementary to it. For example, if the known sequence is G-G-C-T-A-A, then we would synthesize the complementary probe C-C-G-A-T-T. If we make the probe radioactive or fluorescent, the probe will be easy to track, taking us to the proper gene of interest.

▌ **PCR** (polymerase chain reaction) is a method used to amplify a particular piece of DNA without the use of cells. PCR is used to amplify DNA when the source is impure or scanty (as it would be at a crime scene). After 33 cycles, over 1 billion molecules match the target sequence! Figure 5.14 shows the basic steps of the PCR procedure.

▌ **Gel electrophoresis** is a lab technique used to separate macromolecules, primarily DNA and proteins. The steps of this separation of DNA include:

1. An *electric current* is applied to the field. DNA is negatively charged and migrates to the positive electrode.
2. A gel made of a polymer is used as a matrix to separate molecules by size. The gel allows smaller molecules to move more easily than larger fragments of DNA.
3. The DNA must be stained or tagged for visualization.

Follow Figure 5.15 as the specific steps are shown. A more detailed discussion of this process is found in Investigation 9, which begins on page 325.

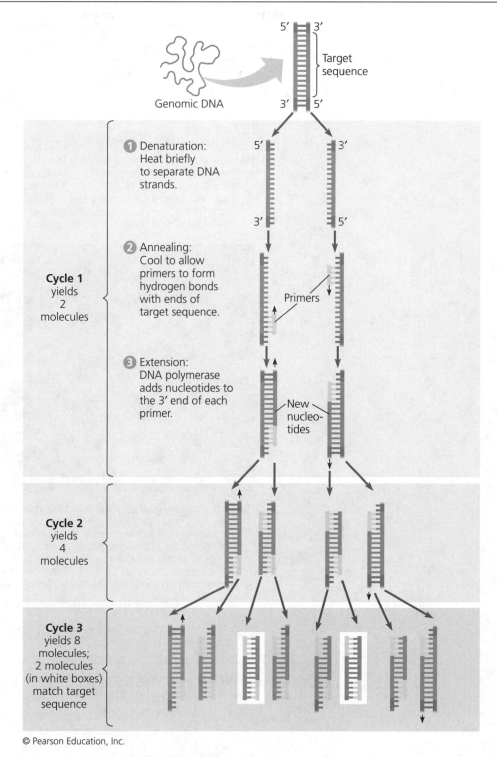

Figure 5.14   Polymerase chain reaction (PCR)

Cycle 1
yields
2
molecules

① Denaturation:
Heat briefly
to separate DNA
strands.

② Annealing:
Cool to allow
primers to form
hydrogen bonds
with ends of
target sequence.

③ Extension:
DNA polymerase
adds nucleotides to
the 3′ end of each
primer.

Cycle 2
yields
4
molecules

Cycle 3
yields 8
molecules;
2 molecules
(in white boxes)
match target
sequence

Target
sequence

Genomic DNA

Primers

New
nucleo-
tides

© Pearson Education, Inc.

▌ **Restriction fragment length polymorphisms (RFLPs)** result from small differences in DNA sequences and can be detected by electrophoresis. The difference in banding patterns after electrophoresis allows for diagnosis of disease or is used to answer paternity and identity questions.

(a) Each sample, a mixture of different DNA molecules, is placed in a separate well near one end of a thin slab of agarose gel. The gel is set into a small plastic support and immersed in an aqueous, buffered solution in a tray with electrodes at each end. The current is then turned on, causing the negatively charged DNA molecules to move toward the positive electrode.

Restriction fragments
(size standards)

(b) Shorter molecules are slowed down less than longer ones, so they move faster through the gel. After the current is turned off, a DNA-binding dye is added that fluoresces pink in UV light. Each pink band corresponds to many thousands of DNA molecules of the same length. The horizontal ladder of bands at the bottom of the gel is a set of restriction fragments of known sizes for comparison with samples of unknown length.

Figure 5.15   Gel electrophoresis

CONNECT WITH THE CURRICULUM FRAMEWORK

Big Idea 3

Be able to explain how heritable information can be manipulated using common technologies. (LO 3.6) Investigation 8 is Bacterial Transformation and Investigation 9 is Restriction Enzyme Analysis of DNA. Be sure that you thoroughly understand both of these processes, and be able to describe PCR. The focus here is how the technology can be used in genetic manipulation, so carefully consider applications of technology. Also, be able to discuss the ethical implications of specific applications of biotechnology.

Biologists use DNA technology to study gene expression and function
(Biology, *11e: 20.2*; Focus, *2e: 15.4*)

▌ Genome-wide studies of gene expression are made possible by the use of **DNA microarray assays**. How can you tell whether a gene is "on" or being expressed? One way is that mRNA is being produced from that gene. DNA microarray chips can determine which genes are "on" in a cell. They work as follows:

1. Small amounts of single-stranded DNA (ssDNA) fragments representing different genes are fixed to a glass slide in a tight grid, termed a *DNA chip*.
2. The mRNA molecules from the cells being tested are isolated and used to make cDNA using reverse transcriptase, then tagged with a fluorescent dye. (cDNA is made from the edited mRNA template, so it lacks introns.)
3. The cDNA bonds to the ssDNA on the chip, indicating which genes are "on" in the cell (actively producing mRNA). This enables researchers, for example, to see differences in gene expression between breast cancer tumors and noncancerous breast tissue.

Cloned organisms and stem cells are useful for basic research and other applications
(Biology, *11e: 20.3*; Focus, *2e: 16.2*)

▌ In animal reproductive cloning, the nucleus of a fertilized egg is removed and replaced with the diploid nucleus of a body cell, a process termed *nuclear transplantation*. The cloned animal would be genetically identical to the donor of the body cell. The ability of a body cell to successfully form a clone decreases with embryonic development and cell differentiation.

▌ The major goal of most animal cloning is reproduction, but not for humans. In humans, the major goal is the production of **stem cells**. A stem cell can both reproduce itself indefinitely and, under the proper conditions, produce other specialized cells. Stem cells have enormous potential for medical applications.

▌ **Embryonic stem cells** are *pluripotent*, which means "capable of differentiating into many different cell types." The ultimate aim is to use the cells to repair damaged or diseased organs, such as insulin-producing pancreatic cells for people with diabetes or certain kinds of brain cells for people with Parkinson's disease.

The practical applications of DNA-based technology affect our lives in many ways
(Biology, *11e: 20.4*)

There are many different uses for DNA technology, some of which are as follows:

▌ **Diagnosis of disease:** A number of diseases can be detected by RFLP analysis (for example, cystic fibrosis, sickle-cell disease) or through amplification of blood samples to test for viruses (for example, HIV).

- **Gene therapy:** This involves alteration of an afflicted individual's genes. Gene therapy holds great potential for treating disorders traceable to a single defective gene, such as cystic fibrosis.
- **The production of pharmaceuticals:** Gene splicing and cloning can be used to produce large amounts of particular proteins in the lab (for example, human insulin and growth hormone).
- **Transgenic** animals are created when eggs are fertilized *in vitro*, and then a desired gene is cloned and inserted into the nucleus of the embryo. If successful, the transgenic animal will express the "foreign" gene, which might be for a human protein that can be produced in large quantities. For example, goats are used to express human antithrombin in milk.
- **Forensic applications:** DNA samples taken from the blood, skin cells, or hair of alleged criminal suspects can be compared to DNA collected from the crime scene. *Genetic profiles* can be compared and used to identify persons at that crime scene.
- **Environmental cleanup:** Scientists engineer metabolic capabilities into microorganisms, which are then used to treat environmental problems, such as removing heavy metals from toxic mining sites.
- **Agricultural applications:** Certain genes that produce desirable traits have been inserted into crop plants to increase their productivity or efficiency. An organism that has acquired by artificial means one or more genes from another species or variety is termed a **genetically modified (GM) organism**. Currently, a debate is in progress over the safety of GM organisms.

Genomes and Their Evolution
(Biology, *11e: Chapter 21;* Focus, *2e: Chapter 18*)

YOU MUST KNOW

- How prokaryotic genomes compare to eukaryotic genomes.
- Applications of bioinformatics to medicine, evolution, and health.
- The activity and role of transposable elements and retrotransposons in generating genetic diversity.
- How evo-devo relates to our understanding of the evolution of genomes.
- The role of homeotic genes and homeoboxes in developmental patterns and sequences.

Scientists use bioinformatics to analyze genomes and their functions
(Biology, *11e: 21.2;* Focus, *2e: 18.2*)

- **Bioinformatics** is the use of computers, software, and mathematical models to process and integrate the incredible volume of data from sequencing projects such as the Human Genome Project. In addition to DNA sequences, protein interactions are analyzed in an approach called *proteomics.*

- *Systems biology* aims to model the behavior of entire biological systems and is enhanced by bioinformatics. This has many applications, including medical ones—for example, in the understanding and treatment of cancers. The Cancer Genome Atlas is an example in which the goal was to find the common mutations in three types of cancer, suggesting possible new targets for therapies. Microarrays (discussed on page 149) can analyze gene expression in the cancer of a particular individual to allow patients' treatments to be tailored to the unique genetic makeup of their cancer.

> ### CONNECT WITH THE CURRICULUM FRAMEWORK
>
> Investigation 3 uses BLAST, a primary tool of bioinformatics. If you did not do this investigation, review the information about it on p. 302. Be sure to understand this powerful tool of modern science!

Genomes vary in size, number of genes, and gene density
(Biology, *11e: 21.3;* Focus, *2e: 18.3*)

- More than 4,300 genomes (about 3,900 of them prokaryotes) have now been sequenced with thousands more in progress. In general, bacteria and archaea have fewer genes than eukaryotes, and the number of genes in eukaryotic genomes is less than was expected.
- There does not seem to be any correlation between the complexity of an organism and its number of genes. The 1 mm nematode *C. elegans* and humans both have between 20,000 and 21,000 genes! The human genome is able to function with relatively few genes by utilizing alternative splicing of RNA transcripts. Recall that this process results in more than one functional protein from a single gene.

Multicellular eukaryotes have much noncoding DNA and many multigene families
(Biology, *11e: 21.4;* Focus, *2e: 18.4*)

- Only a tiny part of the human genome—1.5%—codes for proteins or is transcribed into rRNAs or tRNAs. Much of the rest is **repetitive DNA**, sequences that are present in multiple copies in the genome.
- **Transposable elements** make up much of the repetitive DNA. These are stretches of DNA that can move from one location to another in the genome with the aid of an enzyme, *transposase.*
- Transposons can interrupt normal gene function, if inserted in the middle of a functional gene, or alter gene expression, if inserted into a regulatory element. Although these effects may be harmful or lethal, over many generations some may have small beneficial effects.
- Transposons can account for multiple copies of genes, and the resulting genetic diversity provides raw material for natural selection.
- **Multigene families** are collections of two or more identical or very similar genes. A classic example is the *human α-globin and β-globin* gene families.

In these families, the genes for different human globins are on different chromosomes. This allows for different forms of the β-globin gene to function at different times in the human life cycle. For example, the embryonic and fetal forms of hemoglobin have a higher affinity for oxygen than the adult forms, ensuring the efficient transfer of oxygen from mother to fetus.

Duplication, rearrangement, and mutation of DNA contribute to genome evolution (Biology, *11e: 21.5;* Focus, *2e: 18.5*)

▌ Errors in cell division can lead to extra copies of all or parts of entire chromosome sets. Polyploidy (having an extra set of chromosomes) occurs more often among plants than animals and contributes to speciation.

▌ How might genes with novel functions evolve? Duplication events can lead to the evolution of genes with related functions, such as those of the α-globin and β-globin gene families. Mutations and transpositions can occur, and nonfunctional *pseudogenes* may be found in the clusters. Ultimately, new genes with new functions may occur.

Comparing genome sequences provides clues to evolution and development (Biology, *11e: 21.6;* Focus, *2e: 18.6*)

▌ Determining which genes have remained similar, that is, are *highly conserved,* in distantly related species can help clarify evolutionary relationships among species that diverged from each other long ago.

▌ **Evo-devo** is a field of biology that compares developmental processes to understand how they may have evolved and how changes can modify existing organismal features or lead to new ones.

▌ **Homeotic** genes are master regulatory genes that control placement and spatial organization of body parts by controlling the developmental fate of groups of cells.

▌ A **homeobox** is a widely conserved 180-nucleotide sequence found within homeotic genes. When we say that a sequence is *widely conserved,* this means that it is found in many groups (for example, fungi, animals, and plants) with very few differences. This hints at the relatedness and common evolution of all life forms.

Level 1: Knowledge/Comprehension Questions

The Level 1, Knowledge/Comprehension, questions review essential content knowledge but don't represent the type of question you will see on the AP exam. The Level 2, Synthesis/Application, questions are similar to those you will see on the exam.

1. Which of the following has a DNA genome surrounded by a protein coat?
   (A) a retrovirus
   (B) a virus
   (C) a eukaryotic cell
   (D) a prokaryotic cell

2. Which of the following is a laboratory application of restriction enzymes?
   (A) to block the replication of DNA
   (B) to artificially force the transcription of DNA
   (C) to prevent the translation of mRNA
   (D) to cut DNA molecules at specific locations

Directions: Questions 3–6 consist of four lettered choices followed by a list of numbered phrases or sentences. For each numbered phrase or sentence, select the one choice that is most closely related to it. Each choice may be used once, more than once, or not at all.

Questions 3–6
  (A) Transcription
  (B) Translation
  (C) Transposon
  (D) DNA methylation

3. A mobile segment of DNA that travels from one location on a chromosome to another, making it an important element of genetic change

4. The addition of chemical groups ($-CH_3$, for example) to certain bases of DNA after DNA synthesis; thought to be an important control mechanism for gene expression

5. The synthesis of polypeptides from the genetic information coded in mRNA

6. The synthesis of RNA from a DNA template

7. Which of these processes can cause an increase in the rate of transcription?
  (A) methylation of DNA, particularly the cytosine bases
  (B) acetylation of histone proteins
  (C) binding of the operator in an operon
  (D) negative feedback from accumulating product

8. When a virus infects a bacterium by injecting its DNA and the genome of the virus is incorporated into the host cell, this is
  (A) the lytic cycle of a phage.
  (B) the lysogenic cycle of a phage.
  (C) transposition by a virus.
  (D) retroviral infection.

9. In molecular biology laboratories, DNA ligase is used for which of the following purposes?
  (A) to act as a probe for locating cloned genes
  (B) to create breaks in DNA in order to allow foreign DNA fragments to be inserted
  (C) to seal up nicks created in newly created recombinant DNA
  (D) to ensure that "sticky ends" of like DNA fragments do not reanneal

Directions: Questions 10–13 consist of four lettered choices followed by a list of numbered phrases or sentences. For each numbered phrase or sentence, select the one choice that is most closely related to it. Each choice may be used once, more than once, or not at all.

Questions 10–13
  (A) tRNA
  (B) mRNA
  (C) Poly-A tail
  (D) RNA polymerase

10. An example of a post-transcriptional modification

11. Binds to the promoter on DNA to initiate transcription

12. Binds to free amino acids in the cytoplasm

13. Travels out of the nucleus and into the cytoplasm where it serves as a template in translation

14. After eukaryotic transcription takes place, mRNA undergoes several modifications before leaving the nucleus to take part in translation. One of these is the cutting out of nonessential sections of mRNA and the subsequent splicing together of stretches of mRNA necessary for the final functional molecule. Which of the following mRNA sections are spliced together into the finished mRNA molecule?
  (A) introns   (C) genes
  (B) exons   (D) ribozymes

Level 2: Application/Analysis/Synthesis Questions

1. A goat can produce milk containing the same polymers present in the silk produced by spiders when particular genes from a spider are inserted into the goat's genome. Which of the following reasons describes why this is possible?
   (A) Goats and spiders share a common ancestor and thus produce similar protein excretions.
   (B) Goats retain all the genes that were found in ancestral species and will express these proteins when activated by a gene insertion.
   (C) The proteins in goats' milk and spiders' silk have the same amino acid sequence.
   (D) The universal nature of the genetic code allows for the production of identical proteins from different organisms as long as the DNA sequence is identical.

2. Enzymes and energy are required for the synthesis of DNA and RNA. Which enzyme is correctly linked with its function?
   (A) Telomerase ensures that the transcription machinery starts with the codon AUG.
   (B) DNA ligase joins together Okazaki fragments from the lagging strand.
   (C) DNA polymerase oversees the binding of mRNA to the ribosome.
   (D) Helicase alters the new DNA strands so it will coil into a double helix.

3. PCR (polymerase chain reaction) allows target segments of DNA to be produced quickly by using heat to denature and separate strands of DNA, then cooling to allow primers to attach to the single strands and DNA polymerase to synthesize new strands of the target DNA by adding nucleotides to the 3′ end of each primer on the two strands. Why was this process considered so important that it earned Kary Mullis a Nobel Prize?
   (A) It is useful for isolating the source of DNA.
   (B) It facilitates the introduction of plasmid DNA into a host cell.
   (C) It enables selection of transformed cells that have taken up foreign DNA.
   (D) It can produce multiple copies of even minute samples of DNA.

Questions 4 and 5 refer to an experiment that was performed to separate linear DNA fragments from three samples radioactively labeled with ^{32}P. The fragments were then separated using gel electrophoresis. The visualized bands are depicted as follows:

Completed gel

4. When the electric field was applied, the fragments of DNA in each of the three samples migrated to different locations along the gel. Which of the following explains the pattern shown here?
   (A) The fragments differed in their levels of radioactivity.
   (B) The fragments differed in their charges—some were positively charged, whereas others were negatively charged.
   (C) The fragments differed in size.
   (D) The fragments differed in solubility.

5. How many sites on DNA were cut by the particular restriction enzyme used in Sample 1 (the lane on the far left)?
   (A) 6
   (B) 7
   (C) 8
   (D) 9

6. A bacterium is infected with an experimentally constructed bacteriophage composed of the T2 phage protein coat and T4 phage DNA. The new phages produced by lysis of infected cells would have
   (A) T2 protein and T4 DNA.
   (B) T2 protein and T2 DNA.
   (C) T4 protein and T4 DNA.
   (D) T4 protein and T2 DNA.

7. RNA retroviruses such as HIV discharge both strands of RNA and molecules of reverse transcriptase into cells they infect. What is the purpose of the reverse transcriptase?
    (A) The host cells rapidly destroy the viral RNA so more must constantly be made.
    (B) The host cells lack enzymes that can replicate the viral genome.
    (C) The reverse transcriptase is required to translate viral mRNA into proteins.
    (D) The reverse transcriptase binds to active sites of the lytic enzymes of the host cells.

8. A mutation is any change in a DNA sequence. Of the following mutation events, which one would have the most significant effect on the resulting polypeptide?
    (A) A nucleotide and its complementary base are replaced, resulting in a new amino acid in translation.
    (B) A nucleotide pair is added into a gene near its terminal end, altering the reading frame of the genetic message.
    (C) A nucleotide pair substitution occurs, which results in the introduction of a "stop" codon.
    (D) A nucleotide is altered that results in no change in the amino acid sequence due to redundancy.

9. In analyzing the number of different bases in a DNA sample, which result would be consistent with the base-pairing rules?
    (A) A = G
    (B) A + G = C + T
    (C) A + T = G + T
    (D) A = C

10. Which of the following is a difficulty in getting prokaryotic cells to express eukaryotic genes?
    (A) The signals that control gene expression are different for prokaryotes, thus requiring prokaryotic promoter regions to be added to the vector.

(B) The genetic code differs because prokaryotes substitute the base uracil for thymine.
(C) Prokaryotic cells do not recognize eukaryotic stop and start codons.
(D) The ribosomes of prokaryotes are not large enough to handle long eukaryotic genes.

11. Microarrays use single-stranded pieces of DNA of known genes, which are placed on a slide to determine whether these genes are being expressed in a particular tissue. For example, if the cells come from seedlings that are germinated and kept in the dark, the chlorophyll genes would not be active. Which of the following would you wash across the slide to determine that the chlorophyll genes are active in a plant grown in light?
    (A) single-stranded cDNA made from the mRNA transcribed from the chlorophyll genes
    (B) a portion of the amino acid sequences of the chlorophyll molecules
    (C) mRNA transcribed from the plant grown in the dark
    (D) cell fragments that include ribosomes and both tRNA and rRNA

12. The human genome appears to have only about as many genes as the simple nematode worm, *C. elegans*. Which of the following best explains how the more complex humans can have relatively few genes?
    (A) Human genes have unusually long introns involved in the regulation of gene expression.
    (B) More than one polypeptide can be produced from a gene by alternative splicing.
    (C) The human genome has a high proportion of noncoding DNA.
    (D) The human genome has a large number of SNPs (single nucleotide polymorphisms), which increases genetic variability.

13. The human globin genes are located on two different chromosomes and include variants that are expressed at different times in the life cycle as well as a number of nonfunctional pseudogenes. Which of the following would best describe this gene family?
    (A) All the functional genes in the family have the same transcription control elements.
    (B) This gene family would be equivalent to the operons of prokaryotes.
    (C) Mutations in the hemoglobin gene led to its translocation to two different chromosomes.
    (D) Identical or similar genes have evolved by gene duplication.

After reading the paragraphs, answer the questions that follow.

Exposure to the HIV virus doesn't necessarily mean that a person will develop AIDS. Some people have genetic resistance to infection by HIV. Dr. Stephen O'Brien from the U.S. National Cancer Institute has recently identified a mutant form of a gene, called *CCR5*, which can protect against HIV infection. The mutation probably originated in Europe among survivors of the bubonic plague. The mutated gene prevents the plague bacteria from attaching to cell membranes and, therefore, from entering and infecting body cells.

Although the HIV virus is very different from the bacterium that causes the plague, both diseases affect the exact same cells and use the same method of infection. The presence of the mutated gene in descendants of plague survivors helps prevent them from contracting AIDS. Pharmaceutical companies are using this information as the basis for a new approach to AIDS prevention. This method of prevention would be very important in areas of the world where the mutation is scarce or absent, such as Africa.

14. The most likely method by which the mutated *CCR5* gene prevents AIDS is by
    (A) blocking the protein channels that allow the virus to enter the cell.
    (B) directing the formation of lytic enzymes packaged in the lysosomes.
    (C) being presented on immune system cells to target the virus for attack and destruction.
    (D) coding for a mutant receptor protein on the cell membrane, thus not allowing the entry of the virus.

15. Which of the following shows the steps of a retroviral infection in the proper order?
    (A) Virus locates host cell → enters nucleus → alters host cell DNA → destroys cell membrane.
    (B) Virus locates host cell → alters host cell DNA → host cell produces copies of virus → copies enter host cell nucleus → nucleus leaves cell.
    (C) Virus locates host cell → penetrates cell membrane → enters nucleus → alters host cell DNA → host cell produces copies of virus.
    (D) Virus locates host cell → penetrates cell membrane → viral RNA used to make DNA → host cell produces copies of virus.

16. Lateral gene transfer involves the movement of genes between members of a species without sexual reproduction. In bacteria, there are three mechanisms for this: conjugation, transformation, and transduction. Predict how these processes are most likely to affect bacteria.
    (A) The bacteria's DNA content will be reduced.
    (B) The amount of RNA in the cytoplasm will be increased.
    (C) The bacteria's genetic diversity will be increased.
    (D) The bacteria's metabolic needs will be modified to give a selective advantage.

After reading the paragraph, answer questions 17 and 18.

Four decades after the end of the Vietnam War, the remains of an Air Force pilot were discovered and returned to the United States. A search of Air Force records identified three families to which the remains might possibly belong. Each family had a surviving twin of a missing service member. A DNA comparison was done, and the following STR profiles were obtained from the remains of the pilot and the surviving twins from the three families.

	Air Force Pilot	Family 1	Family 2	Family 3
1		—		
2	—	—		—
3	—			—
4		—		
5	—	—	—	—
6				—
7	—	—		—
8			—	
9		—		
10	—			—
11			—	
12		—		
13	—		—	—

17. In order to match the pilot's remains to the correct family using DNA profiling,
(A) the majority of the STR bands must match.
(B) each of the 13 STR bands must match.
(C) the bands for site 13 must match.
(D) bands 5 and 7 must match.

18. Based on analysis of the STR sites shown, does the missing pilot belong to any of these three families?
(A) No, none of the families match.
(B) Yes, family 1 matches.
(C) Yes, family 2 matches.
(D) Yes, family 3 matches.

19. RNA processing involves some important steps before the final transcript is ready to leave the nucleus. Of the following, which does not represent an event in this process?
(A) Exons are cut out before mRNA leaves the nucleus.
(B) Nucleotides may be added at both ends of the RNA.
(C) Ribozymes may function in RNA splicing.
(D) RNA splicing can be catalyzed by spliceosomes.

20. What is the basis for the difference in how the leading and lagging strands of DNA molecules are synthesized?
(A) The origins of replication occur only at the 5′ end.
(B) Helicases and DNA polymerase work at the 5′ end.
(C) DNA polymerase can join new nucleotides only to the 3′ end of a growing strand.
(D) DNA ligase works only in the 3′ → 5′ direction.

21. Following are amino acid sequences for six species for critical parts of the *FOXP2* gene. Each letter represents a single amino acid. The data can be used to determine the relatedness of the six species. Assuming that mutation rates are equal for all species over time and based only on these data, which number represents the species *most* closely related to species 1?

1. ATETI . . . PKSSD . . . TSSTT . . . NARRD
2. ATKTI . . . PKSSE . . . TSATT . . . NARRD
3. ATETI . . . PKAAD . . . TSSTT . . . NARTD
4. ATETI . . . PKSSD . . . TSSNT . . . SARRN
5. ATETI . . . PKSSD . . . TASTT . . . NARRD
6. VTEPI . . . PSSSD . . . TSSAT . . . NARRD

(A) Species 2
(B) Species 3
(C) Species 4
(D) Species 6 and 4 are equally related to species 1.

Use the graph and information to answer questions 22–25.

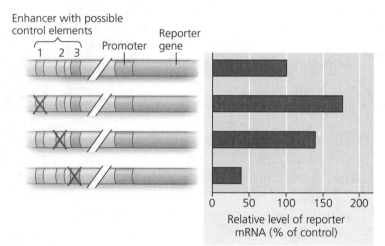

The promoter of a gene includes the DNA immediately upstream of the transcription start site, but expression of the gene can also be affected by control elements. These can be thousands of base pairs upstream of the promoter, grouped in an enhancer. Because the distance and spacing of these control elements make them difficult to identify, scientists begin by deleting sections of DNA that contain possible control elements and measuring the effect on gene expression. In this question set, you will analyze data obtained from DNA deletion experiments that tested possible control elements for the human gene *mPGES-1*. This gene codes for an enzyme that synthesizes a type of prostaglandin, a chemical made during inflammation.

The researchers hypothesized that there were three possible control elements in an enhancer region eight to nine kilobases upstream of the *mPGES-1* gene. Control elements regulate whatever gene is in the appropriate downstream location. To test the activity of the possible elements, researchers synthesized four types of DNA molecules ("constructs"):

- One DNA construct had an intact enhancer region.
- One DNA construct had possible control element #1 deleted from the enhancer region.
- One DNA construct had possible control element #2 deleted from the enhancer region.
- One DNA construct had possible control element #3 deleted from the enhancer region.

In all constructs, the enhancer region was located upstream of a "reporter gene," a gene that would be expressed at the same time as *mPGES-1* and whose mRNA product could be easily measured experimentally.

The researchers then introduced each DNA construct into a separate human cell culture, where the cells took up the artificial DNA molecules. After 48 hours, the amount of reporter gene mRNA made by the cells was measured. Comparing these amounts allowed the researchers to determine if any of the deletions had an effect on expression of the reporter gene, mimicking the effect that deletions would have had on *mPGES-1* gene expression. (The *mPGES-1* mRNA itself couldn't be used to measure expression levels because the cells in culture have their own *mPGES-1* gene with an intact enhancer region. Therefore, the cells produced *mPGES-1* mRNA regardless of which DNA construct they took up.)

22. What was the control treatment in this experiment?
 (A) the reporter gene
 (B) the temperature, pH, and salt concentration of the incubation medium
 (C) the construct that resulted in the lowest amount of reporter mRNA
 (D) the construct that had no DNA deleted from the enhancer

23. Do the data suggest that any of these possible control elements are actual control elements?
 (A) Only control elements 1 and 2 appear to be control elements.
 (B) Only control element 3 appears to be a control element.
 (C) All three appear to be control elements.
 (D) None of the possible control elements appear to be actual control elements.

24. If deletion of a control element causes a reduction in gene expression, what must be the normal role of that control element?
 (A) To activate gene expression; without the control element, repressors are not able to bind to the enhancer, and the level of gene expression increases.
 (B) To repress gene expression; without the control element, repressors are not able to bind to the enhancer, and the level of gene expression decreases.
 (C) To repress gene expression; without the control element, repressors are not able to bind to the enhancer, and the level of gene expression increases.
 (D) To activate gene expression; without the control element, activators are not able to bind to the enhancer, and the level of gene expression decreases.

25. If deletion of a control element causes an increase in gene expression, what must be the normal role of that control element?
 (A) To activate gene expression; without the control element, repressors are not able to bind to the enhancer, and the level of gene expression increases.
 (B) To activate gene expression; without the control element, activators are not able to bind to the enhancer, and the level of gene expression decreases.
 (C) To repress gene expression; without the control element, activators are not able to bind to the enhancer, and the level of gene expression decreases.
 (D) To repress gene expression; without the control element, repressors are not able to bind to the enhancer, and the level of gene expression increases.

Grid-In Questions

The following questions call for a numerical response.

1. A linear strip of DNA has two restriction sites for the restriction enzyme *EcoR1* and three restriction sites for the restriction enzyme *Hind III*. If the strip of DNA were incubated with the restriction enzymes and then the cut DNA were collected and run on an electrophoretic gel, how many bands would be expected on the gel?

2. In *E. coli* the DNA is 24% adenine. Based on this information, what percentage of this DNA is guanine?

Free-Response Question

Genes are located on chromosomes and are the basic unit of heredity that is passed on from parent to child through generations.

(a) For each of the following mutations, **describe** how the genetic information is altered and **predict** one specific effect that could occur with the error.
- nondisjunction
- base-pair deletion resulting in a frameshift mutation within an intron
- base-pair substitution resulting in a different amino acid

(b) **Explain** why it is more common for human males to be colorblind than females.

(c) Proper gene dosages are critical to normal development and function. **Discuss** the mechanism that maintains proper gene dosages related to the X chromosome in females.

Mechanisms of Evolution

Descent with Modification
(Biology, *11e: Chapter 22;* Focus, *2e: Chapter 19*)

YOU MUST KNOW

- Several examples of evidence for evolution from different scientific disciplines and how each supports change of populations over time.
- The difference between structures that are homologous and those that are analogous, and how this relates to evolution.
- The role of adaptations, variation, time, reproductive success, and heritability in evolution.

The Darwinian revolution challenged traditional views of a young Earth inhabited by unchanging species (Biology, *11e: 22.1;* Focus, *2e: 19.1*)

▌ **Carolus Linnaeus** (1707–1778) sought to classify life's diversity. He grouped similar species into increasingly general categories, reflecting what he considered the pattern of their creation.

    ▪ Linnaeus is credited with developing **taxonomy**, the branch of biology dedicated to the naming and classification of all forms of life.

    ▪ Developed **binomial nomenclature**, a two-part naming system that includes the organism's genus and species.

▌ Fossils provide evidence of changing life forms. They are deposited in **strata** (layers of rock), with the older strata being deposited first.

▌ **Charles Lyell** (1797–1875) was an English geologist and friend of Charles Darwin.

    ▪ Lyell developed the idea that the geologic processes that have shaped the planet have been uniform over a long period of time, so the Earth must be much older than the widely accepted age of a few thousand years. ***The Earth must be very old.***

    ▪ *Importance:* An old Earth has time for evolution; a very young Earth does not. Lyell gave Darwin the gift of time.

    ▪ During his journeys, Darwin studied Lyell's *Principles of Geology.*

- **Jean-Baptiste de Lamarck** (1744–1829) proposed a mechanism for evolution based on two principles:

  - **Use and disuse** is the idea that parts of the body that are used extensively become larger and stronger, while those that are not used deteriorate.
  - **Inheritance of acquired characteristics** assumes that characteristics acquired during an organism's lifetime could be passed on to the next generation. *Example:* A weightlifter's child could be born with more muscular anatomy.
  - *Importance:* Lamarck recognized that species evolve, and the match of organisms to their environment occurs through gradual evolutionary change. His explanatory mechanism, however, was flawed.

Descent with modification by natural selection explains the adaptations of organisms and the unity and diversity of life (Biology, *11e: 22.2;* Focus, *2e: 19.2*)

- **Charles Darwin's** voyage on the HMS *Beagle* from 1831 to 1836 was the impetus for the development of his theory of evolution by natural selection.
- Darwin's mechanism for evolution was natural selection. Recall that Lamarck's mechanism was the inheritance of acquired characteristics.
- **Natural selection** explains how adaptations arise.

  - **Adaptations** are heritable characteristics that enhance organisms' ability to survive and reproduce in specific environments. *Example:* Desert foxes have large ears, which radiate heat. Arctic foxes have small ears, which conserve body heat.

- Darwin's theory of natural selection involves these important points:

  1. Members of a population often vary in their inherited traits.
  2. A species can produce far more offspring than its environment can support. With more individuals than the environment can support, competition is inevitable.
  3. Individuals with inherited traits that are better suited to the local environment are more likely to survive and reproduce than individuals that are less suited. This is termed "differential reproductive success."
  4. Evolution occurs as the unequal reproductive success of individuals ultimately leads to the accumulation of favorable traits in the population over generations. Over time, natural selection can improve the match between organisms and their environment.

If an environment changes, or if individuals move to a new environment, natural selection may result in adaptation to these new conditions, sometimes giving rise to new species in the process.

> **TIP FROM THE READERS**
> When explaining evolution, avoid any language that makes it sound like a species "needs" a feature, and so it evolves. Don't write "survival of the fittest"; instead describe how selection favors a feature that results in leaving more offspring. Evolution is not goal oriented.

▌ **Artificial selection** is the process by which species are modified by humans. *Example:* Selective breeding for milk or meat production; development of dog breeds.

▌ *Individuals do not evolve.* **Populations** *evolve.*

Evolution is supported by an overwhelming amount of scientific evidence (Biology, 11e: 22.3; Focus, 2e: 19.3)

> **ORGANIZE YOUR THOUGHTS**
>
> EVIDENCE FOR EVOLUTION is seen in the following ways:
>
> 1. Direct observations
> 2. Homology
> 3. The fossil record
> 4. Biogeography

▌ Evidence for Evolution

1. **Direct observations of evolutionary change** *provide evidence for the theory of evolution.*

   - Insect populations can rapidly become resistant to pesticides such as DDT.
   - Bacteria evolve to become resistant to antibiotics, and viruses evolve to become resistant to other drugs.

2. **Homology and convergent evolution** *provide evidence for the theory of evolution.*

   - **Homology:** Characteristics in related species can have an underlying similarity even though they have very different functions. *Similarity resulting from common ancestry is known as homology.*
   - **Homologous structures** are anatomical signs of evolution. *Examples:* Forelimbs of mammals that are now used for a variety of purposes, such as flying in bats or swimming in whales, were present and used in a common ancestor for walking. (See *Biology,* 11e, Figure 22.15, page 473, or *Focus,* 2e, Figure 19.16, page 389.)
   - **Embryonic homologies:** Comparison of early stages of animal development reveals many anatomical homologies in embryos that are not visible in adult organisms. *Example:* All vertebrate embryos have a post-anal tail and pharyngeal pouches.
   - **Vestigial organs** are structures of marginal, if any, importance to the organism. They are remnants of structures that served important functions in the organisms' ancestors. *Example:* Some snakes have remnants of pelvis and leg bones. We would not expect to see these if snakes had origins separate from other vertebrate animals.

- **Molecular homologies** are shared characteristics on the molecular level. *Example:* All life forms use the same genetic language of DNA and RNA. Amino acid sequences, coding for hemoglobin in primate species, shows great similarity, indicating a common ancestor.
- **Convergent evolution** explains why distantly related species can resemble one another. Convergent evolution has taken place when two organisms developed similarities as they adapted to similar environmental challenges—not because they evolved from a common ancestor. The likenesses that result from convergent evolution are considered **analogous** rather than homologous. Think of it like this: Similar problems have similar solutions. *Examples:*

  - The torpedo shapes of a penguin, dolphin, and shark are the solution to movement through an aqueous environment.
  - Sugar gliders (marsupial mammals) and flying squirrels (eutherian mammals) occupy similar niches in their respective habitats.

> **STUDY TIP**
>
> **Homologous structures** show evidence of common ancestry (whale fin/bat wing).
> **Analogous structures** are similar solutions to similar problems but do *not* indicate close relatedness (bird wing/butterfly wing).

3. **The fossil record** *provides evidence for the theory of evolution.*

   - Fossils are remains or traces of organisms from the past. They are found in sedimentary rock. **Paleontology** is the study of fossils.
   - Fossils show that evolutionary changes have occurred over time and provide evidence of the origin of major new groups of organisms.
   - Darwin's theory of evolution through natural selection explains the succession of forms in the fossil record. Transitional fossils have been found that link ancient organisms to modern species, just as Darwin's theory predicts.

4. **Biogeography** (the geographic distribution of species) *provides evidence for the theory of evolution.*

   - Species in a discrete geographic area tend to be more closely related to each other than to species in distant geographic areas. *Example:* In South America, desert animals are more closely related to local animals in other habitats than they are to the desert animals of Asia. This reflects evolution, not creation.
   - **Continental drift** and the breakup of Pangaea can explain the similarity of species on continents that are distant from each other today.
   - **Endemic species** are found at a certain geographic location and nowhere else. *Example:* Marine iguanas are endemic to the Galápagos Islands.

The Evolution of Populations

(Biology, *11e: Chapter 23;* Focus, *2e: Chapter 21*)

YOU MUST KNOW

- Mutations are the only source of new genes.
- The three ways in which sexual reproduction produces genetic variation.
- The conditions for Hardy-Weinberg equilibrium.
- How to use the Hardy-Weinberg equation to calculate allele frequencies to test whether a population is evolving. (LO 1.4)
- What effects genetic drift, migration, or selection may have on a population, and analyze data to justify your predictions. (LO 1.6–1.8)

Genetic variation makes evolution possible (Biology, *11e: 23.1;* Focus, *2e: 21.1*)

▌ Phenotypic variation often reflects genetic variation. Look at your classmates: Their phenotypic variation may result from either-or differences of a single gene or the range of variation typical of multiple genes. How many students have attached ear lobes, and how many have free ear lobes (an either-or difference resulting from one gene)? What is the range of height in your class (multiple genes yielding variations along a continuum)?

▌ **Mutations** are the only source of *new* genes and *new* alleles.

  ▌ Only mutations in cell lines that produce gametes can be passed to offspring.

▌ **Point mutations** are changes in one nucleotide base in a gene. They can have a significant impact on phenotype, as in sickle-cell disease.

▌ **Chromosomal mutations** delete, disrupt, duplicate, or rearrange many loci at once. They are usually harmful—but not always. Gene duplications (often from mistakes in crossing over) can result in an expanded genome with new genes that may accumulate mutations over generations and take on new functions.

▌ However, most genetic variations within a population result from the sexual recombination of alleles that already exist in a population.

- Sexual reproduction shuffles existing alleles and deals them at random to produce individual genotypes. There are *three mechanisms* for this shuffling of alleles:
  - **Crossing over** during prophase I of meiosis
  - **Independent assortment** of chromosomes during meiosis (2^{23} different combinations possible in the formation of human gametes!)
  - **Fertilization** ($2^{23} \times 2^{23}$ different possible combinations for human sperm and egg)

The Hardy-Weinberg equation can be used to test whether a population is evolving (Biology, *11e: 23.2; Focus, 2e: 21.2*)

- **Population genetics:** The study of how populations change genetically over time
- **Population:** A group of individuals of the same species that live in the same area and interbreed, producing fertile offspring
- **Gene pool:** All of the alleles at all loci in all the members of a population
- In diploid species, each individual has two alleles for a particular gene, and the individual may be either heterozygous or homozygous.
- If all members of a population are homozygous for the same allele, the allele is said to be **fixed**. Only one allele exists at that particular locus in the population. For example, the fruit fly is heterozygous for 1,920 of its 13,700 genes; the remaining 11,780 are fixed. It follows that the greater the number of fixed alleles, the lower the species' genetic diversity.

ORGANIZE YOUR THOUGHTS

Five Conditions for Hardy-Weinberg Equilibrium

1. No change in allelic frequency due to mutation
2. Random mating
3. No natural selection
4. Extremely large population size (no genetic drift)
5. No gene flow (emigration, immigration, transfer of pollen, etc.)

- The **Hardy-Weinberg** equation is used to describe a population that is *not* evolving. It states that the frequencies of alleles and genes in a population's gene pool will remain constant over the course of generations unless they are acted upon by forces *other* than Mendelian segregation and the recombination of alleles. The population is at **Hardy-Weinberg equilibrium**.
- You will find additional discussion of this very important topic in Investigation 2, beginning on page 309.
- However, it is unlikely that all the conditions for Hardy-Weinberg equilibrium will be met. Allele frequencies change. Populations evolve. It is possible to test this idea by applying the **Hardy-Weinberg equation**.
- As you refer to the equation in the box on the following page, note that the dominant phenotype includes both p^2 and $2pq$. For example, if brown eyes are dominant, a person with brown eyes could be homozygous (p^2) or heterozygous ($2pq$). Because the dominant phenotype includes two possible genotypes (and two mathematical variables in p and q), we must look to the recessive phenotype to determine q. The recessive phenotype, blue eyes in our

example, is q^2. Every individual with blue eyes has the same genotype (bb), which is not the case with brown eyes. It is therefore possible to take the square root of the frequency of the recessive phenotype in the population to find q. For example, if 36% of the population has blue eyes, or $q^2 = 0.36$, then $q = 0.6$ and $p = 0.4$. *Here is the rule to remember: Always find* q *first!*

EQUATION FOR HARDY-WEINBERG EQUILIBRIUM

Consider a gene locus that exists in two allelic forms, A and a, in a population.

Let p = the frequency of A, the dominant allele

and q = the frequency of a, the recessive allele.

All the dominant alleles plus all the recessive alleles will equal 100% of the alleles for this gene or, expressed mathematically, $p + q = 1$. Expanding this simple binomial leads to the Hardy-Weinberg equation:

$$p^2 + 2pq + q^2 = 1$$

The three terms of this binomial expansion indicate the frequencies of the three genotypes:

p^2 = frequency of AA (homozygous dominant)
$2pq$ = frequency of Aa (heterozygous)
q^2 = frequency of aa (homozygous recessive)

If we know the frequency of one of the alleles, we can calculate the frequency of the other allele:

$p + q = 1$, so
$p = 1 - q$
$q = 1 - p$

PRACTICE THE PRACTICE: Sample Hardy-Weinberg Problem

Suppose in a plant population that red flowers (R) are dominant to white flowers (r). In a population of 500 individuals, 25% show the recessive phenotype. How many individuals would you expect to be homozygous dominant and heterozygous for this trait? (**The answers are at the ends of items 4 and 5 in bold. Cover the solution and try solving the problem first!**)

1. Let p = frequency of the dominant allele (R) and q = frequency of the recessive allele (r).
2. q^2 = frequency of the homozygous recessive = 25% = 0.25. Since $q^2 = 0.25$, $q = 0.5$.
3. Now, $p + q = 1$, so $p = 0.5$.
4. Homozygous dominant individuals are RR or $p^2 = 0.5^2 = 0.25$ and will represent $(0.25)(500)$ = **125 individuals**.
5. The heterozygous individuals are calculated from $2pq = (2)(0.5)(0.5) = 0.5$. In a population of 500 individuals, **250 individuals** (0.5×500) will be heterozygous dominant.

Natural selection, genetic drift, and gene flow can alter allele frequencies in a population (Biology, *11e: 23.3*; Focus, *2e: 21.3*)

▌ Let's back up before we go on. In nature, is it likely that all the conditions for Hardy-Weinberg equilibrium will be met? NO! Therefore, populations are evolving, which means their allelic frequencies are changing. This concept takes into consideration specific factors that alter allelic frequency. Note that each of the factors represents an exception to one of the five conditions for Hardy-Weinberg equilibrium listed earlier.

▌ Mutations can alter gene frequency, but because mutations are rare, the change from one generation to the next is likely to be very small.

▌ **The three major factors** that alter allele frequencies and bring about most evolutionary change are *natural selection, genetic drift,* and *gene flow.*

  ▪ **Natural selection** results in alleles being passed to the next generation in proportions different from their relative frequencies in the present generation. Individuals with variations that are better suited to their environment tend to survive and produce more offspring than those with variations that are less suited. This concept is called *differential reproductive success.*

  ▪ **Genetic drift** is the unpredictable fluctuation in allele frequencies from one generation to the next. The smaller the population, the greater the chance there is for genetic drift. This is a *random, nonadaptive* change in allele frequencies. Genetic drift can lead to a loss of genetic diversity, even causing some genes to become fixed in the new population. Two examples follow:

    ▪ **Founder effect:** A few individuals become isolated from a larger population and establish a new population whose gene pool is not reflective of the source population. *Example:* A mat of vegetation recently washed up on the shore of a Pacific island. In the vegetation was a small population of lizards—its gene pool randomly different than that of the source population.

    ▪ **Bottleneck effect:** A sudden change in the environment (for example, an earthquake, flood, or fire) drastically reduces the size of a population. The few survivors that pass through the restrictive bottleneck may have a gene pool that no longer reflects the original population's gene pool. *Example:* The population of California condors was reduced to nine individuals. This represents a bottlenecking event.

▌ **Gene flow** occurs when a population gains or loses alleles by genetic additions or subtractions from the population. This change results from the movement of fertile individuals or gametes. *Gene flow tends to reduce the genetic differences between populations*, thus making populations more similar.

Natural selection is the only mechanism that consistently causes adaptive evolution (Biology, *11e: 23.4;* Focus, *2e: 21.4*)

▐ **Relative fitness** refers to the contribution an organism makes to the gene pool of the next-generation relative to the contributions of other members. Fitness does *not* indicate strength or size. Fitness in the context of evolution is measured only by reproductive success.

▐ Natural selection acts more directly on the phenotype and indirectly on the genotype and can alter the frequency distribution of heritable traits in three ways (Figure 6.1).

   ▪ **Directional selection** *Example:* Large black bears survived periods of extreme cold better than smaller ones and so became more common during glacial periods.

   ▪ **Disruptive selection** *Example:* A population has individuals with either large beaks or small beaks but few with the intermediate-sized beaks. Apparently the intermediate-sized beak is not as efficient at cracking either the large or small seeds that are common.

         or Diversyfing

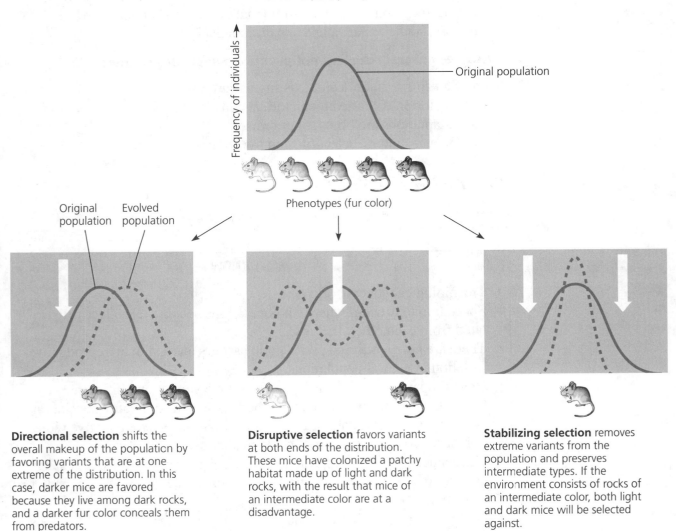

Directional selection shifts the overall makeup of the population by favoring variants that are at one extreme of the distribution. In this case, darker mice are favored because they live among dark rocks, and a darker fur color conceals them from predators.

Disruptive selection favors variants at both ends of the distribution. These mice have colonized a patchy habitat made up of light and dark rocks, with the result that mice of an intermediate color are at a disadvantage.

Stabilizing selection removes extreme variants from the population and preserves intermediate types. If the environment consists of rocks of an intermediate color, both light and dark mice will be selected against.

Figure 6.1   Modes of selection

- **Stabilizing selection** *Example:* Birth weights of most humans lie in a narrow range because babies who are very large or very small have higher mortality.

■ **Sexual selection** is a form of natural selection in which individuals with certain inherited characteristics are more likely than other individuals to obtain mates. It can result in **sexual dimorphism**, a difference between the two sexes in secondary sexual characteristics such as differences in size, color, ornamentation, and behavior.

■ **How is genetic variation preserved in a population?** Why doesn't natural selection eliminate all unfavorable alleles?

- **Diploidy:** Because most eukaryotes are diploid, recessive alleles are hidden from selection in heterozygotes.
- **Heterozygote advantage:** This occurs when individuals who are heterozygous at a certain gene locus have an advantage for survival. *Example:* In sickle-cell disease, individuals homozygous for normal hemoglobin are more susceptible to malaria, whereas homozygous recessive individuals suffer from the complications of sickle-cell disease. Heterozygotes benefit from some protection from malaria and do not have sickle-cell disease, so the mutant allele remains relatively common.

■ **Why does natural selection not produce perfect organisms?**

1. Selection can only edit existing variations.
2. Evolution is limited by historical constraints.
3. Adaptations are often compromises.
4. Chance, natural selection, and the environment interact.

The Origin of Species

(Biology, *11e: Chapter 24;* Focus, *2e: Chapter 22*)

YOU MUST KNOW

- The biological concept of species.
- Speciation may occur when two populations become reproductively isolated from each other. (EK 1.C.2)
- There are prezygotic and postzygotic barriers that maintain reproductive isolation in natural populations.
- How allopatric and sympatric speciation are similar and different.
- How a change in chromosome number can lead to sympatric speciation.
- Why speciation rates are often rapid in situations where adaptive radiation occurs or during times of ecological stress.
- The connection between speciation in an isolated population and a change in gene frequency, a change in the environment, natural selection, and/or genetic drift. (LO 1.24)
- How punctuated equilibrium and gradualism describe two different tempos of speciation.

The biological species concept emphasizes reproductive isolation
(Biology, *11e: 24.1*; Focus, *2e: 22.1*)

▊ **Speciation** is the process by which new species arise.

▊ **Microevolution** is change in allelic frequencies of a population from generation to generation. It refers to adaptations that are confined to a single gene pool.

▊ **Macroevolution** refers to the broad pattern of evolutionary change above the species level, such as the appearance of feathers and other such novelties.

▊ The **biological species concept** defines a species as a group of populations whose members have the potential to interbreed in nature and produce viable, fertile offspring but are unable to produce viable, fertile offspring with members of other groups.

▊ **Reproductive isolation** is the existence of biological barriers that impede members of two species from producing viable, fertile hybrids.

▊ **Prezygotic and postzygotic barriers** are two types of barriers that prevent members of different species from producing offspring that can also successfully reproduce.

▊ **Prezygotic barriers** prevent mating or hinder fertilization if mating has occurred and include the following.

 ▪ **Habitat isolation:** Two species can live in the same geographic area but not in the same habitat; this will prevent them from mating because they will not encounter each other.

 ▪ **Behavioral isolation:** Some species use certain signals or types of behavior to attract mates, and these signals are unique to their species. Members of other species do not respond to the signals; thus, mating does not occur.

 ▪ **Temporal isolation:** Species may breed at different times of day, different seasons, or different years, and this can prevent them from mating.

 ▪ **Mechanical isolation:** Species may be anatomically incompatible.

 ▪ **Gametic isolation:** Even if the gametes of two species do meet, they might be unable to fuse to form a zygote.

▊ **Postzygotic barriers** prevent a hybrid zygote from developing into a fertile adult and include the following:

 ▪ **Reduced hybrid viability:** When a zygote *is* formed, genetic incompatibility may cause development to cease.

 ▪ **Reduced hybrid fertility:** Even if the two species produce a viable offspring, reproductive isolation is still occurring if the offspring is sterile and can't reproduce.

 ▪ **Hybrid breakdown:** Sometimes two species mate and produce viable, fertile hybrids; however, when the hybrids mate, their offspring are weak or sterile.

Speciation can take place with or without geographic separation
(Biology, *11e: 24.2*; Focus, *2e: 22.2*)

▊ In **allopatric speciation** a population forms a new species because it is geographically isolated from the parent population. When the population is geographically isolated, gene flow is interrupted, resulting in reproductive isolation.

- Some **geologic events or processes** that can fragment a population, resulting in geographic isolation of new populations, include the emergence of a mountain range, the formation of a land bridge, or evaporation in a large lake that produces several small lakes.
- Small, newly isolated populations undergo allopatric speciation more frequently because they are more likely to have their gene pools significantly altered. Speciation is confirmed when individuals from the new population are unable to mate successfully with individuals from the parent population.

- A second type of speciation is **sympatric speciation**, in which a small part of a population forms a new species without being geographically separated from the parent population. This speciation can result from part of the population switching to a new habitat; a change in a resource, such as food; or an accident during cell division, resulting in extra sets of chromosomes (polyploidy).

  - An example of a mechanism that can lead to sympatric speciation in plants is the formation of **polyploid** plants through nondisjunction in meiosis. For example, these plants may have a $4n$ chromosome number instead of the normal $2n$ number. They cannot breed with diploid members and produce fertile offspring. Although the formation of new species resulting from the formation of polyploids is rare in animals, it is very common in plants (80% of plant species have been involved in a polyploid event).

- **Adaptive radiation** occurs when many new species arise from a single common ancestor. In adaptive radiations, the new species fill different ecological niches in their communities. For example, when true flight evolved in some reptiles (part of the evolution of birds), a vast array of new niches became available. In addition, catastrophes such as volcanoes, landslides, and mass extinctions have opened a spectrum of new or unfilled niches.

Speciation can occur rapidly or slowly and can result from changes in a few or many genes (Biology, *11e: 24.4;* Focus, *2e: 22.4*)

- **Gradualism** proposes that species descend from a common ancestor and gradually diverge more and more in morphology as they acquire unique adaptations.
- **Punctuated equilibrium** is a term used to describe periods of apparent stasis punctuated by sudden change observed in the fossil record.

TIP FROM THE READERS

Remember this: Individuals do not evolve! They do not "struggle to survive." They cannot change their genetic makeup in response to a catastrophe. The individual lives or dies. Those that live reproduce and pass on adaptive heritable variations. **Individuals do not evolve! Only populations can evolve!**

The History of Life on Earth

(Biology, 11e: Chapter 25; Focus, 2e: Chapters 23, 24.1)

YOU MUST KNOW

- A scientific hypothesis about the origin of life on Earth. (LO 1.27)
- The age of Earth and when prokaryotic and eukaryotic life emerged.
- Characteristics of the early planet and its atmosphere.
- How Miller and Urey tested the Oparin-Haldane hypothesis and what they learned.
- Methods used to date fossils and rocks and how fossil evidence contributes to our understanding of changes in life on Earth.
- Evidence for endosymbiosis.
- How continental drift can explain the current distribution of species (biogeography).
- How extinction events open habitats that may result in adaptive radiation.

Conditions on early Earth made the origin of life possible
(Biology, 11e: 25.1; Focus, 2e: 24.1)

▌ The current hypothesis about how life arose consists of four main stages:

1. Abiotic (nonliving) synthesis of small organic molecules, such as amino acids and nitrogenous bases
2. The joining of these small molecules into macromolecules, such as proteins and nucleic acids
3. The packaging of these molecules into **protocells**, membrane-enclosed droplets, whose internal chemistry differed from that of the external environment
4. The origin of self-replicating molecules that made inheritance possible

▌ Earth was formed about **4.6 billion years ago**, and life on Earth emerged about **3.8 billion years ago**. For the first three-quarters of Earth's history, all of its living organisms were microscopic and primarily unicellular.

▌ Hypothetical early conditions of Earth have been simulated in laboratories, and organic molecules have been produced.

　▪ In the 1920s, **Oparin** and **Haldane** hypothesized that the early atmosphere, thick with water vapor, nitrogen, carbon dioxide, methane, ammonia, hydrogen, and hydrogen sulfide, provided with energy from lightning and UV radiation, could have formed organic compounds, a primitive "soup" from which life arose.

　▪ In the 1950s, **Miller** and **Urey** tested this hypothesis and produced a variety of amino acids. Miller-Urey-type experiments show that the abiotic synthesis of organic molecules is possible under various assumptions about the composition of the early atmosphere.

▌ The "RNA world" hypothesis suggests that **self-replicating RNA** (not DNA) was the **first genetic material**. RNA, which plays a central role in protein synthesis, can also carry out a number of enzyme-like catalytic functions. These RNA catalysts are called **ribozymes**. Some ribozymes can make complementary copies of short pieces of RNA.

The fossil record documents the history of life (Biology, *11e: 25.2;* Focus, *2e: 23.1*)

▌ The **fossil record** is the sequence in which fossils appear in the layers of sedimentary rock that constitute Earth's surface. **Paleontologists** study the fossil record. Fossils, which may be remnants of dead organisms or impressions they left behind, are most often found in sedimentary rock formed from layers of minerals settling out of water. The fossil record is incomplete because it favors organisms that existed for a long time, were relatively abundant and widespread, and had shells or hard bony skeletons.

▌ Rocks and fossils are dated several ways:

  ▪ **Relative dating** uses the order of rock strata to determine the relative age of fossils. The oldest fossils are deposited in the lower strata.

  ▪ **Radiometric dating** uses the decay of radioactive isotopes to determine the age of the rocks or fossils. It is based on the rate of decay, or **half-life** of the isotope. The half-life is the time necessary for 50% of the parent isotope to decay. For example, the half-life of radioactive carbon-14 is 5,730 years (the common isotope carbon-12 is not radioactive). Living organisms accumulate both carbon-12 and carbon-14 in a known ratio. Once the organism dies, there is no more carbon to obtain, but the carbon-14 decays into nitrogen-14. Measuring the carbon-14-to-carbon-12 ratio in a fossil can reveal its age. For example, if the fossil ratio of carbon-14 to carbon-12 is one-eighth the ratio of present-day individuals, the fossil is about 17,190 years old (5780 × 3 half-lives). See the grid-in questions at the end of this topic for a half-life problem.

Key events in life's history include the origins of single-celled and multicelled organisms and the colonization of land (Biology, *11e: 25.3;* Focus, *2e: 23.1, 25.1*)

▌ The earliest living organisms were **prokaryotes** and date to at least 3.5 billion years ago.

▌ About 2.7 billion years ago, **oxygen** began to accumulate in Earth's atmosphere as a result of photosynthesis. The rise of oxygen doomed many prokaryotic groups, but others, including groups capable of cellular respiration, evolved in the new oxygen-rich environment.

▌ **Eukaryotes** appeared about 2.1 billion years ago.

  ▪ The **endosymbiotic hypothesis** proposes that mitochondria and plastids (chloroplasts) were formerly small prokaryotes that began living within larger cells.

  ▪ **Evidence** for the endosymbiotic hypothesis includes the following:

    ▪ Both organelles have enzymes and transport systems homologous to those found in the plasma membranes of living prokaryotes.

    ▪ Both replicate through a splitting process similar to prokaryotes.

    ▪ Both contain a single, circular DNA molecule, not associated with histone proteins, similar to prokaryotes.

- Both have their own ribosomes, which can translate their DNA into proteins.

▌ **Multicellular eukaryotes** evolved about 1.2 billion years ago.

▌ The **colonization of land** occurred about 500 million years ago, when **plants, fungi, and animals** began to appear on Earth.

The rise and fall of groups of organisms reflect differences in speciation and extinction rates (Biology, *11e: 25.4*; Focus, *2e: 23.2*)

▌ **Continental drift** is the movement of Earth's continents on great plates that float on the hot, underlying mantle. The San Andreas Fault is a place where two plates are sliding past each other. Where plates have collided, new mountains have arisen. The Himalayan mountains were formed when the Indian plate crashed into the Eurasian plate 45 million years ago.

- Continental drift can help explain the geographic distribution of certain species, such as a fossil freshwater reptile found in both Brazil (South America) and Ghana (West Africa), which today are widely separated by ocean.
- Continental drift explains why no eutherian (placental) mammals are indigenous to Australia.

▌ **Mass extinctions**, loss of large numbers of species in a short period, have resulted from global environmental changes that have caused the rate of extinction to increase dramatically.

- By removing large numbers of species, a mass extinction can drastically alter a complex ecological community. Evolutionary lineages can disappear. *Example:* The dinosaurs disappeared in a mass extinction 65 million years ago.
- Mass extinctions open niches that new species may occupy. For example, the rise of mammals occurred following the loss of dinosaurs. This is an example of adaptive radiation.

▌ **Adaptive radiations** are periods of evolutionary change in which groups of organisms form many new species whose adaptations allow them to fill different ecological niches. After each of five major extinctions in Earth's history, an adaptive radiation occurred. Adaptive radiations also occur after major evolutionary innovations, such as seeds in plants or feathers in birds, or in newly colonized areas where new species face little competition. *Example:* The Galápagos finch species are the result of an adaptive radiation resulting from the creation of new niches when volcanic action formed new land.

Major changes in body form can result from changes in the sequences and regulation of developmental genes (Biology, *11e: 25.5*; Focus, *2e: 23.3*)

▌ **Evo-devo** is a field of study in which evolutionary biology and developmental biology converge. (Evo = from evolution; devo = from development.) This field is illuminating how slight genetic divergences can be magnified into major morphological differences between species.

- Evolutionary novelty can arise when structures that originally played one role gradually acquire a different one. Structures that evolve in one context but become co-opted for another function are sometimes called **exaptations**. For example, it is possible that feathers of modern birds were co-opted for flight after functioning in some other capacity, such as for thermoregulation.
- **Heterochrony** is an evolutionary change in the rate or timing of developmental events. Changing relative rates of growth even slightly can alter the adult form of organisms substantially, thus contributing to the potential for evolutionary change. The increased rate of growth in bat finger bones provided the underlying support for bat wings, whereas the decreased rate of growth in whale leg and pelvic bones led to the loss of hind limbs.
- **Homeotic genes** are master regulatory genes that determine the location and organization of body parts. Homeotic genes affect where a pair of wings will develop or how a flower's parts are arranged.
- *Hox* genes are one class of homeotic genes. Changes in *Hox* genes and in the genes that regulate them can have a profound effect on morphology, thus contributing to the potential for evolutionary change. An example is seen in the variable expression of a *Hox* gene in a snake limb bud and a chicken leg bud, resulting in no legs in the snake and a skeletal extension in the chicken.

Evolution is not goal oriented (Biology, *11e: 25.6; Focus, 2e: 23.4*)

- Evolution is like tinkering—a process in which new forms arise by the slight modification of existing forms. Even large changes, such as the ones that produced the first mammals, can result from the modification of existing structures or existing developmental genes.

Level 1: Knowledge/Comprehension Questions

The Level 1, Knowledge/Comprehension, questions review essential content knowledge but don't represent the type of question you will see on the AP exam. The Level 2, Application/Synthesis, questions are similar to those you will see on the exam.

1. The condition in which there are barriers to reproduction between individuals of the same species because they are separated by a portion of a mountain range is referred to as
   (A) mechanical isolation.
   (B) geographic isolation.
   (C) gametic isolation.
   (D) temporal isolation.

2. Which of the following statements best expresses the concept of punctuated equilibrium?
   (A) Very small changes in the genome of individuals eventually lead to the evolution of a population.
   (B) The five conditions of Hardy-Weinberg equilibrium will prevent populations from evolving quickly.
   (C) In geologic time, evolution occurs in rapid bursts of change alternating with long periods in which species remain relatively unchanged.
   (D) Profound change over the course of geologic history is the result of an accumulation of slow, continuous processes.

3. In a particular bird species, individuals with average-sized wings survive severe storms more successfully than other birds in the same population with longer or shorter wings. This illustrates which of the following modes of selection?
   (A) directional selection
   (B) stabilizing selection
   (C) diversifying selection
   (D) artificial selection

Directions: Questions 4–7 consist of four lettered choices followed by a list of numbered phrases or sentences. For each numbered phrase or sentence, select the one choice that is most closely related to it. Each choice may be used once, more than once, or not at all.

Questions 4–7
   (A) The bottleneck effect
   (B) Homologous structures
   (C) Analogous structures
   (D) The founder effect

4. Results in a new population with a limited gene pool, often seen when a small population is separated from the larger population

5. One result of evolution from a common ancestor; exhibited by certain structures with similar features having different functions

6. A result of drastic reduction in population size, such as the reduction of the California condor population to nine individuals

7. Features that have evolved independently to serve similar functions but do not represent evolutionary relatedness

8. One general pattern that will maintain two related groups as separate species requires their gametes to not combine. These are called prezygotic barriers. Select the one example that does not describe this type of isolating mechanism.
   (A) hybrid breakdown
   (B) behavioral isolation
   (C) temporal isolation
   (D) mechanical isolation

9. A marsupial species found only in Australia has evolved to eat tree leaves, be diurnal, and raise its young until they are of reproductive age. A grazing placental mammal species found in Africa has also evolved to eat tree leaves, be diurnal, and raise its young until they are of reproductive age. This is an example of which of the following types of evolution?
   (A) divergent evolution
   (B) species-specific evolution
   (C) convergent evolution
   (D) neutral evolution

10. Banded iron formations in marine sediments provide evidence of
   (A) the crashing of meteorites onto Earth, possibly transporting abiotically produced organic molecules from space.
   (B) oxidized iron layers in terrestrial rocks.
   (C) the accumulation of oxygen in the seas from the photosynthesis of cyanobacteria.
   (D) the evolution of photosynthetic archaea near deep-sea vents.

11. Which of the following constitutes the smallest unit capable of evolution?
   (A) an individual
   (B) a family unit
   (C) a population
   (D) a community

12. Which of the following would not be important in Darwin's theory of evolution?
    (A) Acquiring genetic change during the life span of the organism contributes to evolution.
    (B) More individuals are born in a population than will survive to reproduce.
    (C) Natural selection occurs as a result of the differing reproductive success of individuals in a population.
    (D) A result of evolution is the adaptation of a population of organisms to their environment.

Level 2: Application/Analysis/Synthesis Questions

1. In a certain group of rabbits, the presence of yellow fur is the result of a homozygous recessive condition in the biochemical pathway producing hair pigment. If the frequency of the allele for this condition is 0.09, which of the following is closest to the frequency of the dominant allele in this population? (Assume that the population is in Hardy-Weinberg equilibrium and only two alleles are present for this gene.)
    (A) 0.01
    (B) 0.19
    (C) 0.70
    (D) 0.91

2. In a population of squirrels, the allele that causes bushy tail (B) is dominant, whereas the allele that causes bald tail is recessive (b). If 64% of the squirrels have a bushy tail, what is the frequency of the dominant allele?
    (A) 0.8
    (B) 0.6
    (C) 0.4
    (D) 0.36

3. Mice that are homozygous for a lethal recessive allele die shortly after birth. In a large breeding colony of mice, you find that a surprising 5% of all newborns die from this trait. In checking lab records, you discover that the same proportion of offspring have been dying from this trait in this colony for the past three years. (Mice breed several times a year and have large litters.) Calculate the frequency of the recessive allele. How might you explain the persistence of this lethal allele at such a high frequency?
    (A) Homozygous recessive mice have a reproductive advantage, which helps to maintain the frequency of the allele.
    (B) The rapid reproductive rate is coupled with a large mutation rate, which results in multiple copies of this lethal allele.
    (C) There is some sort of heterozygote advantage and perhaps selection against the homozygous dominant trait.
    (D) Because this is a diploid species, the recessive allele cannot be selected against when it is in the heterozygote.

4. Morphological and genetic comparisons group 30 species of snapping shrimp (genus *Alpheus*) into 15 pairs of closely related species. In sympatric speciation, a new species may arise in the same area as an existing species, whereas in allopatric speciation, some geographical isolating mechanism is present. What is the best explanation for the fact that one member of each pair lives on the Atlantic side of the Isthmus of Panama, whereas the other member of each pair lives on the Pacific side?
   (A) Different predator pressures in the Atlantic and Pacific selected for differences, resulting in the reproductive isolation of these species.
   (B) The pairs of species arose by allopatric speciation when the Isthmus of Panama separated their ancestral species.
   (C) The 30 species of snapping shrimp evolved by sympatric speciation before the Isthmus of Panama formed.
   (D) These 15 pairs of species illustrate the pattern of punctuated equilibrium, in which most speciation events take place in a short period of time.

5. Sympatric evolution occurs when a new species arises in the same area as an existing ancestral species. Which of the following can lead to sympatric speciation?
   (A) A small number of individuals migrate to a geographically remote area.
   (B) A natural disaster cuts off contact between members of a population.
   (C) A flood causes a new river to form, separating segments of a population.
   (D) A mutation event results in offspring that are fertile tetraploids.

6. Mitochondria and plastids contain DNA and ribosomes and make some, but not all, of their proteins. Some of their proteins are coded for by nuclear DNA and are produced in the cytoplasm. What may explain this division of labor?
   (A) Over the course of evolution, some of the original endosymbiont's genes were transferred to the host cell's nucleus.
   (B) The host cell's genome has always included genes for making mitochondrial and plastid proteins.
   (C) The smaller prokaryotic ribosomes in these organelles cannot produce the eukaryotic proteins required for their functions.
   (D) Some mitochondria and plastid genes were contributed by early bacterial prokaryotes that shared genes with other primitive cells.

7. Mothers and teachers have often said that they need another pair of eyes on the backs of their heads. Another pair of hands would come in handy in many situations also. You can imagine that these traits would have been advantageous to our early hunter–gatherer ancestors as well. According to sound evolutionary reasoning, what is the most likely explanation for why humans do not have these traits?
   (A) These traits actually would not be beneficial to the fitness of individuals who possessed them. Natural selection always produces the most beneficial traits for a particular organism in a particular environment.
   (B) Every time these traits have arisen, the individual mutants bearing these traits have been killed by chance events. Chance and natural selection interact.
   (C) These variations have probably never appeared in a healthy human. Tetrapods share a four-limbed, two-eyed body plan; natural selection can only edit existing variations.
   (D) Humans are a relatively young species. Given enough time for adaptation, it is inevitable that the required adaptations will arise.

8. The following figure shows the change of a population over time. Which statement best describes the mode of selection depicted in the figure?

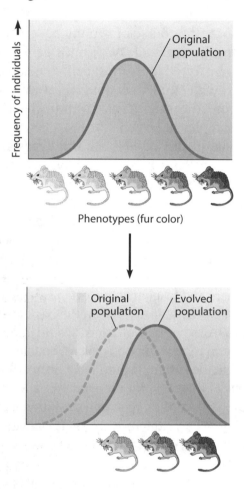

Phenotypes (fur color)

(A) stabilizing selection, which causes the average color of the population to be pushed toward an intermediate value
(B) directional selection, which causes the average color to become darker over time
(C) diversifying selection, which causes the average color to become either darker *or* lighter over time
(D) no selection, because too many of the original population are lost over time

After reading the paragraphs, answer questions 9 and 10.

In 2004, scientists announced the discovery of the fossil remains of some extremely short early humans on the Indonesian island of Flores. The new species has been named *Homo floresiensis*. One hypothesis is that *H. floresiensis* evolved from *Homo erectus*, another early human species. How did a population of *H. erectus* become isolated on this remote island? Early humans constructed boats and rafts, so perhaps they were blown far off course by strong winds during a storm.

H. erectus averaged almost 6 feet in height, but the remains show that adults of *H. floresiensis* were only about 3 feet tall. Scientists hypothesize that limited resources on this hot and humid island (only 31 square miles) exerted selection pressure, and succeeding generations began to shrink in size. Small bodies require less food, use less energy, and are easier to cool than larger bodies. Evolution of small size in similar circumstances has been observed in many other species but never before in humans. This find demonstrates that evolutionary forces operate on humans in the same way they do on all other organisms.

9. The evolution of *Homo floresiensis* is an example of
(A) sympatric speciation, which occurs when a new species develops in the midst of an ancestral species, often by polyploidy.
(B) allopatric speciation, in which a new species arises when two populations are geographically separated.
(C) adaptive radiation, which occurs when new niches become available and are filled by new species.
(D) hybridization, which occurs when two species interbreed.

10. If *H. floresiensis* were reunited with *H. erectus* at a much later date, but the two populations could no longer interbreed, which would be a scientifically plausible conclusion about their incompatibility?
    (A) *H. floresiensis* is no longer fertile as a species.
    (B) *H. floresiensis* had been isolated for more than 50,000 years.
    (C) *H. floresiensis* has become less fit than *H. erectus*.
    (D) Reproductive barriers had evolved between the two species.

Use the following table and paragraph to answer questions 11–15.

Number of Seedlings				
Time (days)	Green (C^GC^G)	Green-yellow (C^GC^Y)	Yellow (C^YC^Y)	Total
7	49	111	56	216
21	47	106	20	173

One way to test whether evolution is occurring in a population is to compare the observed genotype frequencies at a locus with those expected for a non-evolving population based on the Hardy-Weinberg equation. Students planted soybean seeds and then counted the number of seedlings of each genotype at day 7 and again at day 21. Seedlings of each genotype could be distinguished visually because the C^G and C^Y alleles show incomplete dominance: C^GC^G seedlings have green leaves, C^GC^Y seedlings have green-yellow leaves, and C^YC^Y seedlings have yellow leaves. The two alleles, C^G and C^Y affect chlorophyll production and hence leaf color, which affects photosynthesis and therefore the viability of the plant.

11. The first step in testing whether a population is in Hardy-Weinberg equilibrium is to calculate the allele frequencies in the population. Remember that the frequency of an allele in a gene pool is the number of copies of that allele divided by the total number of copies of all alleles at that locus. Using the day 7 data, what is the frequency of the C^G allele (p)?
    (A) 0.113
    (B) 0.484
    (C) 0.613
    (D) 0.968

12. Using the day 7 data, what is the frequency of the C^Y allele (q)?
    (A) 0.234
    (B) 0.484
    (C) 0.516
    (D) 1.484

13. Use the values for p and q from day 7 and the Hardy-Weinberg equation ($p^2 + 2pq + q^2 = 1$) to calculate the expected percentage of genotype C^GC^Y (green-yellow plants) for a population in Hardy-Weinberg equilibrium.
    (A) 23%
    (B) 27%
    (C) 46%
    (D) 50%

14. The expected genotypic percentage of yellow plants (C^YC^Y) at Hardy-Weinberg equilibrium is 26.6%. However, in the day 21 readings, the observed genotypic ratio is 11.6%. Which of the following statements is best supported by the data?
    (A) The population is evolving, and there appears to be selection against genotype C^GC^Y.
    (B) The population is in Hardy-Weinberg equilibrium.
    (C) The population is evolving, and there appears to be selection against genotype C^YC^Y.
    (D) The population is evolving, and there appears to be selection against genotype C^GC^G.

15. Based on the data presented, predict the frequencies of the C^G and C^Y alleles after six more generations.

(A) The frequency of the C^Y allele will decrease, and the frequency of the C^G allele will increase.

(B) The frequencies of the C^Y and C^G alleles will stay the same.

(C) The frequency of the C^Y allele will increase, and the frequency of the C^G allele will decrease.

(D) The frequency of the C^Y allele will decrease, and the frequency of the C^G allele will stay the same.

Use the reading and the table to answer questions 16–18.

Did you ever wonder if the fish you ordered in a restaurant or bought in a market was really the fish you thought it was? Substitution of one fish species for another in stores or restaurants is called "market substitution." To determine the degree of market substitution, a gene comparison study compared DNA sequences in muscle cells among all species. Then samples of fish being sold as Pacific salmon were taken from restaurants in Tacoma, Washington, for comparison.

Pacific salmon include five closely related species within the genus *Oncorhynchus:* chinook (*O. tshawytscha*), chum (*O. keta*), coho (*O. kisutch*), pink (*O. gorbuscha*), and sockeye (*O. nerka*). The DNA sequencing and phylogenetic analysis of salmon served at the restaurants revealed that about 24% of the salmon sold as Pacific salmon was actually Atlantic salmon (*Salmo salar*), and another 14% of the salmon sold was a different species of Pacific salmon than the one listed on the menu.

	S. salar	O. gorbuscha	O. keta	O. kisutch	O. nerka	O. tshawytscha	Test sample
S. salar	self	16%	15%	14%	14%	14%	1%
O. gorbuscha		self	5%	10%	9%	10%	16%
O. keta			self	10%	9%	10%	15%
O. kisutch				self	9%	4%	15%
O. nerka					self	10%	14%
O. tshawytscha						self	15%
Test sample							self

Within the matrix, the intersection of a given row and column contains the percentage difference between the row species and the column species. (Some of the cells are gray because they would duplicate comparisons made elsewhere in the matrix.) You can use the pattern of differences to infer the relationships among each of the samples or standards.

16. Which of the following is most likely the species of the test sample fish?
    (A) *O. tshawytscha*
    (B) *O. nerka*
    (C) *O. gorbuscha*
    (D) *S. salar*

17. When a phylogenetic tree is formed using the data in the chart, *O. kisutch* is closely related to another species of salmon. Which is the closely related species?
    (A) *O. tshawytscha*
    (B) *O. nerka*
    (C) *O. gorbuscha*
    (D) *O. nerka*

18. Which of the following trees is the best match for the relationships shown in the chart?

(A)

(B)

(C)

(D)
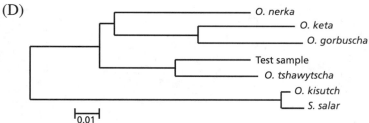

Grid-In Questions

The following questions require a numerical response.

1. The radioisotope potassium-40 can help date past events older than 60,000 years. Potassium-40 has a half life of 1.3 billion years, decaying into argon-40. If the igneous rock layer that scientists wish to date shows a ratio of potassium-40 to argon-40 at one-fourth the current ratio, what is the age of the rock layer? Express your answer in billions of years to the nearest tenth.

2. In a population of king snakes, the banded pattern (*B*) is dominant to no banding (*b*). If 12% of the population shows no banding, what percentage of the population, to the nearest tenth, is heterozygous for banding?

3. In a population of turtles, the allele that causes a yellow shell (*Y*) is dominant to the allele that results in a red shell (*y*). If the dominant allele is present in the population at the 0.72 level and the population is in Hardy-Weinberg equilibrium, what percentage of the population would be expected to have a red shell? Express your answer to the nearest tenth of a percentage point.

Free-Response Question

1. *Various experimental investigations have provided evidence that the conditions early in Earth's history provided an environment capable of generating complex organic molecules and simple cell-like structures.*

   (a) Describe one scientific model for the origin of organic molecules on Earth.

   (b) Explain how RNA has the essential features of the earliest genetic material.

   (c) Predict the effect that introduction of free oxygen into the atmosphere had on the prokaryotic species of the time.

The Evolutionary History of Life

Phylogeny and the Tree of Life
(Biology, *11e: Chapter 26;* Focus, *2e: Chapter 20*)

YOU MUST KNOW

- The taxonomic categories and how they indicate relatedness.
- How systematics is used to develop phylogenetic trees.
- How to construct a phylogenetic tree that represents processes of biological evolution. (LO 1.13)
- The three domains of life, including their similarities and their differences.
- The significance of widely conserved processes across the three domains.

CONNECT WITH THE CURRICULUM FRAMEWORK

This chapter is a rich source of possible questions. Note these specific objectives, and be sure you can do each of these tasks.

- The student is able to pose scientific questions about a group of organisms whose relatedness is described by a phylogenetic tree or cladogram to (1) identify shared characteristics, (2) make inferences about the evolutionary history of the group, and (3) identify character data that could extend or improve the phylogenetic tree. (LO 1.17)
- The student is able to evaluate evidence provided by a data set in conjunction with a phylogenetic tree or a simple cladogram to determine evolutionary history and speciation. (LO 1.18)
- The student is able to create a phylogenetic tree or simple cladogram that correctly represents evolutionary history and speciation from a provided data set. (LO 1.19)

Phylogenies show evolutionary relationships (Biology, *11e: 26.1;* Focus, *2e: 20.1*)

- **Phylogeny** is the evolutionary history of a species or a group of related species. It is constructed by using evidence from **systematics**, a discipline that focuses on classifying organisms and their evolutionary relationships.

▌ Many different disciplines provide evidence that supports biological evolution and may be used to determine phylogeny. These tools include fossils, morphology, DNA and genetic analysis, and molecular evidence.

▌ **Taxonomy** is an ordered division of organisms into categories based on a set of characteristics used to assess similarities and differences.

▌ **Binomial nomenclature** is a two-part naming system that consists of the **genus** to which the species belongs as well as the organisms' **species** within the genus, such as *Canis familiaris*, the scientific name of the common dog. This system was developed by **Carolus Linnaeus**.

▌ The hierarchical classification of organisms consists of the following levels, beginning with the most general or inclusive: **domain, kingdom, phylum, class, order, family, genus,** and **species**. Each categorization at any level is called a **taxon**.

> ***STUDY TIP*** Use a mnemonic device, such as "Dear King Phillip climbed over the fence and got shot," to remember the categories in order. Know that the degree of relatedness increases with each successive level down (in other words, the organisms share more common traits).

▌ Systematists use branching diagrams called **phylogenetic trees** to depict hypotheses about evolutionary relationships. The branches of such trees reflect the hierarchical classifications of groups nested within more inclusive groups. (See Figure 7.1.)

▌ Notice in Figure 7.1 that two branch points are numbered. Each number represents a *common ancestor* of the two branches. Can you mark the point where all carnivores shared a common ancestor?

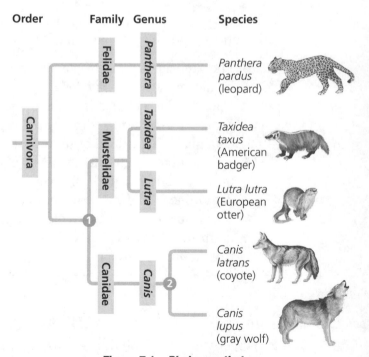

Figure 7.1   Phylogenetic tree

▌ Examine the phylogenetic tree in Figure 7.2. Carefully work through the explanations near Figure 7.2.

Figure 7.2   How to read a phylogenetic tree

PRACTICE THE PRACTICE: Understanding and Using Phylogenetic Trees

1. Redraw the tree shown in Figure 7.2, rotating the branches around branch points 2 and 4. Does your new version tell a different story about the evolutionary relationship between the taxa? Explain.

2. Which of the trees shown here depicts an evolutionary history different from the other two? Explain.

3. Suppose new evidence indicates that taxon E in Figure 7.2 is the sister taxon of a group consisting of taxa D and F. Redraw the tree accordingly.

You can find answers at the end of this topic, on page 203.

Phylogenies are inferred from morphological and molecular data
(Biology, *11e: 26.2;* Focus, *2e: 20.2*)

- ■ **Homologous structures** are similarities resulting from shared ancestry, such as the bones of a whale's flipper and a tiger's front limb.
- ■ **Convergent evolution** has taken place when two organisms developed similarities as they adapted to similar environmental challenges—not because they evolved from a common ancestor. *Example:* The streamlined bodies of a tuna and a dolphin show convergent evolution.

- The likenesses that result from convergent evolution are considered **analogous** rather than homologous. They do not indicate relatedness but rather similar solutions to similar problems. *Example:* The wing of a butterfly is analogous to the wing of a bat. Both are adaptations for flight.
- **Molecular systematics** uses DNA and other molecular data to determine evolutionary relationships. The more alike the DNA sequences of two organisms are, the more closely related the organisms are evolutionarily.

Shared characters are used to construct phylogenetic trees (Biology, *11e: 26.3*; Focus, *2e: 20.3*)

- A **cladogram** depicts patterns of shared characteristics among taxa and forms the basis of a **phylogenetic tree**.
- A **clade**, within a tree, is defined as a group of species that includes an ancestral species and all its descendants. Clades are monophyletic.
- **Shared derived characters** are used to construct cladograms. They are evolutionary novelties unique to a particular clade. For example, hair is a shared derived character of mammals.
- A **shared ancestral characteristic** is one that originated in an ancestor of the taxon. For example, all mammals have backbones, but a backbone does not distinguish a mammal from other vertebrates because all vertebrates have a backbone.
- Study Figure 7.3 to understand why a clade is *monophyletic* and what is meant by paraphyletic and polyphyletic groupings. Each cladogram is a hypothesis about the evolutionary relatedness of the organisms included. The goal of taxonomy is to understand the lines of descent from ancestral forms well enough to produce monophyletic cladograms. This means the cladogram reflects the common ancestor and all of its descendants. Many times, however, scientists lack the data to make a monophyletic cladogram, resulting in paraphyletic

(a) Monophyletic group (clade)

Group I

Group I, consisting of three species (A, B, C) and their common ancestor ❶, is a clade, also called a monophyletic group. A monophyletic group consists of an ancestral species and *all* of its descendants.

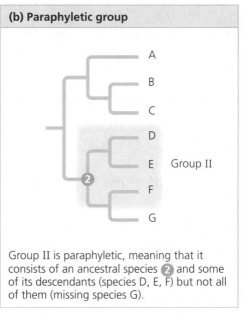

(b) Paraphyletic group

Group II

Group II is paraphyletic, meaning that it consists of an ancestral species ❷ and some of its descendants (species D, E, F) but not all of them (missing species G).

(c) Polyphyletic group

Group III

Group III, consisting of four species (A, B, C, D), is polyphyletic, meaning that the common ancestor ❸ of its members is *not* part of the group.

Figure 7.3   Cladograms

or polyphyletic groupings. As data become available, the cladograms are improved until, we hope, a monophyletic cladogram can be formed.

▌ The terms *monophyletic, paraphyletic*, and *polyphyletic* are not in the curriculum framework, but questions about these ideas are common. The terms help organize your learning and will be ones your college professors will expect you to know.

Molecular clocks help track evolutionary time (Biology, *11e: 26.5;* Focus, *2e: 20.4*)

▌ **Molecular clocks** are tools used to measure the absolute time of evolutionary change based on the observation that some genes and regions of the genome appear to evolve at constant rates. The underlying assumption for molecular clocks is that the number of nucleotide substitutions in related genes is proportional to the time that has elapsed since the genes branched from their common ancestor.

▌ What causes differences in the speed at which genes evolve? Some mutations are selectively neutral, but many new mutations are harmful and quickly removed by natural selection. Can you predict which would accumulate mutations more rapidly—a gene for a critical enzyme for glycolysis or a gene that results in a difference in human eye color?

▌ Differences in the rate of mutation in different genes are a function of how important the gene is to survival. Glycolysis is a universal pathway for the oxidation of glucose to obtain energy, and genes in this pathway are remarkably similar among all organisms. We say the genes are "highly conserved." Because natural selection would result in selection against genes that alter this essential process in a negative way, the mutation rate would be very slow in this type of gene.

Our understanding of the tree of life continues to change based on new data (Biology, *11e: 26.6;* Focus, *2e: 20.5*)

▌ Taxonomy is in flux! When the authors of this book were in high school, we were taught that there were two kingdoms, plants and animals; then in our college courses, we were introduced to five kingdoms: Monera, Protista, Plantae, Fungi, and Animalia.

▌ Now biologists have adopted a **three-domain** system, which consists of the domains Bacteria, Archaea, and Eukarya. This system arose from the finding that there are two distinct lineages of prokaryotes.

▌ The domains Bacteria and Archaea contain *prokaryotic* organisms, and Eukarya contains *eukaryotic* organisms. As we gain more tools for analysis, earlier ideas about evolutionary relatedness change, so taxonomy continues to evolve. The Practice the Practice box that follows compares the three domains in current use.

▌ **Horizontal gene transfer** occurs when genes are transferred from one genome to another. The mechanisms of horizontal gene transfer include the exchange of transposable elements and plasmids, viral infections and perhaps the fusion of organisms.

▌ Comparisons of complete genomes from the three domains show that there have been substantial movements of genes between organisms in the different domains. Horizontal gene transfer has played a key role throughout the evolutionary history of life and continues to occur today.

Phylogenetic trees are constructed based on the assumption that genes are passed vertically from one generation to the next. The occurrence of horizontal transfer events helps explain why trees built using different genes can give inconsistent results. The DNA evidence from different genes can be interpreted to tell more than one story.

PRACTICE THE PRACTICE: Evaluating Information from a Chart

A Comparison of the Three Domains of Life

Characteristic	Bacteria	Archaea	Eukarya
Nuclear envelope	No	No	Yes
Membrane-enclosed organelles	No	No	Yes
Introns	No	Yes	Yes
Histone proteins associated with DNA	No	Yes	Yes
Circular chromosome	Yes	Yes	No

1. List three ways in which Bacteria and Archaea are similar.
2. Archaea are more closely related to Eukarya than Bacteria. Provide evidence from the chart to justify this statement.

You can find solutions at the end of this topic, on page 203.

TIP FROM THE READERS

We have seen great emphasis placed on the importance of using data from several sources to develop cladograms or of using cladograms to infer relatedness in both multiple-choice and free-response questions. You will be glad you invested your time on working with cladograms and phylogenetic trees!

Chapter 27: Bacteria and Archaea

(Biology, *11e: Chapter 27;* Focus, *2e: Chapter 24*)

YOU MUST KNOW

- The key ways in which prokaryotes differ from eukaryotes with respect to genome, membrane-bound organelles, size, and reproduction.
- How horizontal acquisition of genetic information occurs in prokaryotes via transformation, conjugation, and transduction.
- How these mechanisms, plus mutation, contribute to genetic diversity in prokaryotes. (EK 3.C.2)

Structural and functional adaptations contribute to prokaryotic success (Biology, *11e: 27.1;* Focus, *2e: 24.2*)

▌ Life is divided into three domains: **Archaea, Bacteria**, and **Eukarya**. Both domain Bacteria and domain Archaea are made up of prokaryotes.

▌ Prokaryotes are perhaps 1/10 the size of typical eukaryotic cells.

▌ As you read the following sections, study Figure 7.4. Prokaryotes have *no true nuclei* or internal compartmentalization. The DNA is concentrated in a *nucleoid region* and has little associated protein. The small genome consists of a single circular chromosome. Prokaryotes reproduce through an asexual process called **binary fission** and have short generation times.

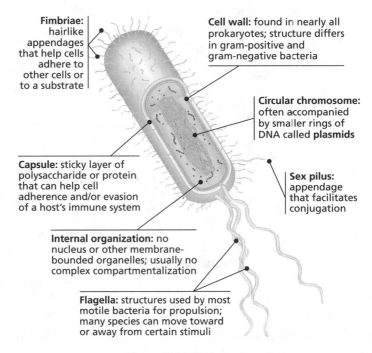

Fimbriae: hairlike appendages that help cells adhere to other cells or to a substrate

Cell wall: found in nearly all prokaryotes; structure differs in gram-positive and gram-negative bacteria

Circular chromosome: often accompanied by smaller rings of DNA called **plasmids**

Capsule: sticky layer of polysaccharide or protein that can help cell adherence and/or evasion of a host's immune system

Sex pilus: appendage that facilitates conjugation

Internal organization: no nucleus or other membrane-bounded organelles; usually no complex compartmentalization

Flagella: structures used by most motile bacteria for propulsion; many species can move toward or away from certain stimuli

Figure 7.4 Prokaryote

▌ In addition to their one major chromosome, prokaryotic cells may also possess smaller, circular, self-replicating pieces of DNA called **plasmids**. In biotechnology plasmids are often used to carry the gene of interest into a prokaryotic cell.

▌ Outside their cell membranes, most prokaryotes possess a cell wall that contains **peptidoglycans**. (It is worth noting that cell walls occur in three kingdoms: Plants have cell walls of cellulose, fungi have cell walls of chitin, and bacteria have cell walls of peptidoglycans.)

▌ About half of the prokaryotes are **motile**, because they possess whiplike **flagella**. The flagellum of a bacterium is structurally different from the eukaryotic flagellum; this is another example of analogous structures.

Rapid reproduction, mutation, and genetic recombination promote genetic diversity in prokaryotes (Biology, *11e: 27.2;* Focus, *2e: 24.3*)

▌ It is important for you to know that there are many ways for genetic information to be transferred between bacterial cells. In eukaryotes, the sexual processes of meiosis and fertilization combine DNA from two individuals. Meiosis and fertilization do not occur in prokaryotes. However, genetic recombination—the combining of DNA from two different sources—can occur in prokaryotes through the three mechanisms explained in the next bulleted section. When the individuals are different species, this movement is called **horizontal gene transfer**. Note that all three processes result in increased genetic variation without sexual reproduction.

▌ Three mechanisms by which bacteria can transfer genetic material between each other are:

   ▪ **Transformation**, in which a prokaryote takes up DNA from its environment. The foreign DNA is integrated into the chromosome by the exchange of homologous DNA segments. Investigation 8 uses transformation to introduce a gene into *E. coli*. We have reviewed the investigation in the lab section of this book on page 333.

   ▪ **Transduction** is a process by which a bacteriophage (virus) transfers genes between one prokaryote and another. A random piece of DNA is accidently packaged into the head of the bacteriophage, which is then introduced to the next host during infection. Recombination may occur when the newly introduced DNA replaces its homologous section in the host cell's chromosome.

   ▪ **Conjugation** occurs when genes are transferred directly from one prokaryote to another when they are temporarily joined by a "mating bridge." Once again, recombination may occur when the newly introduced DNA replaces its homologous section in the host cell's chromosome.

▌ Although **mutations** are rare, they are the major source of genetic variation in prokaryotes because of the short generation time and large population sizes of bacteria.

Diverse nutritional and metabolic adaptations have evolved in prokaryotes (Biology, *11e: 27.3;* Focus, *2e: 24.2*)

▌ Prokaryotes have diverse strategies for taking in carbon and obtaining energy. Some prokaryotes are photosynthetic, and others get their energy from organic and inorganic compounds.

▌ **Obligate aerobes** cannot grow without oxygen because they need oxygen for cellular respiration.

▌ **Obligate anaerobes** are poisoned by oxygen. Many obligate anaerobes live exclusively by fermentation.

▌ **Facultative anaerobes** use oxygen if it is available but can also carry out fermentation.

▌ In the early period of evolution on Earth, life-forms were anaerobic prokaryotes. Once oxygen began to accumulate in the atmosphere as a result of photosynthesis, many species of anaerobic prokaryotes became extinct.

Prokaryotes have radiated into a diverse set of lineages (Biology, *11e: 27.4;* Focus, *2e: 24.4*)

▌ Horizontal gene transfer has played a key role in the evolution of prokaryotes. A study of sequenced bacterial genomes found that an average of 75% of the genes in each genome had been transferred horizontally at some point in their evolutionary history.

▮ Since their origin 3.5 billion years ago, prokaryotes have evolved into two separate lineages: Bacteria and Archaea. Although this chapter concentrates on Bacteria, Archaea are also important. The first prokaryotes that were classified in the domain Archaea are known as **extremophiles** and live in extreme environments.

▪ **Extreme halophiles** live in saline environments (highly concentrated with salt) such as the Great Salt Lake.
▪ **Extreme thermophiles** live in very hot environments, such as geyser pools.

▮ Other Archaea do not live in extreme environments. **Methanogens**, found in deep sea vents as well as swamps, use carbon dioxide to oxidize H_2 and produce methane as a waste product.

Prokaryotes play crucial roles in the biosphere (Biology, *11e: 27.5;* Focus, *2e: 24.5*)

▮ Many prokaryotes are **decomposers,** breaking down dead organisms and waste products. Decomposition recycles chemical elements between the living and nonliving components of the environment.

▮ Many prokaryotes are **symbiotic,** meaning they form relationships with other species:

▪ **Mutualism:** Both symbiotic organisms benefit. An example would be the relationship between humans and their gut bacteria. The bacteria synthesize certain vitamins while living in a nutrient-rich environment.
▪ **Commensalism:** One organism benefits, whereas the other is neither helped nor harmed. An example would be some of the numerous bacterial species that live on the surface of your body that receive food and a place to live from the host (you) and neither harm nor benefit you.
▪ **Parasitism:** One organism benefits at the expense of the other. An example would be the relationship between you and a *Streptococcus* infection.

Concept 54.1 in *Biology,* 11e, and Concept 41.1 in *Focus*, 2e, further explore these topics.

Prokaryotes have both beneficial and harmful impacts on humans (Biology, *11e: 27.6;* Focus, *2e: 24.5*)

▮ Some bacteria are **pathogens**, parasites that cause disease.
▮ **Antibiotics** are chemicals that can kill prokaryotes. They are *not* effective against viruses. Many bacterial plasmids contain resistance genes to different antibiotics.
▮ Horizontal gene transfer can spread genes associated with virulence or antibiotic resistance between bacterial strains.
▮ Humans use prokaryotes in many diverse ways:

▪ The CRISPR-Cas9 (clustered, regularly interspaced, short palindromic repeat) system, a powerful new tool for altering genes in virtually any organism. A DNA sequence can be precisely cut, offering tremendous promise for the treatment of disease.

- **Bioremediation**, removing pollutants from soil, air, or water, which includes treating sewage, cleaning up oil spills, and precipitating radioactive materials
- Symbionts in the gut manufacturing vitamins and digesting foods
- Gene cloning and producing transgenic organisms
- Production of cheese and yogurt and other products

Protists

(Biology, *11e: Chapter 28;* Focus, *2e: Chapter 25*)

> **WHAT'S IMPORTANT TO KNOW?**
> The Curriculum Framework does not include specific information that you must know about the taxonomy of protists. However, this chapter contains information that may be the basis of both multiple-choice and essay questions. A general understanding of the protists will help you be more confident in dealing with potential questions.

Most eukaryotes are single-celled organisms (Biology, *11e: 28.1;* Focus, *2e: 25.3 and 25.4*)

- **Protist** is now a term used to refer to eukaryotes that are not plants, animals, or fungi. Biologists no longer consider Protista a kingdom because it is *paraphyletic*. Refer back to Figure 7.3 to review what this means. Some protists are more closely related to plants, fungi, or animals than to other protists.
- Protists vary in structure and function more than any other group of eukaryotes. Here are some general commonalities, but even these are not true for all groups:

  - Most are unicellular.
  - Most use aerobic metabolism and have mitochondria.

- There is evidence that the enormous diversity of protists has its origins in endosymbiosis. According to current theory, mitochondria and chloroplasts evolved through **endosymbiosis**. They were originally unicellular organisms engulfed by other cells that ultimately became organelles in the host cell.
- Protists can be divided into three categories: photosynthetic (plantlike) algae, ingestive (animal-like) protozoans, and absorptive (fungus-like) organisms.
- Most protists are aquatic and are important constituents of plankton. Many other protists live as symbionts in other organisms.
- Protists are such a diverse group that their classification continues to undergo revision. Here are some common protists that you may recognize:

  - *Giardia intestinalis* (causes "hiker's diarrhea"; always treat your water!)
  - *Trypanosoma* species (sleeping sickness and Chagas disease)
  - *Euglena* (remember seeing the tiny flagellated green cell with a red eyespot in Biology I?)
  - Dinoflagellates (blooms cause "red tides"; many are bioluminescent)
  - *Plasmodium* (causative agent of malaria)
  - Ciliates (*Paramecium* and *Stentor* are examples)

- Amoebas (move by pseudopodia)
- Brown algae (kelp)
- Red algae (multicellular; some found at great depths; sushi wraps)
- Green algae (*Clamydomonas, Ulva, Volvox*; this group is the closest relative of land plants)
- Slime molds (often seen as flat, yellowish oozes in damp mulch)

How Plants Colonized Land

(Biology, *11e: Chapter 29;* Focus, *2e: Chapter 26*)

WHAT'S IMPORTANT TO KNOW?

Plant evolution is not an explicit topic of the Curriculum Framework, but your teacher may choose to introduce you to this material. This chapter contains information that may be the basis of both multiple-choice and essay questions. Having a general understanding of plant evolution will help you be more confident in dealing with potential questions. Here are what we consider to be the main points of this chapter:

- Evidence that land plants have evolved from green algae
- Disadvantages and advantages of life on land
- The major evolutionary characteristics of bryophytes and seedless vascular plants
- Plants' unique life cycle, termed *alternation of generations*, with a gametophyte generation and a sporophyte generation
- The typical life cycle pattern of plants, as demonstrated by ferns

---

Plants evolved from green algae (Biology, *11e: 29.1;* Focus, *2e: 26.1*)

- Land plants evolved from green algae more than 500 million years ago. Plants have enabled other life-forms to survive on land. Plants supply oxygen and are the ultimate provider of most of the food eaten or absorbed by animals and fungi.
- Movement onto land had both advantages and challenges:

  - Advantages included increased sunlight unfiltered by water, more carbon dioxide in the atmosphere than the water, soils rich in nutrients, and fewer predators.
  - Challenges included a lack of water, desiccation, and a lack of structural support against gravity.

- All land plants have a life cycle that consists of two multicellular stages, called **alternation of generations**.
- The two stages are the haploid **gametophyte,** which produces gametes, and the diploid **sporophyte,** which makes spores by meiosis.

  - During *fertilization*, the egg and sperm fuse to form a diploid zygote, which divides by mitosis to form the sporophyte.
  - The zygote develops within the tissues of the female parent, deriving nutrients from it.

Mosses and other nonvascular plants have life cycles dominated by gametophytes (Biology, *11e: 29.2;* Focus, *2e: 26.3)*

- Bryophytes include three phyla: mosses, liverworts, and hornworts.
- The bryophytes are **nonvascular** plants (no xylem or phloem tissue to conduct water and nutrients). The lack of vascular tissue accounts for the small size of bryophytes.
- Unlike vascular plants, in all three bryophyte phyla the haploid gametophytes are the dominant stage of the life cycle. The organs that produce sperm and egg are found on the gametophytes. Bryophytes require water for the sperm to swim to the egg during fertilization.
- Bryophytes have the smallest, simplest sporophytes of all plant groups. Even though the sporophytes are photosynthetic when young, they must absorb water, sugars, and other nutrients from parental gametophytes.

Ferns and other seedless vascular plants were the first plants to grow tall (Biology, *11e: 29.3;* Focus, *2e: 26.3)*

- The evolution of vascular tissues allowed vascular plants to grow taller than bryophytes, gaining access to sunlight. Ferns and other seedless vascular plants, however, still require a film of water for the sperm to reach the egg.
- In this group—as with all other groups of plants except mosses—the diploid sporophyte is the dominant stage. Meiosis produces haploid spores and occurs within the sporangia. The haploid spores may grow into gametophytes, where swimming sperm fertilize eggs, yielding the diploid zygote, which will grow into the sporophyte generation.

The Evolution of Seed Plants

(Biology, *11e: Chapter 30;* Focus, *2e: Chapter 26)*

WHAT'S IMPORTANT TO KNOW?

Plant evolution is not an explicit topic of the Curriculum Framework, but your teacher may choose to introduce you to this material. This chapter contains information that may be the basis of both multiple-choice and essay questions. Having a general understanding of plant evolution will help you be more confident in dealing with potential questions. Here are what we consider to be the main points of this chapter:

- The evolutionary significance of seeds and pollen as key adaptations to life on land
- The evolutionary significance of flowers and fruits in angiosperm reproduction

Seeds and pollen grains are key adaptations for life on land (Biology, *11e: 30.1;* Focus, *2e: 26.4*)

▋ **Seeds** are plant embryos packaged with a food supply in a protective coat. Mature seeds are dispersed from their parent by wind or other means.

▋ Seeds have several advantages over spores. Seeds are multicellular, with several layers of protective tissue, safeguarding the embryo. Unlike spores, seeds have a supply of stored energy, which allows the seed to wait for good germination conditions and use stored energy to finance the early growth of the embryo.

▋ *The evolution of pollen was a key adaptation to life on land.* A pollen grain is a male gametophyte containing two sperm nuclei. The pollen grain has a waterproof coating, allowing for transfer by the wind. Before the evolution of pollen, water was required for sperm transfer.

Gymnosperms bear "naked" seeds, typically on cones (Biology, *11e: 30.2;* Focus, *2e: 26.4*)

▋ Gymnosperms are plants that have "naked" seeds that are not enclosed in ovaries. Their seeds are often exposed on modified leaves that form cones. To compare, angiosperms (flowering plants) have seeds enclosed in fruits, which are mature ovaries. Gymnosperms do not have fruits.

▋ The most ecologically significant group of gymnosperms is the conifers, which include pines, spruces, firs, and redwoods.

The reproductive adaptations of angiosperms include flowers and fruits (Biology, *11e: 30.3;* Focus, *2e: 26.4*)

▋ **Angiosperms** are seed plants that produce the reproductive structures called flowers and fruits. Today, angiosperms account for about 90% of all plant species.

▋ The **flower** is a unique angiosperm structure specialized for sexual reproduction. The flower greatly improved the efficiency of pollination compared with gymnosperms, which rely entirely on the wind for pollen dispersal. Flowers attract insects and other animals, which transfer pollen from the *anthers* (male structures) of one flower to the *carpels* (female structures) of another flower, resulting in fertilization. However, not all flowers attract pollinators. Some plants, like the grasses, produce large quantities of wind-borne pollen.

▋ **Fruits** are mature ovaries of the plant. As seeds develop from ovules after fertilization, the wall of an ovary thickens to become the fruit. Fruits help disperse the seeds of angiosperms.

▋ Angiosperms have traditionally been divided into monocots and eudicots:

▪ **Monocots** have one cotyledon in the seed, parallel leaf venation, and flowering parts in multiples of three. Examples include corn, orchids, lilies, and grasses.

▪ **Eudicots** have two cotyledons in the seed, net leaf venation, and flowering parts usually in multiples of four or five. Examples include roses, peas, beans, and oaks.

Fungi
(Biology, *11e: Chapter 31;* Focus, *2e: Chapter 26*)

WHAT'S IMPORTANT TO KNOW?

The study of fungi is not an explicit topic of the Curriculum Framework, but your teacher may choose to introduce you to this material. This chapter contains information that may be the basis of both multiple-choice and essay questions. Having a general understanding of fungi will help you be more confident in dealing with potential questions. Here are what we consider to be the main points of this chapter:

- The characteristics of fungi
- Important ecological roles of fungi including their mycorrhizal associations and as decomposers and parasitic plant pathogens

---

Fungi are heterotrophs that feed by absorption (Biology, *11e: 31.1;* **Focus,** *2e: 26.2*)

- Fungi are eukaryotes with these characteristics:

  - They are **multicellular heterotrophs** that obtain nutrients by **absorption**. Fungi secrete hydrolytic enzymes, digest food outside their bodies, and absorb the small molecules. Note that this is an example of extracellular digestion.
  - The cell walls of fungi are made of *chitin,* a polysaccharide that also makes up the exoskeleton of arthropods.
  - Bodies are composed of filaments called **hyphae** that are entwined to form a mass, the **mycelium**.
  - Fungi reproduce by spores.
  - Modes of nutrition include decomposers, parasites, and mutualists.

Fungi play key roles in nutrient cycling, ecological interactions, and human welfare (Biology, *11e: 31.5;* Focus, *2e: 26.2, 26.5*)

- Fungi are important decomposers of organic material, including cellulose and lignin.
- **Mycorrhizal fungi** are found in association with plant roots and may improve delivery of minerals to the plant, while being supplied with organic nutrients. This is a fine example of mutualism.
- **Lichens** are symbiotic associations of photosynthetic microorganisms (algae) embedded in a network of fungal hyphae. They are very hardy organisms that are pioneers on rock and soil surfaces.
- Thirty percent of known species of fungi are parasites. Many are plant pathogens (for example, Dutch elm disease, chestnut blight, dogwood anthracnose, and wheat rust). Some fungi infect animals (for example, ringworm, athlete's foot, and *Candida*).

- **Yeasts** are unicellular fungi that figure prominently in molecular biology and biotechnology. Current research includes exploration of the genes involved in Parkinson's disease and Huntington's disease by examining homologous genes in yeast (*Saccharomyces cerevisiae*). In addition, of course yeasts are used to make dough rise and ferment sugars to alcohol.
- Humans use fungi for food and to make antibiotics.

The Rise of Animal Diversity

(Biology, *11e: Chapters 32, 33, 34;* Focus, *2e: Chapter 27*)

WHAT'S IMPORTANT TO KNOW?

Animal diversity is not an explicit topic of the Curriculum Framework, but your teacher may choose to introduce you to this material. This chapter contains information that may be the basis of both multiple-choice and essay questions. Having a general understanding of animal diversity will help you be more confident in dealing with potential questions. Here are what we consider to be some main points of this topic:

- The unique characteristics of animals
- Important events in evolution of animals with respect to symmetry and the development of a body cavity
- Adaptations that made life on land possible, including amniote eggs

---

Animals are multicellular, heterotrophic eukaryotes with tissues that develop from embryonic layers (Biology, *11e: 32.1;* Focus, *2e: Overview, 27.1*)

- Animals have the following characteristics:
  - They are multicellular heterotrophs.
  - Most have muscle and nervous tissue.
  - Most reproduce sexually, with a flagellated sperm and a large egg uniting to form a diploid *zygote*. The diploid stage dominates the life cycle.
- Some animals have **larvae**, an immature form distinct from the adult stage that will undergo **metamorphosis**.
- Animals share *Hox* genes, a unique homeobox-containing family of genes that plays important roles in development.

Animals can be characterized by "body plans" (Biology, *11e: 32.3;* Focus, *2e: Overview, 27.3*)

- **No symmetry:** the sponges.
- **Radial symmetry** occurs in jellyfish and other organisms, so any cut through the central axis of the organism would produce mirror images.
- **Bilateral symmetry** occurs in lobsters, humans, and many other organisms. These animals have a right side and a left side, and a single cut would divide the animal into two mirror-image halves. There is also a *dorsal* (back) side, a *ventral* (belly) side, and *anterior* (head) and *posterior* (tail) ends.

- **Cephalization** is the concentration of sensory equipment at one end (usually the anterior, or head end) of the organism.
- A **coelom** is a fluid or air-filled space located between the digestive tract and the outer body wall (also referred to as the *body cavity*). Body cavities have several functions, including cushioning suspended organs, acting as a hydrostatic skeleton, and enabling internal organs to grow and move independently.
- Evolutionary relationships among living animals provide a useful framework in studying the rise of animals. They include the following key points:
  1. All animals share a common ancestor.
  2. Most animals belong to the clade Bilateria. Bilateral symmetry is a shared derived characterfor this clade, which includes the majority of animal phyla.
  3. Most animal phyla are invertebrates—animals that lack a backbone. Only one animal phylum, Chordata, includes vertebrates, such as fish, amphibians, reptiles, and mammals.

The Invertebrates

- **Phylum Porifera** (pore-bearing animals) includes the sponges.

  - Sponges lack true tissues and are *diploblastic* (their body consists of only two layers of cells).
  - Sponges have no nerves or muscles. The body of a sponge looks like a sac with holes in it. Water is drawn in through the pores and flows out through the top through the movement of flagellated cells, circulating nutrients and removing wastes.

- **Phylum Cnidaria** includes hydras, jellyfish, and corals. All have radial symmetry, a central digestive compartment known as a gastrovascular cavity, tentacles to capture food, and nerves and muscles in their simplest form.
- **Phylum Platyhelminthes** (flatworms) includes planarians, tapeworms, and flukes. This group also has a gastrovascular cavity and no coelom. Their bodies are thin and flat, providing sufficient surface area for gas exchange and circulation without special organs. There are sensory cells clustered in the anterior end, which is called *cephalization*. This group and all other animal phyla have **bilateral symmetry,** placing them in the clade Bilateria.
- **Phylum Nematoda** (roundworms) includes pinworms, hookworms, and the model organism, *C. elegans*. These small, cylindrical worms are *pseudocoelomates,* which means they have a body cavity but it is lined with mesoderm on only one side.
- **Phylum Mollusca** includes slugs, clams, snails, squids, and octopuses. They have a true coelom (a body cavity lined on both sides with mesoderm) as do all the phyla that follow. They use a muscular "foot" for locomotion.
- **Phylum Annelida** is the segmented worms and includes earthworms and leeches. They show internal and external segmentation and have a digestive system with specialized regions (the crop, gizzard, esophagus, and intestine).

- **Phylum Arthropoda** includes insects, arachnids, millipedes, centipedes, and crustaceans. They all have an *exoskeleton* of *chitin*, which must be *molted* to grow, and jointed appendages.
- Insects undergo metamorphosis during development.
  - **Incomplete metamorphosis:** egg, nymph, adult (for example, grasshoppers)
  - **Complete metamorphosis:** egg, larva, pupa, adult (for example, butterflies)

Clade Deuterostomia

The clade Deuterostomia contains a diverse array of organisms, from sea stars to chordates. All have radial cleavage during embryonic development. You are a chordate . . . so what other animals are deuterostomes and therefore more closely related to you than grasshoppers? Read on.

- **Phylum Echinodermata** includes starfish, brittle stars, sea urchins, and sand dollars. Echinoderm larvae have bilateral symmetry, but adults radiate from the center, often as five spokes.
- **Phylum Chordata** includes two invertebrate subphyla as well as all vertebrates.
  - There are four shared derived characteristics of all chordates. Note that some of these are present only during embryonic development (Figure 7.5).
    1. A **notochord** is a long, flexible rod that provides skeletal support and appears during embryonic development between the digestive tube and the dorsal nerve cord. This is *not* the spinal cord or the vertebral column! Students commonly confuse all of these.
    2. A **dorsal, hollow nerve cord** is formed from a plate of ectoderm that rolls into a hollow tube and develops into the brain and spinal cord. Other animals have a *ventral* nerve cord.
    3. **Pharyngeal slits** are grooves that separate a series of pouches along the sides of the pharynx. In most chordates (but not tetrapods, the critters with four legs), the slits allow water to enter and exit the mouth without going through the digestive tract.
    4. Chordates also have a muscular **tail** posterior to the anus.

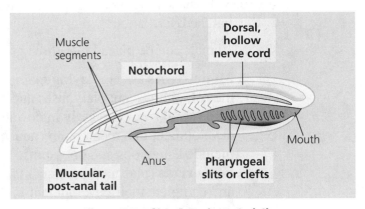

Figure 7.5 Chordate characteristics

The Vertebrates

▌ **Vertebrates** derive their name from the **vertebrae**, a series of bones that make up the backbone. In the majority of vertebrates, vertebrae enclose the spinal cord and have assumed the roles of the notochord.

▌ Vertebrates are members of the phylum Chordata.

▌ Let's look at features of several groups of vertebrates.

- **Chondrichthyes** have flexible endoskeletons composed of cartilage, possess streamlined bodies, are denser than water, and will sink if they stop swimming. Some examples are sharks and rays (such as stingrays).

- **Osteichthyes** are the bony fishes. They have a bony endoskeleton, are covered in scales, and possess a swim bladder for buoyancy control. Some examples are trout and salmon.

- **Amphibians** include frogs, toads, salamanders, and newts. Some gas exchange occurs across their thin, moist skin, although many members have lungs. Some amphibians, such as frogs, have an aquatic larval stage with gills and metamorphose into an adult stage with lungs. All have external fertilization and external development in an aquatic environment.

- **Reptiles** include turtles, lizards and snakes, alligators and crocodiles, birds, and the extinct dinosaurs. Modern reptiles have scales containing keratin, which are an adaptation for terrestrial living because they reduce water loss. They also have *amniote eggs,* which we describe in the following section. Most reptiles are *ectothermic,* regulating body temperature through behavioral adaptations rather than by metabolism. **Birds** are *endothermic* (warm blooded) and have *feathers* and a *four-chambered heart*.

- **Mammals** share certain characteristics:

  - All possess **mammary glands** that produce milk and have a body covering of **hair**. These two characteristics are excellent examples of shared, derived characters.

  - They have a four-chambered heart and are **endothermic**. (The four-chambered heart of some reptiles, including birds, is analogous—not homologous—to the four-chambered heart of mammals.)

  - Mammals have internal fertilization, and most are born rather than hatched.

- Mammals can be placed into three groups:

  1. **Monotremes** are egg-laying mammals that have hair and produce milk. Examples are platypuses and spiny anteaters.
  2. **Marsupials** are born early in development and complete embryonic development in a marsupium (pouch) while nursing. Examples include kangaroos and opossums.
  3. **Eutherians** (placental mammals) have a longer period of pregnancy and complete their development in the uterus. Examples include mice, dogs, and humans.

- One important evolutionary development that allowed extensive colonization of dry habitats was the **amniotic egg**, which has a shell that retains water and so can be laid in a dry environment.
- Amniotic eggs have four specialized **extraembryonic membranes**:

  - The **amnion** encloses a fluid compartment that bathes the embryo and absorbs shock.
  - The **chorion**, **allantois**, and **yolk sac** function in gas exchange, waste storage, and transfer of stored nutrients.

Answer to PRACTICE THE PRACTICE: Understanding and Using Phylogenetic Trees, p. 187

1. The new version does not alter any of the evolutionary relationships shown in the original figure. For example, although you rotated taxon B and C about point 4, B and C remain sister taxa. Taxon A is still as closely related to taxon B as it is to taxon C, and so on. Always consider that the branches on a cladogram work like the arms of a mobile hung from a ceiling. *Rotations around branch points do not alter the relationships.*
2. The tree in (c) shows a different pattern of evolutionary relationships. In (c), C and B are sister taxa, whereas C and D are sister taxa in (a) and (b).
3.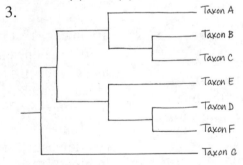

Answer to PRACTICE THE PRACTICE: Evaluating Information from a Chart, p. 190

1. Bacteria and Archaea lack a nuclear membrane, have no membrane-bound organelles, and have a circular chromosome.
2. Archaea and Eukarya have introns as part of their gene complexes and have histones complexed with DNA to form a chromosome. Prokaryotes do not have these characteristics.

Level 1: Knowledge/Comprehension Questions

The Level 1, Knowledge/Comprehension, questions review essential content knowledge but don't represent the type of question you will see on the AP exam. The Level 2, Application/Synthesis, questions are similar to those you will see on the exam.

1. Which of the following groups is best characterized as being eukaryotic, multicellular, heterotrophic, and without a cell wall?
   (A) Plantae
   (B) Animalia
   (C) Fungi
   (D) Viruses

2. Systematists categorize all living creatures into what three domains?
   (A) Bacteria, Animalia, Eukarya
   (B) Bacteria, Archaea, Eukarya
   (C) Archaea, Plantae, Eukarya
   (D) Protista, Plantae, Eukarya

3. Which of the following is a symbiotic relationship in which both organisms benefit?
   (A) parasitism
   (B) commensalism
   (C) mutualism
   (D) predation

4. The evolution of which feature enabled vertebrates to reproduce successfully on land?
   (A) the amniotic egg
   (B) origin of limbs with digits
   (C) flagellated sperm
   (D) keratinized body covering

5. Genetic variation in bacterial populations is introduced in several ways. Select the one process that will not introduce genetic variation in bacteria.
   (A) transduction
   (B) transformation
   (C) conjugation
   (D) meiosis

6. Shared derived characters are used to develop cladograms. Which is a correct description of them?
   (A) They are features that characterize all the species on a branch of a phylogenetic tree.
   (B) They can be determined through a BLAST comparison of related genes in a group of species.
   (C) They are homologous structures that develop during adaptive radiation.
   (D) They can be used to identify species but not higher taxa.

Level 2: Application/Analysis/Synthesis Questions

1. In a comparison of birds and mammals, having four appendages is
   (A) a shared ancestral characteristic because it originates in an ancestor of the taxa.
   (B) a shared derived characteristic because it is shared by all mammals.
   (C) a characteristic useful for distinguishing birds from mammals.
   (D) an example of analogy rather than homology.

2. An outgroup is a species from an evolutionary lineage that is known to have diverged before the lineage under study. If you were using cladistics to build a phylogenetic tree of cats, which of the following would be the best outgroup?
   (A) lion
   (B) domestic cat
   (C) wolf
   (D) leopard

3. In the 1920s, Frederick Griffith conducted an experiment in which he mixed the dead cells of a bacterial strain that can cause pneumonia with live cells of a bacterial strain that cannot. When he cultured the live cells, some of the daughter colonies proved able to cause pneumonia. Which of the following processes of bacterial DNA transfer does this experiment demonstrate?
   (A) transduction
   (B) conjugation
   (C) transformation
   (D) transposition

4. Molecular data can be used to assess relationships among the major groups of living organisms whose common ancestors lived millions or billions of years ago. Similar techniques can be used to assess relationships among populations within a species. How can molecular techniques be useful for such varied comparisons?
   (A) Studying the relationships among different populations of a single species can be just as effective as studying the relationships of major biological groups if you look at many more genes.
   (B) The same data can be used for any comparison with equal accuracy.
   (C) Faster-evolving gene sequences provide better data for comparisons among close relatives, whereas very slowly evolving sequences work best for distantly related taxa.
   (D) The relationships between very different groups such as bacteria and whales cannot be assessed.

After reading the paragraph, answer the question that follows.

The first fossil of *Archaeopteryx*, which lived about 150 million years ago, was found in the Solnhofen Quarry in Germany. *Archaeopteryx* has an interesting collection of characteristics that led to the hypothesis that it represents an evolutionary transition between modern-day birds and small bipedal dinosaurs. The fossil reveals the imprint of feathers, which connect *Archaeopteryx* to birds, although they don't present direct evidence of flight.

Unlike birds, however, the fossil record reveals that *Archaeopteryx* had teeth, functional claws on the wings that may have been used for climbing trees or holding prey, and a long, bony tail. Birds have a fused collarbone, and so did *Archaeopteryx*. However, there were differences in the structure of the sternum. In birds, the sternum is keeled (raised and slightly concave). The keel of the sternum serves as an attachment site for the flight muscles. *Archaeopteryx* had a flat sternum, similar to that found in reptiles.

5. If you were constructing a phylogenetic tree for the evolution of birds, which characteristics found in *Archaeopteryx* might provide evidence that birds and dinosaurs had a common ancestor?
   (A) feathers, wings, wishbone
   (B) teeth, feathers, keeled sternum
   (C) teeth, flat sternum, claws
   (D) keeled sternum, claws, long forelimbs

6. An experimental forest ecosystem is enclosed in a sealed greenhouse. The entire ecosystem, including the air and soil, is treated with an extremely potent fungicide that kills all fungal life stages including spores. What will probably happen next?
   (A) Tree growth will increase because the dead fungi will act as a fertilizer.
   (B) Plants will enjoy a long-term increase in growth and survival because of the removal of fungal pathogens.
   (C) Dead organic matter will accumulate on the forest floor; plant growth will decline because of a lack of nutrients and the loss of mycorrhizal partners.
   (D) Certain animal populations may decrease due to loss of their fungal food sources, but otherwise the forest will be largely unchanged.

7. The movement of life onto land required numerous adaptations to obtain water, prevent water loss, and reproduce. Plants have a waxy covering on their leaves, known as cuticle, which helps them conserve water. Seeds help several plant groups to reproduce effectively on dry land by protecting the embryo from water loss. Which of these pairs correctly shows a trait that prevents water loss and a trait that protects the embryo?
   (A) Reptiles have keratinized scales and produce amniote eggs.
   (B) Mammals have fur or hair and internal fertilization.
   (C) Amphibians have a moist skin and external fertilization.
   (D) Roundworms have a cuticle and are hermaphroditic.

8. This is a figure in which viruses that infect bacteria carry genes from one host cell to another. There is a process in sexually reproducing eukaryotes that uses enzymes similar to the ones that result in the incorporation of the A^+ gene into the host genome shown in the figure. Which of these represents the similar process in eukaryotes?

① A phage infects a bacterial cell that carries the A^+ and B^+ alleles on its chromosome (brown). This bacterium will be the "donor" cell.

② The phage DNA is replicated, and the cell makes many copies of the proteins encoded by its genes. Meanwhile, certain phage proteins halt the synthesis of proteins encoded by the host cell's DNA, and the host cell's DNA may be fragmented, as shown here.

③ As new phage particles assemble, a fragment of bacterial DNA carrying the A^+ allele happens to be packaged in a phage capsid.

④ The phage carrying the A^+ allele from the donor cell infects a recipient cell with alleles A^- and B^-. Crossing over at two sites (dotted lines) allows donor DNA (brown) to be incorporated into recipient DNA (green).

⑤ The genotype of the resulting recombinant cell (A^+B^-) differs from the genotypes of both the donor (A^+B^+) and the recipient (A^-B^-).

Phage DNA

A^+ B^+

Donor cell

A^+ B^+

A^+

Crossing over

A^+
A^- B^-

Recipient cell

Recombinant cell

A^+ B^-

(A) fertilization during sexual reproduction
(B) independent assortment during mitosis
(C) transduction during bacterial recombination
(D) crossing over during meiosis

9. Monophyletic clades include a common ancestor and all its descendants. According to this figure, which grouping represents a monophyletic clade?

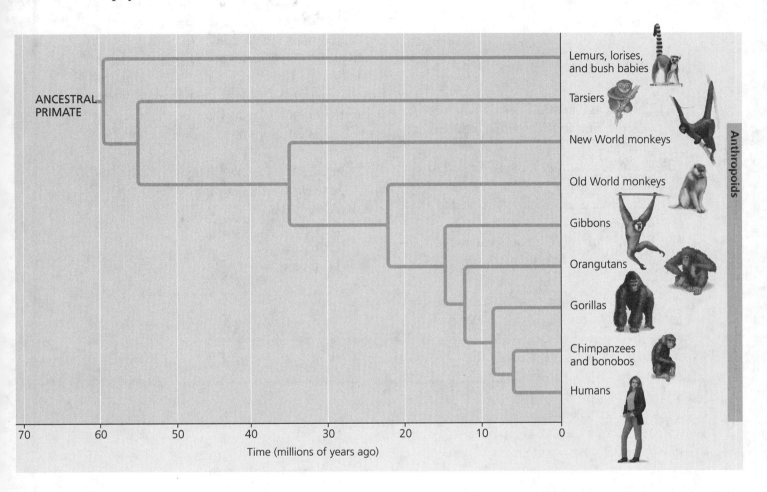

(A) lemurs, tarsiers, New World monkeys, and Old World monkeys
(B) New World monkeys and Old World monkeys
(C) gibbons, orangutans, gorillas, chimpanzees, and bonobos
(D) gorillas, chimpanzees, bonobos, and humans

10. Which of these relationships is depicted on this cladogram?
(A) Humans have descended from chimpanzees.
(B) Gibbons are the common ancestor of orangutans, gorillas, chimpanzees, and humans.
(C) Old World monkeys and New World monkeys diverged approximately 35 million years ago.
(D) Gorillas are equally related to orangutans and chimps.

11. Which statement is not supported by the cladogram?

(A) The lineage leading to salamanders was the first to diverge from the other lineages.
(B) Humans are more closely related to goats than to lizards.
(C) Salamanders are as closely related to goats as to humans.
(D) Lizards are more closely related to salamanders than to humans.

Use the following phylogenetic tree to answer question 12.

This tree was constructed by comparing sequences of homologs of a gene that plays a role in development. *Drosophila* was used as an outgroup. All the other animals are chordates (have a notochord), and all but the lancelet are vertebrates (have a backbone). The branch lengths are proportional to the amount of genetic change in each lineage; varying branch lengths indicate that the gene has evolved at different rates in different lineages.

12. In which *vertebrate* lineage has the studied gene evolved most rapidly?
(A) lancelet
(B) zebrafish
(C) human
(D) mouse

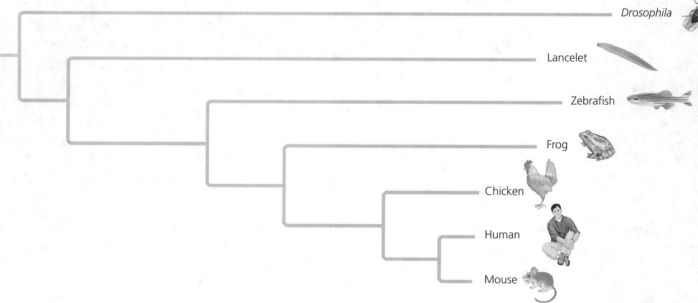

Use the following graph to answer question 13

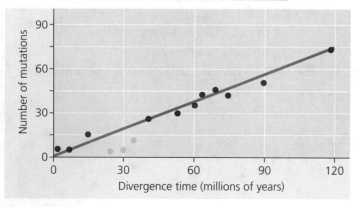

The number of accumulated mutations in seven proteins has increased over time in a consistent manner for most mammal species. The divergence time for each data point was based on fossil evidence.

13. Use the graph to estimate the divergence time for a mammal with 30 mutations in the seven proteins.
(A) 18 million years
(B) 30 million years
(C) 45 million years
(D) 60 million years

Use the following information to answer questions 14–16.

Carotenoids are colored molecules that have diverse functions in many organisms, such as photosynthesis in plants and light detection in animals. Plants and many microorganisms can synthesize carotenoids from scratch, but animals generally cannot (they must obtain carotenoids from their diet).

One exception is the pea aphid, *Acyrthosiphon pisum*, a small plant-dwelling insect whose genome includes a full set of genes for the enzymes needed to make carotenoids. Because other animals lack these genes, it is unlikely that aphids inherited them from a single-celled common ancestor shared with microorganisms and plants. So where did they come from? Evolutionary biologists hypothesize that an aphid ancestor acquired these genes by horizontal gene transfer from distantly related organisms.

Scientists obtained the DNA sequences for the carotenoid-biosynthesis genes from several species, including aphids, fungi, bacteria, and plants. A computer "translated" these sequences into amino acid sequences of the encoded polypeptides and aligned the amino acid sequences. This allowed the team to compare the corresponding polypeptides in the different organisms, as shown in the chart. Identical amino acid sites are in bold type.

Organism	Alignment of Amino Acid Sequences						
Acyrthosiphon (aphid)	IKIIIIGSGV	GGTAAAARLS	KKGFQVEVYE	KNSYNGGRCS	IIR_HNGHRF	DQGPSL__YL	
Pantoea (bacterium)	KRTFVIGAGF	GGLALAIRLQ	AAGIATTVLE	QHDKPGGRAY	VWQ_DQGFTF	DAGPTV__IT	
Staphylococcus (bacterium)	MKIAVIGAGV	TGLAAAARIA	SQGHEVTIFE	KNNNVGGRMN	QLK_KDGFTF	DMGPTI__VM	
Ustilago (fungus)	KKVVIIGAGA	GGTALAARLG	RRGYSVTVLE	KNSFGGGRCS	LIH_HDGHRW	DQGPSL__YL	
Gibberella (fungus)	KSVIVIGAGV	GGVSTAARLA	KAGFKVTILE	KNDFTGGRCS	LIH_NDGHRF	DQGPSL__LL	
Arabidopsis (plant)	WDAVVIGGGH	NGLTAAAYLA	RGGLSVAVLE	RRHVIGGAAV	TEEIVPGFKF	SRCSYLQGLL	

14. Which species is most similar in its amino acid sequence to the aphid's sequence?
(A) *Pantoea* (bacterium)
(B) *Staphylococcus* (bacterium)
(C) *Ustilago* (fungus)
(D) *Arabidopsis* (plant)

15. Do the data from the chart support the hypothesis that aphids acquired the gene for this polypeptide by horizontal gene transfer? Why or why not?
(A) No; the aphid's sequence is similar to the sequences of distantly related organisms.
(B) Yes; the aphid's sequence is completely different from the sequences of distantly related organisms.

(C) No; the aphid's sequence is completely different from the sequences of distantly related organisms.
(D) Yes; the aphid's sequence is similar to the sequences of distantly related organisms.

16. What additional sequence data would best support your hypothesis?
(A) sequence data from a more distantly related plant species
(B) sequence data from other polypeptides involved in carotenoid biosynthesis
(C) sequence data from polypeptides not involved in carotenoid biosynthesis
(D) sequence data from an insect that does not synthesize carotenoids

Grid-In Questions
These questions call for a numerical response.

1. Using the figure for question 9, approximately what percentage of the time, to the nearest whole number, have humans been a species on the primate phylogenetic tree?

2. Using the figure for question 13, note that the molecular clock for seven proteins in a group of mammals covers 120 million years. Over the time period covered in the graph, what is the average mutation rate per 1,000,000 years to the nearest tenth?

Free-Response Question

1. *Prokaryotes do not undergo sexual reproduction but use several unique mechanisms to promote genetic diversity. For* **each** *of the following mechanisms,* **describe** *the biological process and* **explain** *how it increases genetic diversity.*

(a) mutation
(b) transformation
(c) transduction
(d) conjugation

Plant Form and Function

Plant Structure, Growth, and Development
(Biology, *11e: Chapter 35;* Focus, *2e: Chapter 28*)

WHAT'S IMPORTANT TO KNOW?

Much of plant anatomy is not an explicit topic of the Curriculum Framework, but your teacher may choose to use plant anatomy for illustrative examples. This chapter contains information that might appear in multiple-choice and essay questions, and a general understanding of plant structures will make you more confident in dealing with such questions. Here are what we consider to be the main points of this chapter:

- Plants grow only at meristems.
- Leaf anatomy relates to photosynthesis.
- Root hairs and mycorrhizae are essential for resource acquisition.
- Roots, stems, and leaves interact in essential plant life functions. (EK 4.A.4)

Plants have a hierarchical organization consisting of organs, tissues, and cells (Biology, *11e: 35.1;* Focus, *2e: 28.1*)

- Plants have a **root system** beneath the ground that anchors the plant, absorbs water and minerals, and often stores sugars and starches. Additional structural characteristics of roots include the following:

  - At the tips of the roots, vast numbers of tiny *root hairs*, which are extensions of root epidermal cells, increase the surface area enormously, making efficient absorption of water and minerals possible.
  - Plants may also have a symbiotic relationship with fungi at the tips of the roots, termed **mycorrhizae** ("fungus roots"). Mycorrhizae assist in the absorption process and exist in the vast majority of plants. In turn, plants provide the mycorrhizae with carbohydrates. The relationship between plant roots and fungi is an excellent example of mutualism.

- Plants have a **shoot system** above the ground consisting of stems and leaves.

  - **Stems** function primarily to display the leaves.
  - **Leaves** are the main photosynthetic organ in most plants.

▌ Plant organs—leaf, stem, and root—are composed of a couple of tissue types:

- **Dermal tissue** is a single layer of closely packed cells that cover the entire plant and protect it against water loss and invasion by pathogens such as viruses and bacteria.
- **Vascular tissue** is continuous throughout the plant and transports materials between the roots and shoots. Vascular tissue is made up of **xylem**, which transports water and minerals up from the roots and is dead at maturity, and **phloem**, which transports sugars and other organic compounds from the leaves to the other parts of the plant.

Meristems generate cells for primary and secondary growth (Biology, *11e: 35.2; Focus, 2e: 28.2*)

▌ **Meristems** are perpetually embryonic tissues. Unlike growth in animals, growth in plants occurs only as a result of cell division in the meristems.

- **Apical meristems** are located at the tips of roots and in buds of shoots, allowing the plant's stems and roots to extend. Note that this means elongating growth occurs only from the tips of the roots and shoots. If you place a basketball hoop at 10 feet on a tree, and the tree grows 6 feet taller over several years, the basketball hoop will not move—it stays at 10 feet. Growth occurs only from the tip or apical meristem; this is *primary growth*.
- **Lateral meristems** cause growth that thickens the shoots and roots.
- There are two lateral meristem tissues. The **vascular cambium** produces secondary xylem (wood) and phloem. The **cork cambium** produces a tough, waterproof covering that replaces the epidermis early in secondary growth.
- **Bark** is all the tissue outside the vascular cambium. Bark includes the living phloem derived from the vascular cambium. Almost all of the wood (xylem) of a large tree is dead when it functions. The living part of the trunk of a large tree is almost exclusively bark. Injuries to the bark may result in the death of the tree when they damage the phloem and interfere with movement of organic compounds through the plant.

Tissue Organization of Leaves (Biology, *11e: 35.3; Focus, 2e: 28.3*)

▮ Refer to Figure 8.1 as you review tissue organization. The epidermis of the underside of the leaf is interrupted by **stomata**, which are small pores flanked by *guard cells* that open and close the stomata. The stomata allow for gas exchange in the leaf: CO_2 necessary for photosynthesis can enter, and O_2 and water vapor can escape the leaf. The process of water loss from the leaf is part of the Curriculum Framework and is covered in the next chapter under transpiration.

▮ Study actively! How does water enter the leaf for photosynthesis? How does water leave? How does CO_2 enter the leaf? Draw arrows and label each of these events on Figure 8.1.

▮ In Investigation 5, Photosynthesis, leaf disks float until you use a vacuum to eliminate the gases. Note the air spaces within the leaf where gases can accumulate and diffuse into and out of the cells of the leaf. As photosynthesis produces oxygen, these air spaces will refill and float the disks.

(a) Cutaway drawing of leaf tissues

(b) Surface view of a spiderwort (*Tradescantia*) leaf (LM)

(c) Cross section of a lilac (*Syringa*) leaf (LM)

Figure 8.1   Leaf anatomy

Resource Acquisition and Transport in Vascular Plants

(Biology, *11e: Chapter 36;* Focus, *2e: Chapter 29*)

> **YOU MUST KNOW**
>
> - How passive transport, active transport, and cotransport function to move materials across plant cell membranes.
> - The role of water potential in predicting movement of water in plants.
> - How the transpiration cohesion-tension mechanism explains water movement in plants.
> - How bulk flow affects movement of solutes in plants.
> - Mechanisms by which plant cells communicate with other distant cells. (EK 3.D.2)

> ### CONNECT WITH THE CURRICULUM FRAMEWORK
>
> This chapter ties together concepts from Big Idea 2 and Big Idea 4. You will apply information that you have learned about transport across membranes to movement of materials through plants. Focus on integrating your content and knowledge. If your class does AP Lab Investigation 11, Transpiration, you will find this an important chapter.

Adaptations for acquiring resources were key steps in the evolution of vascular plants (Biology, *11e: 36.1;* Focus, *2e: 29.1*)

▌ Study Figure 8.2, where you will see an overview of resource acquisition and transport. Take time to understand the figure because it has a lot of important information.

Different mechanisms transport substances over short or long distances (Biology, *11e: 36.2;* Focus, *2e: 29.2*)

▌ Transport begins with the movement of water and solutes across a cell membrane.

  ▪ Solutes diffuse down their electrochemical gradients. Electrochemical gradients are the combined effects of the concentration gradient of the solute and the voltage or charge differential across the membrane. (See Chapter 7 in *Biology,* 11e, or Chapter 5 in *Focus*, 2e.)

  ▪ If no energy is required to move a substance across the membrane, the movement is termed *passive transport*. Diffusion is an example of passive transport.

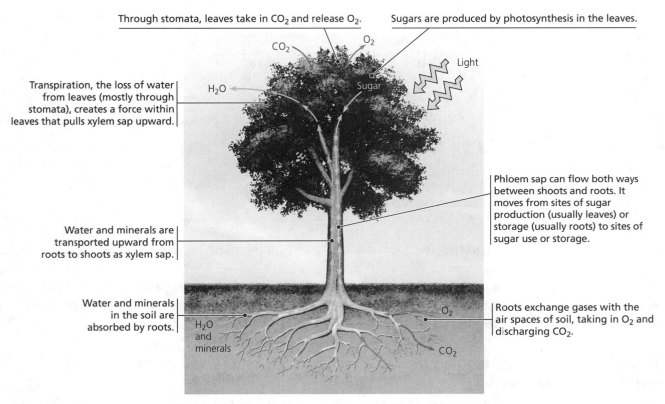

Through stomata, leaves take in CO_2 and release O_2.

Sugars are produced by photosynthesis in the leaves.

Transpiration, the loss of water from leaves (mostly through stomata), creates a force within leaves that pulls xylem sap upward.

Phloem sap can flow both ways between shoots and roots. It moves from sites of sugar production (usually leaves) or storage (usually roots) to sites of sugar use or storage.

Water and minerals are transported upward from roots to shoots as xylem sap.

Water and minerals in the soil are absorbed by roots.

Roots exchange gases with the air spaces of soil, taking in O_2 and discharging CO_2.

Figure 8.2   Overview of resource acquisition and transport

- If energy is required to move solutes across the membrane, the movement is termed *active transport*. Because most solutes cannot move across the phospholipid barrier of the membrane, a **transport protein** is required. The most important transport protein in plants is the **proton pump**.
- A proton pump creates an electrochemical gradient by using the energy of ATP to pump hydrogen ions against their gradient across the membrane. This potential energy can then be used in the process of **cotransport**—the coupling of the steep gradient of one solute (hydrogen in our example) with another solute such as sucrose. The drop in potential energy experienced by the hydrogen ion pays for the transport of the sucrose.

- The uptake of water across cell membranes occurs through *osmosis*, the passive transport of water across a membrane.

  - Water moves from areas of high water potential to low water potential. **Water potential** includes the combined effects of solute concentration and physical pressure.
  - The water potential equation is $\Psi = \Psi_s + \Psi_p$, where Ψ is water potential, Ψ_s is solute potential, and Ψ_p is the pressure potential.
  - By definition, the Ψ_s of pure water is 0. Adding solutes to pure water always lowers water potential. The solute potential of a solution is therefore always negative.

- Pressure potential is the physical pressure on a solution. An example of positive Ψ_p occurs when the cell contents press the plasma membrane against the cell wall, a force termed *turgor pressure*. If the cell loses water, the pressure potential becomes more negative, resulting in wilting.

> ### CONNECT WITH THE CURRICULUM FRAMEWORK
>
> You can expect to encounter water potential problems on the exam; you will find the necessary formulas on the Equations and Formulas Sheet (p. 358). Refer to Investigation 4 (p. 317) for a detailed explanation of how to solve these problems.

- **Aquaporins** are channel proteins in the plasma membrane specifically for the passage of water.
- Long-distance transport in plants occurs through **bulk flow**, the movement of liquid in response to a pressure gradient. Bulk flow always occurs from regions of high pressure to regions of low pressure.

Transpiration drives the transport of water and minerals from roots to shoots via the xylem (Biology, *11e: 36.3;* Focus, *2e: 29.5*)

- Water and minerals from the soil enter the plant through the root epidermis, cross the body of the root, and then flow up the xylem.
- Once in the root xylem, water and minerals are transported long distances—to the rest of the plant—by bulk flow. The water and minerals, termed *xylem sap*, flow out of the root and up through the shoot, eventually exiting the plant, primarily through the leaves.
- **Transpiration** is the loss of water vapor from the leaves and other parts of the plant that are in contact with air. It plays a key role in the movement of water from the roots.

  - The **cohesion-tension hypothesis** describes how transpiration provides the pull for the ascent of xylem sap, and the cohesion of water molecules transmits this pull along the entire length of the xylem from shoots to roots.
  - Water is lost through transpiration from the leaves of the plant because of the lower water potential of the air. The *cohesion* of water resulting from hydrogen bonding plus the *adhesion* of water to the plant cell walls enables the water to form a water column. Water is drawn up through the xylem as water evaporates from the leaves, each evaporating water molecule pulling on the one beneath it through the attraction of *hydrogen bonds*.

> ### TIP FROM THE READERS
> Hydrogen bonding plays a key role in cohesion-tension mechanisms. Be able to explain the importance of cohesion, adhesion, transpiration, and tension in this mechanism.

The rate of transpiration is regulated by stomata (Biology, *11e: 36.4;* Focus, *2e: 29.6*)

▌ Large leaf surface area increases photosynthesis but also increases water loss by the plant through stomata. **Guard cells** open and close the **stomata**, controlling the amount of water lost by transpiration but also the amount of carbon dioxide available from the atmosphere for photosynthesis.

▌ Guard cells control the size of the stomatal opening by changing shape, widening or closing the gap between them. When the guard cells take up K^+ from the surrounding cells, water potential in the guard cells is decreased, causing them to take up water. The guard cells then swell and buckle, increasing the size of the pore between them. When the guard cells lose K^+, the cells lose water and become less bowed; then the pore closes. Follow this sequence of events in Figure 8.3.

▌ Guard cells are stimulated to open by the presence of light, loss of carbon dioxide in the leaf, and normal circadian rhythms. Notice the critical interactions between environmental stimuli and internal molecular changes. This area of study has many essay possibilities!

▌ Circadian rhythms are part of the plant's internal clock mechanism and cycle with intervals of about 24 hours. Even plants kept in the dark will open their stomata as dawn approaches.

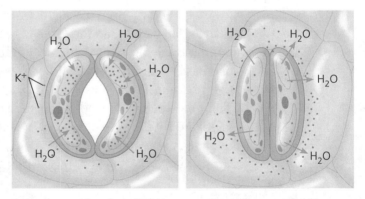

Role of potassium ions (K^+) in stomatal opening and closing.

Figure 8.3   Mechanisms of stomatal opening and closing

Sugars are transported from sources to sinks via the phloem (Biology, *11e: 36.5;* Focus, *2e: 29.7*)

▌ Phloem transports organic products of photosynthesis from the leaves throughout the plant, a process called **translocation**. The mechanism for translocation is **pressure flow**.

▌ Phloem always carries sugars from a sugar source to a sugar sink. A **sugar source** is an organ that is a net producer of sugar, such as the leaves. A **sugar sink** is an organ that is a net consumer or storer of sugar, such as a fruit or roots during the summer. Analyze Figure 8.4, noting the key steps.

Vessel (xylem)   **Sieve tube (phloem)**   **Source cell** (leaf)

H₂O

Sucrose

H₂O

Bulk flow by negative pressure

Bulk flow by positive pressure

Sink cell (storage root)

Sucrose

H₂O

① Loading of sugar (dots) into the sieve tube at the source reduces water potential inside the sieve-tube elements. This causes the tube to take up water by osmosis.

② This uptake of water generates a positive pressure that forces the sap to flow along the tube.

③ The pressure is relieved by the unloading of sugar and the consequent loss of water at the sink.

④ In leaf-to-root translocation, xylem recycles water from sink to source.

Figure 8.4   Pressure flow in a sieve tube

1. Sucrose is loaded into the sieve tubes at the sugar source. Proton pumps create an electrochemical gradient to load sucrose. This process decreases water potential and causes the uptake of water, creating positive pressure.

2. The pressure is relieved at the sugar sink by the unloading of sucrose followed by the loss of water. In leaf-to-root translocation, xylem recycles the water back to the sugar source. Translocation via pressure flow is a second example of bulk flow.

Movement of material from cell to cell often occurs through the plasmodesmata (Biology, *11e: 36.6*)

▌ **Plasmodesmata** are cytoplasmic connections between plant cells. They allow for the movement of informational molecules such as RNA and protein, which coordinate development between cells. Plasmodesmata are dynamic and can open or close rapidly in response to changes such as turgor pressure, pH, or calcium levels in the cytoplasm.

▌ In some plants, the phloem carries out rapid, long-distance electrical signaling. This may lead to changes in gene transcription, respiration, photosynthesis, and other cellular functions in widely spaced organs. This is a nerve-like function, allowing for swift communication.

Soil and Plant Nutrition

(Biology, *11e: Chapter 37;* Focus, *2e: Chapter 29*)

WHAT'S IMPORTANT TO KNOW?

This chapter provides illustrative examples that your teacher might select, but they are not required content. Here are what we consider to be the main points of this chapter:

▮ Mutualistic relationships between plant roots and the bacteria and fungi that grow in the rhizosphere help plants acquire important nutrients.

▮ Some plants are epiphytic, parasitic, or carnivorous.

▮ Interactions between populations (such as competition, predation, mutualism, and commensalism) can influence patterns of species distribution and abundance. (EK 4.B.3)

Plant nutrition often involves relationships with other organisms
(Biology, *11e: 37.3;* Focus, *2e: 29.4*)

▮ A *mutualistic* relationship occurs between nitrogen-fixing bacteria and plants. Nitrogen-fixing bacteria from the genus *Rhizobium* live in the root nodules of the legume plant family, including plants such as peas, soybeans, alfalfa, peanuts, and clover. *Rhizobium* bacteria fix atmospheric nitrogen into a form that plants can use.

▮ Bacteria also play a critical role in the nitrogen cycle (discussed in *Biology*, 11e, Chapter 55, or *Focus*, 2e, Chapter 42). Bacteria recycle ammonia in the soil into forms that can be absorbed and used by plants.

▮ *Mycorrhizae* are another example of mutualistic relationships with roots—this time between the roots and fungi in the soil. In mycorrhizae, the fungus benefits from a steady supply of sugar donated by the host plant. In return, the fungus increases the surface area for water uptake, selectively absorbs minerals that the plant takes up, and secretes substances that stimulate root growth and antibiotics that protect the plant from invading bacteria.

▌ Some plants form symbiotic relationships that are not mutualistic. (See Figure 37.16 in *Biology*, 11e, or Figure 29.15 in *Focus*, 2e).

  ▪ **Parasitic plants**, such as dodder or Indian pipe, are not photosynthetic and rely on other plants for their nutrients. Many parasitic plants have completely lost the ability to undergo photosynthesis. Would you consider these plants producers or consumers?
  ▪ **Epiphytes** are not parasitic but just grow on the surfaces of other plants instead of the soil. Many orchids grow as epiphytes.
  ▪ **Carnivorous plants** are photosynthetic, but they get some nitrogen and other minerals by digesting small animals. They are commonly found in nitrogen-poor soil, such as in bogs.

Angiosperm Reproduction and Biotechnology

(Biology, *11e: Chapter 38;* Focus, *2e: Chapter 30*)

> **WHAT'S IMPORTANT TO KNOW?**
> Most of this chapter's information is not required knowledge, but the following are what we consider to be the main points:
>
> ▋ The difference between pollination and fertilization.
> ▋ The biology of pollination and pollination strategies (wind, insects, birds, other animals).
> ▋ Many plants and their pollinators are examples of coevolution.
> ▋ The relationship between seed and fruit.
> ▋ Factors that affect seed germination, such as temperature and moisture. (EK 2.E.1)
> ▋ The role of seed dormancy in promoting survival of the species.
> ▋ How different modes of plant reproduction affect genetic diversity.

Flowers, double fertilization, and fruits are unique features of the angiosperm life cycle (Biology, *11e: 38.1;* Focus, *2e: 30.1*)

▨ **Pollination** is the transfer of pollen from an anther (where pollen is made) to a stigma (the sticky top of the female reproductive structure). This transfer is accomplished by wind, water, and animals, with animals doing the most pollination.

▨ Many species of flowering plants have evolved with specific animal pollinators in classic examples of *mutualism*. The joint evolution of two interacting species, each in response to selection imposed by the other, is called *coevolution*. Pollination is an excellent and uncomplicated example of mutualism and coevolution!

▨ The ripe ovary develops into the **fruit**. The ovules within the ovaries develop into seeds. The fruit protects the enclosed seeds and aids in their dispersal by wind or animals.

As the seed matures, it enters dormancy, in which it has a low metabolic rate and its growth and development are suspended. The seed resumes growth when there are suitable environmental conditions for germination. If you did a laboratory activity on cellular respiration, such as AP Investigation 6, you will know that dry seeds have a very low rate of respiration because they are dormant, not dead.

- Seed **dormancy** allows the embryo to wait until a suitable environment exists for the growth and development of the new plant. Seed dormancy can be broken by a number of environmental factors including fire, rain (desert plants), or cold temperatures.
- Seed **germination** (sprouting) depends on the uptake of water as a result of the low water potential of the dry seed. Imbibing water causes the seed to expand and rupture its coat and also triggers metabolic changes in the embryo that enable it to resume growth.
- Note the importance of timing and coordination with the breaking of seed dormancy and initiation of germination. The seed receives environmental cues and cell signaling responses turn on genes and stimulate the embryo to start the process of growth.
- Seeds must be widely dispersed to germinate in suitable sites with minimum competition. See if you can give an example of a fruit or its seed(s) dispersed by each of the following mechanisms: water, wind, animals. (*See* Biology, *11e, Figure 38.12;* Focus, *2e, Figure 30.11*)

Flowering plants reproduce sexually, asexually, or both
(Biology, *11e:* 38.2; Focus, *2e:* 30.2)

- Asexual reproduction, or **vegetative reproduction**, produces clones. Fragmentation is an example in which pieces of the parent plant break off to form new individuals that are exact genetic replicas of the parent.
- Some flowers self-fertilize, but others have methods to prevent self-fertilization and maximize genetic variation. One of these methods is **self-incompatibility**, in which a plant rejects its own pollen or that of a closely related plant, thus ensuring cross-pollination.
- Agriculture uses several techniques of artificial vegetative reproduction to maintain named cultivated varieties, such as grafting, cuttings, and test-tube cloning.

People modify crops by breeding and genetic engineering
(Biology, *11e:* 38.3; Focus, *2e:* 30.3)

- Humans have intervened in the reproduction and genetic makeup of plants for thousands of years through **artificial selection**.
- **Genetically modified organisms** are engineered to express a gene from another species. *Examples*: "Golden Rice," engineered to include large amounts of vitamin A; and *Bt* corn, engineered to contain a toxin that kills specific crop pests. There is some debate over the creation of these genetically modified (GM) crops because of fear of human allergies and possible effects on nontarget organisms, among other concerns.

Plant Responses to Internal and External Signals
(Biology, *11e: Chapter 39;* Focus, *2e: Chapter 31*)

YOU MUST KNOW

- The three components of a signal transduction pathway and how changes could alter cellular responses.
- The role of auxins in plants.
- How phototropism and photoperiodism use changes in the environment to modify plant growth and behavior. (EK 2.E.2)
- How plants respond to attacks by herbivores and pathogens.

Signal transduction pathways link signal reception to response
(Biology, *11e: 39.1;* Focus, *2e: 5.6*)

> *TIP FROM THE READERS*
> Essays on the AP Biology Exam often cover ideas in different units in the textbook. Cell signaling in plants brings together the general topic of cell communication from Chapter 11 with specific examples of cell communication. Focus on mechanisms by which plant cells receive information and the responses that occur from these inputs. Also, consider the evolutionary significance of the response or mechanism. This would be an excellent topic for an essay question!

▌ Let's begin with a review (Concept 11.1 in *Biology*, 11e, or Concept 5.6 in *Focus*, 2e). Signal transduction pathways involve three steps:

1. **Reception:** Cell signals are detected by receptors that undergo changes in shape in response to a specific stimulus. Two common plasma membrane receptors are *G protein-coupled receptors* and *receptor tyrosine kinase.*
2. **Transduction:** Transduction is a multistep pathway that amplifies the signal. This allows a small number of signal molecules to produce a large cellular response.
3. **Response:** Cellular response is primarily accomplished by two mechanisms: (1) turning genes on or off and thereby increasing or decreasing mRNA production or (2) activating existing enzyme molecules.

▌ Just as in animal cells, signal transduction pathways may involve second messengers, phosphorylation cascades activated by protein kinases, and a means to turn off the pathway such as protein phosphatases.

Plant hormones help coordinate growth, development, and responses to stimuli (Biology, *11e: 39.2;* Focus, *2e: 31.1*)

▌ **Hormones** are signaling molecules produced in small amounts in one part of an organism and transported to other parts. Hormones act as chemical messengers that coordinate the different parts of a multicellular organism.

▌ A **tropism** is a plant growth response that results in the plant growing either toward or away from a stimulus. Tropisms result from hormone production.

▌ **Phototropism** is the growth of a shoot in a certain direction in response to light. **Positive phototropism** is the growth of a plant organ (the shoot, for example) toward light; **negative phototropism** is the growth of a plant organ (roots, for example) away from light. The hormone most directly involved with positive phototropism is auxin.

▌ The natural auxin in plants is *indoleacetic acid*, usually abbreviated as *IAA*. Auxins have many functions and play key roles in phototropisms and gravitropisms (plants' responses to gravity).

▌ **Auxins** stimulate elongation of cells within young developing shoots. Auxins produced in the apical meristems activate proton pumps in the plasma membrane, which results in a lower pH (acidification of the cell wall). This weakens the cell wall, allowing turgor pressure to expand the cell wall, resulting in cell elongation.

▌ Phototropism directs shoot growth toward the sunlight that powers photosynthesis. This response results from cells on the darker side elongating faster than the cells on the lighter side. This causes the shoot to grow faster on the side away from the light, bending the plant toward the light source. Can you explain the adaptive value of this response?

▌ Synthetic auxins are often used as herbicides. Monocots, such as grasses, can quickly inactivate synthetic auxins, but eudicots cannot. Thus, high concentrations of auxins kill broadleaf weeds (dicots), whereas auxins do not harm grasses (monocots such as turf grass or corn).

> **STUDY TIP** You are not required to know the names and functions of the plant hormones. However, you should be able to explain the plant responses of phototropism and photoperiodism. Knowledge of how auxins work will help you understand tropisms.

Responses to light are critical for plant success (Biology, *11e: 39.3;* Focus, *2e: 31.2*)

▌ Plants can detect not only the presence of light but also its direction, intensity, and wavelength. Action spectra reveal that red and blue light are the most important colors in plant responses to light.

▌ *Blue-light photoreceptors* initiate various plant responses to light including phototropisms and the light-induced opening of stomata.

▌ Light receptors termed **phytochromes** absorb mostly red light.

▌ Phytochromes exist in two isomer forms, P_r and P_{fr}, which can switch back and forth depending on the wavelength of light in greatest supply. P_{fr} is the form of phytochrome that triggers many of a plant's developmental responses to light.

The plant produces phytochrome in the P_r form, but upon illumination, the P_{fr} level increases by rapid conversion from P_r. The relative amounts of the two pigments provide a baseline for measuring the amount of sunlight in a day.

▌ **Circadian rhythms** are physiological cycles that have a frequency of about 24 hours and that are not paced by a known environmental variable. In plants, the surge of P_{fr} at dawn resets the biological clock. The combination of a phytochrome system and a biological clock allows the plant to accurately assess the amount of daylight or darkness and hence the time of year.

▌ A physiological response to a photoperiod (the relative lengths of night and day), such as flowering, is called **photoperiodism**. Photoperiodism controls when plants will flower. When scientists first discovered photoperiodism, they thought the critical factor was the length of the day. They later determined that the length of the night is the actual critical factor. The old terminology, however, is still used, so take note of that in the following categories:

  ▪ Study the response of a short-day plant, such as the chrysanthemum shown in Figure 8.5(a), to day length. Notice that if an amount of *uninterrupted* darkness does not *exceed* the critical period, the plant will not flower. **Short-day plants** flower in early spring or fall. Short-day plants are actually long-night plants; that is, what the plant measures is the length of the night.

  ▪ **Long-day plants** flower only if the night is *shorter* than a critical period. Study the iris in the long-day plant example in Figure 8.5(b). Long-day plants often flower in the late spring or early summer. Long-day plants are actually short-night plants.

  ▪ **Day-neutral plants** can flower in days of any length.

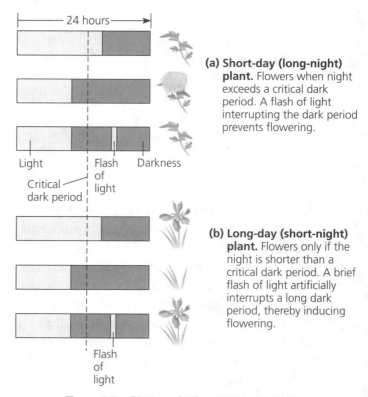

(a) Short-day (long-night) plant. Flowers when night exceeds a critical dark period. A flash of light interrupting the dark period prevents flowering.

(b) Long-day (short-night) plant. Flowers only if the night is shorter than a critical dark period. A brief flash of light artificially interrupts a long dark period, thereby inducing flowering.

Figure 8.5   Photoperiodic control of flowering

Plants respond to a wide variety of stimuli other than light
(Biology, *11e: 39.4;* Focus, *2e: 31.3*)

▮ What environmental cue causes the shoot of a young seedling to grow up and the root to grow down? **Gravitropism** is a plant's response to gravity. Roots show **positive gravitropism** and grow toward the source of gravity, whereas shoots show **negative gravitropism** and grow away from gravity.

▮ The hormone **auxin** plays a key role in gravitropism in both roots and stems. In the young root, gravity indirectly causes a high concentration of auxin on the root's lower side. *Higher than normal* concentrations of auxins inhibit cell elongation, causing the lower side to grow more slowly, whereas more rapid elongation of cells on the upper side causes the root to curve as it grows.

▮ **Thigmotropism** is directional growth in a plant as a response to a touch. Vines display thigmotropism when their tendrils coil around supports.

▮ Plants have various responses to stresses. In times of drought, the guard cells lose turgor. This causes the stomata to close; young leaves will stop growing, and they will roll into a shape that slows transpiration rates. Also, deep roots continue to grow, whereas those near the surface (where there isn't much water) do not grow very quickly.

▮ Continue to consider why these different plant responses to environmental stimuli are adaptive. What is the value of the behavior in evolutionary terms?

Plants respond to attacks by herbivores and pathogens
(Biology, *11e: 39.5;* Focus, *2e: 31.4*)

▮ Some physical defenses that plants have against predators (herbivores) are thorns and chemicals such as bitter or poisonous compounds. Some plants produce airborne attractants to recruit other animals to kill the herbivores. (Remember reading how parasitoid wasps lay their eggs on caterpillars, and the emerging wasp larva eats the caterpillar from the inside out?)

▮ The first line of defense against viruses for a plant (as for a human) is the epidermal layer. Plant immune responses involve both localized, specific responses as well as plant-wide responses. The lesions or dead spots you may have seen on leaves can be the result of the plant responding to a pathogen by sealing off the pathogen and then killing the cells in the area. This response kills the pathogen and prevents the spread of the disease to the rest of the plant. Both plant and animal immune systems depend heavily on signal transduction pathways.

Level 1: Knowledge/Comprehension Questions

The Level 1, Knowledge/Comprehension, questions review essential content knowledge but don't represent the type of question you will see on the AP exam. The Level 2, Application/Synthesis questions are similar to those you will see on the exam.

1. Which of the following processes is responsible for the bending of the stem of a plant toward a light source?
   (A) The amount of chlorophyll produced on the side facing the light increases.
   (B) The rate of cell division on the side facing the light increases.
   (C) The rate of cell division on the side away from the light increases.
   (D) The cells on the side of the stem away from the light elongate.

2. Which of the following mechanisms is most important in the movement of water from roots to leaves in the xylem?
   (A) the effect of gravity
   (B) root pressure
   (C) transpiration
   (D) osmosis

3. Hydrogen bonding plays a particularly important role in which plant process?
   (A) bulk flow of solutes from source to sink
   (B) photoperiodism resulting in flowering
   (C) attraction of the sperm and egg
   (D) the transpiration-cohesion-tension mechanism

4. In a mesophyll cell of a leaf, the synthesis of ATP takes place in which of the following cell organelles?
   (A) chloroplasts and mitochondria
   (B) mitochondria only
   (C) nucleoli and mitochondria
   (D) ribosomes and mitochondria

5. Which of these does not play a significant role in enhancing the uptake of water by a plant?
   (A) root hairs
   (B) large leaf surface area
   (C) mycorrhizae
   (D) gravitational force

6. How does the sperm of flowering plants reach the egg?
   (A) via a pollen tube that grows from the pollen grain through the carpel tissues to the egg
   (B) via raindrops of a dew film that allows the sperm to swim from the male plant to the female plant
   (C) usually via an insect, which places sperm in the ovary while probing for nectar
   (D) by actively swimming down through the style to the egg

7. Which of the following plant structures will become the seed?
   (A) a flower
   (B) an embryo
   (C) an ovule
   (D) an ovary

Level 2: Application/Analysis/Synthesis Questions

1. In order to flower, short-day plants require a period of
   (A) light greater than a critical period.
   (B) darkness greater than a critical period.
   (C) light less than a critical period.
   (D) darkness less than a critical period.

2. If a long-day plant has a critical length of 9 hours, which 24-hour cycle would prevent flowering?
   (A) 16 hours light/8 hours dark
   (B) 14 hours light/10 hours dark
   (C) 15.5 hours light/8.5 hours dark
   (D) 4 hours light/8 hours dark/4 hours light/ 8 hours dark

3. Select the activity that does not occur in a signal transduction pathway.
   (A) activation of the receptor by a relay molecule
   (B) expression of specific genes
   (C) activation of protein kinases
   (D) phosphorylation of transcription factors

Use the following information to answer questions 4–6.

In 1926, Frits Went experimented with how seedlings grow toward the light. He placed seedlings in the dark and removed their tips, putting some tips on agar cubes, which he predicted would absorb the growth-promoting chemical. The figure shows key elements of Went's experiment.

4. Which plant shows auxin stimulating elongation in the left side of the plant only?
   (A) plant A
   (B) plant B
   (C) plant C
   (D) plant D

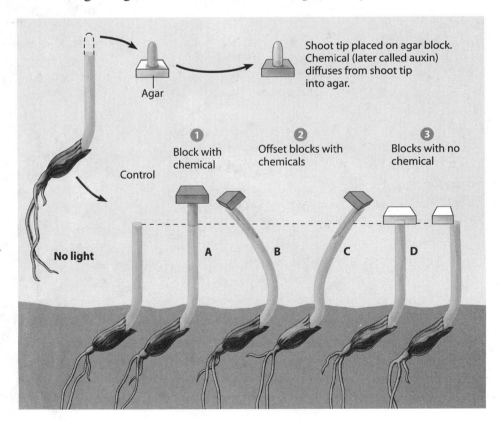

5. What prior knowledge must Went have had to design this experiment as shown?
   (A) Plants respond to gravity as well as light.
   (B) Compounds produced in the shoot tip have an effect on phototropism.
   (C) Placing an agar block on a seedling will stimulate its growth.
   (D) Photosynthesis is concentrated in cells of the shoot tip.

6. In Went's experiment, observe what happens to both plants with treatment D (agar blocks with no chemicals). What *conclusion* can you draw from this?
   (A) These plants serve as the control because they have no chemical.
   (B) It is necessary to add chemical to the block to get bending.
   (C) The addition of the chemical causes elongation of cells.
   (D) The mechanical irritation of the agar block is responsible for the bending.

7. You are given the task of preventing grass seedlings from rotating toward the light. Using your knowledge of phototropism, which of the following experimental procedures would you use to complete the task?
   (A) Cover the growing tip of the grass seedling with black paper.
   (B) Cover only the base of the grass seedling with black paper.
   (C) Illuminate the seedlings with a high wattage bulb at a 45° angle.
   (D) Supply the seedling with a nutrient-rich fertilizer solution.

8. In plants, the movement of sugars, hormones, and other organic molecules takes place in the phloem. Which of the following mechanisms would best explain this movement?
   (A) a difference in water potential between a sugar source and a sugar sink
   (B) the evaporation of water through the stomata
   (C) the cohesion of water molecules to each other and adhesion to the transport tubes
   (D) the release of auxins in response to a loss of water in the xylem

Use the following information to answer questions 9 and 10.

When a seed germinates and the growing plant shoot reaches light, the plant undergoes profound changes known as de-etiolation or greening. Stem elongation slows, leaves expand, roots elongate, and the shoot produces chlorophyll. You can see this pathway in the accompanying figure.

9. Which step in this pathway begins the amplification of the signal resulting in numerous active molecules?
   (A) Step 1
   (B) Step 2
   (c) Step 3
   (D) Both Steps 1 and 3

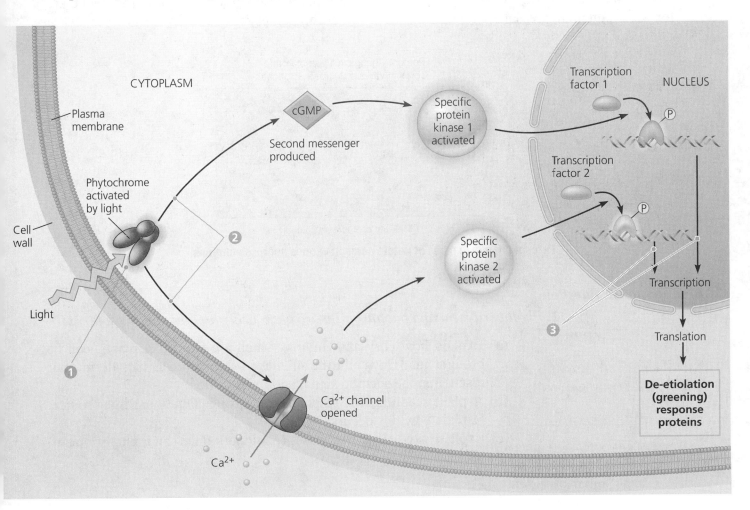

10. Which of the following describes a significant difference between the phytochrome and the calcium channel protein in the figure?
    (A) When activated, phytochromes allow the plant to skip the transduction stage and go directly to cellular responses.
    (B) Phytochrome molecules do not require an environmental stimulus to be activated.
    (C) Phytochrome molecules are intracellular rather than membrane bound and do not respond to a molecular stimulus.
    (D) Phytochrome activation causes the transduction and cellular response sequences to occur in the nucleus.

Grid-In Questions

The following questions require a numerical response.

A group of students placed potato cores in various sucrose solutions to determine the molarity of the cores. The students measured the mass of the potato cores before and after immersion in the various sucrose solutions. The figure shows the results.

1. Calculate the solute potential of the potato cores if the temperature in the beaker is 25°C. (Hint: On the exam you will find the formula for water potential, pressure potential, and solute potential. Anytime you have a numerical question that doesn't include the formula, check the Equations and Formulas sheet that accompanies the exam.)

Percent change in mass of potato cores in various sucrose solutions

Free-Response Question

1. *Photoperiodism and phototropism are plant behaviors that increase fitness.*

    (a) Explain how chrysanthemums, which are short-day plants, can be brought into flower in the middle of the summer. Include in your discussion the specific signal and its reception.

    (b) A plant seedling will respond to a strong directional light source. Explain how this occurs.

    (c) Explain how each response (photoperiodism and phototropism) increases biological fitness.

Animal Form and Function

Chapter 40: Basic Principles of Animal Form and Function

(Biology, *11e: Chapter 40;* Focus, *2e: Chapter 32*)

YOU MUST KNOW
• How feedback systems function to maintain homeostasis.
• One example of positive feedback and one example of negative feedback.

Animal form and function are correlated at all levels of organization
(Biology, *11e: 40.1;* Focus, *2e: 32.1*)

▌ **Tissues** are groups of cells that have a common structure and function. Tissues are further organized into functional units called **organs**. Groups of organs that work together make up **organ systems** (for example, the digestive, circulatory, and excretory systems).

▌ For animals to survive, their tissues, organs, and organ systems must act in a coordinated manner. Two major organ systems specialize in control and coordination:

▪ In the **endocrine system**, chemical signals called **hormones** are released into the bloodstream and are broadcast throughout the body. Different hormones cause specific effects but only in cells with specific receptors for the released hormone.

▪ In the **nervous system, neurons** transmit information between specific locations. Only three types of cells receive nerve impulses: neurons, muscle cells, and endocrine cells.

Feedback control maintains the internal environment in many animals
(Biology, *11e: 40.2;* Focus, *2e: 32.1*)

▌ **Homeostasis** is the maintenance of a relatively stable condition, and it requires a control system, generally a feedback mechanism. For example, animals maintain a relatively constant internal environment even when the external environment changes significantly.

▌ Homeostatic control systems function by having a **set point** (such as a body temperature to maintain), **sensors** to detect any stimulus above or below the set point, and a physiological **response** that helps return the body to its set point.

▌ In **negative-feedback systems**, the animal responds to the stimulus in a way that reduces the stimulus. For example, in response to exercise, the body temperature rises, which initiates sweating, which cools the body. As the body moves away from the set point, negative-feedback systems return the body to the set point. Homeostasis relies primarily on negative-feedback systems. *More gets you less.*

▌ In **positive-feedback systems**, a change in some variable triggers mechanisms that amplify rather than reverse the change. For example, during childbirth, pressure of the baby's head against receptors near the opening of the uterus stimulates greater uterine contractions, which cause greater pressure against the uterine opening, which heightens the contractions, and so forth. *More gets you more.*

Homeostatic processes for thermoregulation involve form, function, and behavior (Biology, *11e: 40.3;* Focus, *2e: 32.1*)

▌ **Thermoregulation** refers to how animals maintain their internal temperature within a tolerable range. It may involve *physiological changes,* such as panting, sweating, shivering, or *behaviors,* such as burrowing and sunning.

▌ **Endotherms** (such as mammals and birds) are warmed mostly by heat generated by metabolism. **Ectotherms** (such as most invertebrates, fishes, amphibians, and reptiles) generate relatively little metabolic heat, gaining most of their heat from external sources.

▌ In many birds and mammals, reduction of heat loss relies on **countercurrent exchange**. Heat transfer involves antiparallel arrangement of blood vessels such that warm blood from the core of the animal, en route to the extremities, transfers heat to colder blood returning from the extremities. Heat that would have been lost to the environment is conserved in the blood returning to the core of the animal.

Energy requirements are related to animal size, activity, and environment (Biology, *11e: 40.4;* Focus, *2e: 33.5*)

▌ An animal's **metabolic rate** is the total amount of energy it uses in a unit of time. Metabolic rates are generally higher for endotherms than for ectotherms.

▌ Metabolic rate is inversely related to body size among similar animals. For example, elephants have a lower metabolic rate per gram of body mass, whereas mice have a much higher metabolic rate per gram.

Animal Nutrition

(Biology, *11e: Chapter 41;* Focus, *2e: Chapter 33*)

> **WHAT'S IMPORTANT TO KNOW?**
> Digestion is not an explicit topic of the Curriculum Framework, but your teacher may choose to introduce you to this material. This chapter contains information that may be the basis of both multiple-choice and essay questions. Having a general understanding of digestion will help you be more confident in dealing with potential questions. Pay particular attention to examples of feedback circuits on page 236.

An animal's diet must supply chemical energy, organic molecules, and essential nutrients (Biology, *11e: 41.1;* Focus, *2e: 33.1*)

▌ The **essential nutrients** required by an animal are those that the animal cannot produce from raw materials. These include essential amino acids, essential fatty acids, vitamins, and minerals.

Food processing involves ingestion, digestion, absorption, and elimination (Biology, *11e: 41.2;* Focus, *2e: 33.2*)

▌ **Intracellular digestion** occurs within a cell enclosed by a protective membrane. Sponges digest their food this way.

▌ **Extracellular digestion** is carried out by most animals; in this type of digestion, food is broken down outside of cells. This process allows the animal to devour much larger sources of food than can be handled using only intracellular digestion.

Organs specialized for sequential stages of food processing form the mammalian digestive system (Biology, *11e: 41.3;* Focus, *2e: 33.3*)

> *STUDY TIP* You will not be expected to name the enzymes of digestion or know the anatomy of this system. It is important to understand how the large chunks of food you ingest are reduced to monosaccharides, amino acids, fatty acids, and glycerol and are able to enter your cells. Required knowledge of digestion includes how enzymes work and the role of passive and active transport in moving nutrients in and out of cells.

▌ The movement of food through the digestive system is controlled by the rhythmic waves of contraction (peristalsis) by smooth muscle in the walls of the alimentary canal and by muscular, ring-like valves that regulate the passage of material between digestive compartments.

▌ One of the primary functions of the digestive system is to break down polymers to monomers. Recall that we studied how cells make polymers by dehydration synthesis, the removal of water to join two organic molecules chemically. In digestion, enzymes will add the water back, splitting the large compounds into smaller and smaller pieces.

▌ Dehydration synthesis reactions require energy, whereas hydrolysis reactions release free energy into the system. The calories from food come from this release of free energy. We take in polymers and through digestive hydrolysis reduce them to monomers. In general, only monomers can be absorbed into the body to serve as raw materials to build new molecules or to serve as fuel for cellular respiration.

> **STUDY TIP** The bulleted items that follow feature structures of the digestive system in bold and give their functions. In this section, consider questions such as the following: How does the structure fit its function? How is the surface area of the intestine increased for digestion and absorption? How does the epithelial lining of the intestine aid in absorption of nutrients?

▌ When food is in the **mouth**, a nervous reflex occurs that causes saliva to be secreted into the mouth. Saliva lubricates the food to facilitate swallowing. It also starts chemical digestion because saliva contains an enzyme that hydrolyzes the polysaccharide starch.

▌ Food moves from the mouth down to the stomach via the **esophagus**. Rhythmic muscular contractions called *Peristalsis* will move digestive contents through the entire tract.

▌ The **stomach's** functions include storing food and secreting *gastric juice*. Two components of gastric juice, hydrochloric acid and pepsin, carry out chemical digestion.

  ▪ *Hydrochloric acid*, with a pH of about 2, breaks down the extracellular matrix of meat and plant materials, and it also kills most of the bacteria ingested with food.

  ▪ *Pepsin* is an enzyme in gastric juice that begins to hydrolyze proteins into smaller polypeptides. Pepsin is secreted in an inactive form and is activated by hydrochloric acid in the stomach. This enzyme functions best in a very acidic environment. The inactive form protects the cells that produce the protein-digesting enzyme from self-digestion.

▌ The **small intestine** is the major site of digestion and absorption. Here, the mixture of ingested food and digestive juice mixes with secretions from the pancreas and the liver. Enzymes will complete the digestion of fats, proteins, carbohydrates, and nucleic acids to their respective monomers and components.

▌ The lining of the small intestine has tiny finger-like projections called *villi*; the epithelial cell membranes are highly folded into *microvilli*. This greatly increases the surface area of the small intestine and maximizes absorption of nutrients into the circulatory system, an example of how structure enhances function.

▌ In each villus are capillaries where the absorption of monomers, including monosaccharides and amino acids, occurs. Also included is a lymph vessel, which absorbs small fatty acids. Passive, facilitated diffusion and active transport move monomers across the intestinal membrane and into blood vessels.

▌ The **pancreas** releases a complex mix of digestive enzymes and alkaline fluid rich in bicarbonate into the small intestine. This fluid acts as a buffer against the acidic contents from the stomach. The pancreas produces enzymes for the digestion of all four major organic groups—carbohydrates, fats, proteins, and nucleic acids. The digestive enzymes found in the small intestine have an alkaline-optimum pH.

▌ The **liver** makes bile, which is then stored in the gallbladder until released into the small intestine. Bile emulsifies fats; that is, bile coats fat droplets, turning large fat droplets into small fat droplets, which are easier to digest.

▌ To summarize, the small intestine is the location of the complete chemical digestion of nutrients as well as where absorption of nutrient components occurs.

▌ *Review the final products of each nutrient category. You should be familiar with these components from your earlier study of organic molecules in Topic 1.*

- **Carbohydrates:** The breakdown of starch and glycogen that begins in the mouth ends in the small intestines with the production of monosaccharides such as glucose. Glucose can now be absorbed into the bloodstream.

- **Proteins:** Pepsin begins the breakdown of proteins in the stomach. In the small intestine, polypeptides are further broken into their monomers, amino acids. The amino acids are then absorbed into the bloodstream.

- **Nucleic acids:** The breakdown of nucleic acids starts with the hydrolysis of DNA and RNA to their respective nucleotides. The nucleotides are then broken down to nitrogenous bases, sugars, and phosphate groups, which are absorbed into the bloodstream.

- **Fats:** Chemical digestion of fats begins in the small intestine, where fats are emulsified by bile secreted by the liver. The enzyme lipase hydrolyzes the small fat droplets into fatty acids and glycerol, which are then absorbed into the bloodstream.

STUDY TIP Consider questions such as the following: How are the foods we eat reduced to molecules that can cross into the circulatory system? What adaptations of the digestive system contribute to this? How do passive diffusion and active transport function in absorption?

▌ The **large intestine** is connected to the small intestine. Its main functions are to compact waste and reabsorb water from the digestive fluid.

▌ The large intestine includes a rich flora of mostly harmless bacteria, including *Escherichia coli*. Some of these bacteria are important symbionts, producing several vitamins including B vitamins and vitamin K. The presence of *E. coli* in lakes and streams is a useful indicator of contamination by untreated sewage.

▌ At the end of the large intestine is the **rectum**, where feces are stored until they are eliminated.

Evolutionary adaptations of vertebrate digestive systems correlate with diet (Biology, *11e: 41.4;* Focus, *2e: 33.4*)

▌ One type of adaptation to diet is seen in the **dentition** of mammals. For example, carnivores have large canine teeth for the tearing of food, whereas herbivores such as horses show well-developed molars and premolars, the teeth at the rear of the mouth that grind food.

- Another category of adaptation to diet is seen in the length of the digestive tract. Herbivores generally have longer alimentary canals than carnivores, reflecting the longer time needed for digestion of vegetation and the greater surface area available for absorption.
- Mutualistic adaptations include the coexistence of humans and many of our gut bacteria. Much of the chemical energy in herbivore diets comes from the cellulose of plant cell walls. Many vertebrates (as well as termites) house large populations of symbiotic bacteria and protists, whose enzymes actually digest the cellulose. Some intestinal bacteria produce vitamins, whereas others help regulate the function of the innate immune system.
- The exploration of the importance of our **microbiome** (all the microbes living on our body) is just beginning. The microbiome is now known to play a significant role in human health and disease.

Feedback circuits regulate digestion, energy storage, and appetite (Biology, *11e: 41.5*; Focus, *2e: 33.5*)

- Vertebrates store excess calories as *glycogen* in the liver and muscles and as fat.
- Blood glucose is maintained within a narrow range through the antagonistic effects of two hormones. *Insulin* decreases blood glucose by moving glucose into the cells, and *glucagon* increases blood glucose by promoting release of glucose from the stored glycogen in the liver.

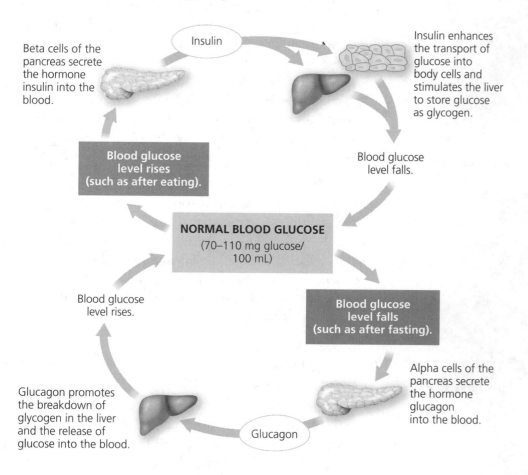

Beta cells of the pancreas secrete the hormone insulin into the blood.

Insulin

Insulin enhances the transport of glucose into body cells and stimulates the liver to store glucose as glycogen.

Blood glucose level rises (such as after eating).

Blood glucose level falls.

NORMAL BLOOD GLUCOSE
(70–110 mg glucose/ 100 mL)

Blood glucose level rises.

Blood glucose level falls (such as after fasting).

Glucagon promotes the breakdown of glycogen in the liver and the release of glucose into the blood.

Glucagon

Alpha cells of the pancreas secrete the hormone glucagon into the blood.

> **STUDY TIP** Several times we have suggested that you should be able to describe specific feedback loops and consider this to be a common example that you should know. Follow the legend with the figure on the previous page to see how glucagon and insulin maintain blood glucose homeostasis. Is this an example of positive or negative feedback?

Circulation and Gas Exchange
(Biology, *11e: Chapter 42;* Focus, *2e: Chapter 34*)

> **WHAT'S IMPORTANT TO KNOW?**
> Circulation and gas exchange are not explicit topics of the Curriculum Framework, but your teacher may choose to introduce you to this material and use it for illustrative examples. Consider these ideas, which link to the Curriculum Framework:
> ▌ Common ancestry and divergence resulting from adaptation in different environments are shown through the different types of respiratory and circulatory systems seen in various animal groups. (EK 2.D.2)
> ▌ The respiratory and circulatory systems exchange molecules between the environment and the cells. The concepts of diffusion and surface area can explain both anatomy and processes in these two systems.

Here are what we consider to be the main points of this chapter:

▌ How red blood cells (RBCs) demonstrate the relationship of structure to function
▌ The general characteristics of a respiratory surface
▌ How O_2 and CO_2 are transported in the blood
▌ The roles of diet, blood pressure, and genetics in cardiovascular disease
▌ The pathway a molecule of oxygen takes from the air until it is delivered by a red blood cell to the tissues

Circulatory systems link exchange surfaces with cells throughout the body
(Biology, *11e: 42.1;* Focus, *2e: 34.1*)

▌ The exchange of gases, nutrients, and wastes occurs at the cellular level. Because diffusion is rapid only across small distances, natural selection has led to two general solutions.

    1. Body size and shape keep many or all cells in direct contact with the environment, such as with sponges. Cnidarians and flatworms possess a **gastrovascular cavity** that serves both in digestion and distribution of substances throughout the body.

    2. Larger animals have a **circulatory system** that moves fluid to the tissues and cells for exchange.

- A *circulatory system* has three components: **blood** (a circulatory fluid), **vessels** (tubes through which blood moves), and a **heart** (a structure that pumps the blood).
- There are three main types of blood vessels:
  - **Arteries** carry blood *away* from the heart and branch into smaller **arterioles**. Their walls are relatively thick and include a significant amount of smooth muscle. The *pulse* is felt in an artery.
  - **Capillaries** are microscopic vessels that are composed of only a single layer of cells. All diffusion occurs here.
  - **Veins** carry the blood back to the heart. They have valves to prevent backflow.
- **Atria** are heart chambers that receive blood and convey it to **ventricles**, which pump blood.

Coordinated cycles of heart contraction drive double circulation in mammals (Biology, *11e: 42.2;* Focus, *2e: 34.2*)

- The **sinoatrial (SA) node** is the pacemaker of the heart. It is located in the upper wall of the right atrium. It generates electrical impulses that set the rate at which cardiac muscle cells contract.
- The **atrioventricular (AV) node**, located in the lower wall of the right atrium, delays the impulses from the SA node to allow the atria to completely empty before the ventricles contract. The AV node generates electrical impulses that cause the ventricles to contract.
- Heart rate is regulated by at least three factors. The sympathetic nerves accelerate heart rate, and the parasympathetic nerves slow it down. Hormones such as epinephrine increase heart rate, as does an increase in body temperature.

Patterns of blood pressure and flow reflect the structure and arrangement of blood vessels (Biology, *11e: 42.3;* Focus, *2e: 34.3*)

- **Blood pressure** is highest when the ventricles contract (systole) and decreases when the ventricles relax (diastole).
  - *Short-term regulation of blood pressure* occurs when the smooth muscle of the arterioles contracts or relaxes because of changes in activity or hormonal signals.
  - *Long-term regulation of blood pressure* is accomplished by changes in blood volume because of a negative-feedback system involving the kidney and the endocrine system. (See Chapter 42 on page 927.)
- Blood moves through the veins and venules propelled by rhythmic contractions of smooth muscle in the walls of the blood vessels. Blood flow in veins is also enhanced by the contraction of skeletal muscles during exercise, pushing the blood toward the heart. Valves prevent the backflow of blood in veins and venules.
- Exchange of substances between the blood and surrounding interstitial fluid takes place across the thin walls of the capillaries. Large molecules such as proteins are carried across in vesicles by endocytosis, while small molecules, such as O_2 and CO_2, simply diffuse across the walls. Fluid can be forced from the capillaries as a result of pressure; it returns to the blood through the *lymphatic system*.

Blood components function in exchange, transport, and defense
(Biology, *11e: 42.4*; Focus, *2e: 34.4*)

▌ **Plasma** is mostly water, but it also contains ions, electrolytes, and plasma proteins. It transports nutrients, metabolic wastes, gases, and hormones. In addition, blood plasma carries the following:

  ▪ **Red blood cells (erythrocytes or RBCs)**, which transport oxygen via *hemoglobin* (an iron-containing protein).
  ▪ **White blood cells (leukocytes or WBCs)**, which are part of the immune system.
  ▪ **Platelets**, which are fragments of cells responsible for blood clotting.

> **TIP FROM THE READERS**
> *Structure fits function* is a major theme in AP Biology and is the basis for many essay questions. The red blood cell, as described next, is an excellent example of the correlation of structure and function.

▌ Red blood cells are *biconcave disks*. This shape increases surface area to enhance oxygen uptake and release. Each RBC contains about 250 million molecules of hemoglobin, and each hemoglobin molecule can bind up to four molecules of oxygen.

▌ RBCs lack nuclei, which increases space for hemoglobin.

▌ RBCs lack mitochondria, so the oxygen they carry is not consumed.

Gas exchange occurs across specialized respiratory surfaces
(Biology, *11e: 42.5*; Focus, *2e: 34.5*)

▌ **Gas exchange**, or **respiration**, is the uptake of molecular oxygen (O_2) from the environment and the discharge of carbon dioxide (CO_2) to the environment.

▌ The **respiratory medium** is the source of the O_2. It is air for terrestrial animals and water for most aquatic animals.

▌ The **respiratory surface** is the part of an animal's body where gases are exchanged with the surrounding environment. It can be the body wall, the skin, gills, tracheae, or lungs.

  ▪ General characteristics of respiratory surfaces include:

    ▪ They are moist.
    ▪ They have a favorable surface area–volume ratio. Respiratory surfaces are often extensively folded or branched. (Think structure/function.)
    ▪ They are closely associated with the vascular system of larger animals.

▌ **Gills** are respiratory organs in aquatic animals. Water flows through them, and blood flowing through capillaries within the wall of the gill picks up oxygen from the water. Blood flows in a direction opposite to the flow of water. This is called **countercurrent exchange**, and it maximizes the absorption of oxygen.

■ Countercurrent exchange mechanisms allow for more diffusion to occur than would otherwise be possible. Follow the countercurrent flow of blood and oxygen-rich water in Figure 9.1. Examine the figure until all the numbers make sense in the context of diffusion.

Figure 9.1   Countercurrent exchange

■ The **alveoli** are air sacs clustered at the ends of bronchioles in the lungs. They are thin and moist, and they have a large surface area (in a human, the size of a tennis court if spread out!). They are associated with capillary beds. O_2 diffuses into the blood by passing through the thin membrane of an alveolus and through the thin membrane of a capillary, into the blood, and attaches to a hemoglobin molecule in a red blood cell. Again, think structure/function.

> **STUDY TIP** Refer again to the characteristics of a respiratory surface and note how the mammalian lung fulfills the requirements.

Breathing ventilates the lungs (Biology, *11e: 42.6*; Focus, *2e: 34.6*)

■ Breathing is under the control of regions located in the brain (the medulla and the pons). It is influenced by pH, which is an indirect indication of blood CO_2 levels.

■ Increased metabolic activity lowers pH by increasing the concentration of CO_2 in the blood. CO_2 reacts with water to form carbonic acid, which dissociates into a bicarbonate ion and a hydrogen ion. As blood pH drops, the rate and depth of respiration increase.

Adaptations for gas exchange include pigments that bind and transport gases (Biology, *11e: 42.7*; Focus, *2e: 34.7*)

■ **Hemoglobin** is the respiratory pigment found in almost all vertebrates. It consists of four subunits, each of which has a *heme group* with an embedded iron atom. Each iron atom binds O_2, allowing each hemoglobin to carry four oxygen molecules.

■ A lowering of the pH in blood (as occurs with exercise) lowers the affinity of hemoglobin for oxygen, and oxygen dissociates from hemoglobin. This delivers more O_2 to the tissues during times of heavy exercise.

■ CO_2 is most commonly carried in the blood in the form of bicarbonate ions (70%). Less commonly, it is transported via hemoglobin (23%) and in solution in the blood plasma (7%).

The Immune System

(Biology, *11e: Chapter 43*; Focus, *2e: Chapter 35*)

YOU MUST KNOW

- The roles of innate and adaptive immunity.
- Elements of an innate immune response.
- The differences between B and T cells relative to their activation and actions in adaptive immunity.
- How antigens are recognized by immune system cells.
- How clonal selection explains humoral immunity.
- How T cells function in cell-mediated immunity.
- Why helper T cells are central to immune responses of both B cells and T cells.

STUDY TIP The immune system is one of three human systems explicitly included in the Curriculum Framework. As you work through this chapter, pay particular attention to the ways cells communicate with each other to defend against pathogens.

In innate immunity, recognition and response rely on traits common to groups of pathogens (Biology, *11e: 43.1*; Focus, *2e: 35.1*)

- **Innate immune responses** rely on traits common to groups of organisms, so they are nonspecific. Innate immune responses are the same whether or not the pathogen has been encountered previously. All animals have an innate immune response system.

    - **Barrier defenses** provide a physical barrier to pathogens and include skin and the mucous membranes that cover the surface and line the openings of the animal body. Body secretions result in a skin pH from 3 to 5 and create an environment that is hostile to many pathogens. The antimicrobial enzyme **lysozyme**, which breaks down bacterial cell walls, is found in saliva, mucus, and tears.
    - **Cellular innate defenses** combat pathogens that get through the skin—for example, in a cut. They include phagocytic white blood cells and antimicrobial proteins.
    - Some phagocytic white blood cells recognize microbes using **toll-like receptors (TLRs)**. TLRs recognize fragments of molecules that are characteristic of a particular type of pathogen but absent from the vertebrate body. For example, a TLR might recognize a polysaccharide found on the surface of many bacteria but not found on the surface of vertebrate cells. TLRs increase the efficiency of phagocytosis.

        - A variety of other phagocytic white blood cells (especially neutrophils and macrophages) are also attracted by signals from infected tissues.

■ A local **inflammatory response** is triggered by damage to tissue by physical injury or the entry of pathogens. It leads to the release of numerous chemical signals. For example, **histamines** are released by *mast cells* in response to injury. Histamines trigger the dilation and permeability of nearby capillaries, which aids in delivering clotting agents and phagocytic cells to the injured area. Systemic inflammatory responses include fever and increased production of white blood cells to fight infection.

In adaptive immunity, receptors provide pathogen-specific recognition (Biology, *11e: 43.2;* Focus, *2e: 35.2*)

■ Vertebrates have two types of lymphocytes: **B lymphocytes (B cells)**, which proliferate in the bone marrow, and **T lymphocytes (T cells)**, which mature in the thymus. They circulate through the blood and lymph, and both recognize specific antigens. All blood cells proliferate from stem cells in the bone marrow.

■ **Antigens** are foreign molecules that elicit a response by lymphocytes. B and T cells recognize the antigens through specific receptors embedded in their plasma membranes.

■ **Antibodies** are soluble proteins secreted by B cells during an immune response.

■ **B** or **T cell activation** begins when an antigen binds to a B or T cell receptor. B cell activation is enhanced by cytokines. Cytokines are small proteins that regulate the function of other cells and thus play an important role in cell communication. B cells form two clones of cells in a process called **clonal selection**, which results in thousands of cells, all specific to a specific antigen. A thorough review of clonal selection will clarify the humoral (B cell) response to infection.

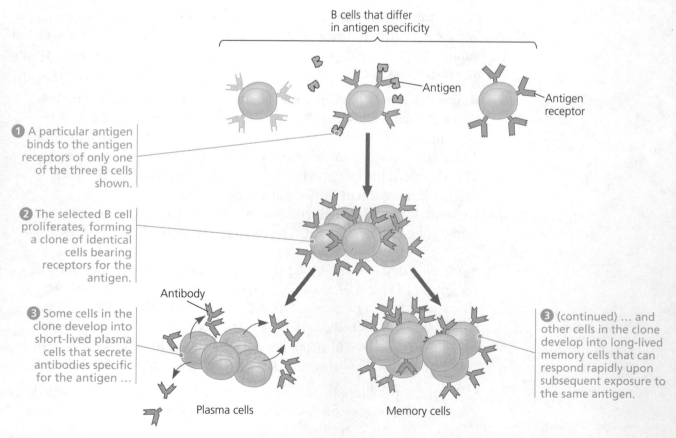

B cells that differ in antigen specificity

Antigen

Antigen receptor

❶ A particular antigen binds to the antigen receptors of only one of the three B cells shown.

❷ The selected B cell proliferates, forming a clone of identical cells bearing receptors for the antigen.

❸ Some cells in the clone develop into short-lived plasma cells that secrete antibodies specific for the antigen ...

Antibody

❸ (continued) ... and other cells in the clone develop into long-lived memory cells that can respond rapidly upon subsequent exposure to the same antigen.

Plasma cells

Memory cells

- One clone of cells forms **plasma cells** that combat the antigen by producing antibodies *specific* to that antigen.
- The second clone forms **memory cells**, which are long-lived and bear receptors for the same antigen. This allows memory cells to quickly mount an immune response in subsequent infections. Notice the large increase in the antibodies produced in the secondary immune response in Figure 9.2. The large increase, compared with the primary response, results from the cloning of memory cells, all making the same antibody.
- A **primary immune response** occurs when the body is first exposed to a foreign antigen and a B cell is activated, producing plasma cells that make antibodies against the specific antigen.
- A **secondary immune response** occurs when the same antigen is encountered at a later time. It is faster and of greater magnitude. (Refer to Figure 9.2.) Because the initial exposure to the antigen not only resulted in plasma cells but also produced memory cells, the secondary immune response occurs faster with a much higher production of antibodies. Notice how long the primary response takes and the low level of antibody produced. No wonder we get sick on first exposures to pathogens!

▌T cell receptors bind antigens that are displayed by **antigen-presenting cells (APCs)**. When a pathogen enters a host cell, enzymes inside the cell cleave the foreign molecules into smaller peptides that can be combined with host proteins and moved to the cell surface. This presentation, a host protein displaying a foreign molecule, works like a flag, signaling to the body that the cell is infected.

▌B cells defend against extracellular pathogens in blood and lymph by secreting antibodies that bind to antigens, thereby neutralizing pathogens or making them better targets for phagocytic cells.

▌T cells defend against intracellular pathogens and cancer by binding to and lysing the infected cells or cancer cells. When a cell becomes cancerous, it can display new peptide molecules on its surface, signaling that it is aberrant.

Figure 9.2   Primary and secondary immune responses

Adaptive immunity defends against infection of body fluids and body cells (Biology, *11e: 43.3; Focus, 2e: 35.3*)

▌ Adaptive immunity has two branches:

▪ **Humoral immune response** involves the activation and clonal selection of plasma and memory B cells, which produce antibodies that circulate in the blood and lymph.

▪ **Cell-mediated immune response** involves the activation and clonal selection of *cytotoxic T cells*, which identify and destroy infected cells.

▌ **Helper T cells** aid both responses. Helper T cells are activated by binding with the antigen presented by a host body cell. The combination of binding to the presented antigen and the release of *cytokines* from the helper T cell will stimulate and activate both B cells and cytotoxic T cells. Refer to Figure 9.3 to see the essential, central role of helper T cells.

▌ **Cytotoxic T cells (Tc)** bind to antigenic fragments displayed on the surface of infected body cells. Cytotoxic T cells destroy infected body cells.

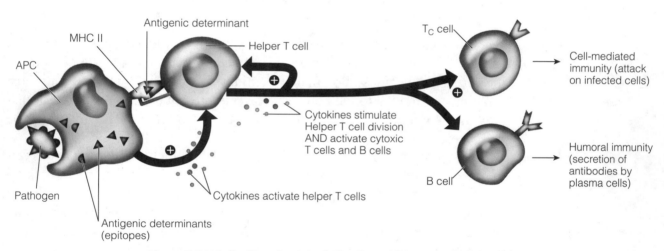

Figure 9.3   Activation of cytotoxic T cells and B cells by helper T cells

---

ORGANIZE YOUR THOUGHTS

Confused by all the different cell names?

1. **B cells** make antibodies, which provide humoral immunity. The antibodies help fight pathogens that are circulating in blood and lymph.
2. **Cytotoxic T cells** destroy body cells that are infected by a pathogen or cancer cells.
3. **Helper T cells** activate both B and T cells.

▌ **Active immunity** occurs when exposure to an antigen leaves behind circulating memory cells. Immunity can develop naturally in response to an infection; it also can develop artificially by immunization (vaccination). In immunization, a nonpathogenic form of a microbe or part of a microbe elicits an immune response, resulting in immunological memory for that microbe.

- **Passive immunity** occurs when an individual receives antibodies, such as those passed to the fetus across the placenta and to infants via breast milk.

Disruptions in immune system function can elicit or exacerbate disease
(Biology, *11e: 43.4;* Focus, *2e: 35.3*)

- In localized **allergies**, such as hay fever, antibodies produced after first exposure to an allergen attach to receptors on mast cells. Mast cells produce and store histamines. The next time the same allergen enters the body, it bonds to mast cell molecules, inducing the cell to release histamine and other mediators that cause typical allergy symptoms.
- **Lupus, rheumatoid arthritis, type I diabetes mellitus**, and **multiple sclerosis** are examples of autoimmune diseases. In each case, the immune system turns against particular molecules of the body, allowing cytotoxic T cells to attack and damage the body's own healthy cells.
- **HIV** infects helper T cells. Refer again to Figure 9.3. Can you see why people with AIDS are immune suppressed? Note that helper T cells are essential in both humoral and cell-mediated immunity.

CONNECT WITH THE CURRICULUM FRAMEWORK

LO 2.29 asks you to create a representation or model to describe immune responses. Do not underestimate the importance of mastery in this area! (EK 2.D.4) In addition, EK 3.D.2 looks at cell signaling, and you are expected to know how cells within the immune system communicate. Can you describe or explain the relationships between all of the following: Cell mediated response, humoral response, B cells, T cells, cytotoxic T cells, antigens, antibodies, and memory cells?

Osmoregulation and Excretion

(Biology, *11e: Chapter 44;* Focus, *2e: Chapter 32*)

WHAT'S IMPORTANT TO KNOW?

This topic is not a required part of the Curriculum Framework, but the removal of nitrogenous wastes and maintenance of water balance are essential for the maintenance of homeostasis. This chapter provides many illustrative examples related to transport, exchange of materials with the surrounding environment, feedback regulation, homeostasis, and evolutionary adaptations.

Osmoregulation balances the uptake and loss of water and solutes
(Biology, *11e: 44.1;* Focus, *2e: 32.3, 32.4*)

- **Osmoregulation** is the process by which animals control solute concentrations and balance water gain and loss.
- Adaptations for osmoregulation reflect the habitat of the species and often require energy for the movement of salts or water.

- **Nitrogenous wastes** from the breakdown of proteins and nucleic acids are toxic and are removed by **excretion**.
- The form of nitrogenous waste reflects the animal's phylogeny and habitat: ammonia for aquatic species, urea or uric acid for terrestrial species.

The nephron is organized for stepwise processing of blood filtrate (Biology, *11e*: 44.4; Focus, *2e*: 32.4, 32.5)

- Animals across a wide range of species produce a fluid waste (urine) in a four-step process. In mammals, this occurs in the nephrons of the kidney, so we will focus on this area as a specific example.
- **Nephrons** are the functional units of the kidney. Each kidney has approximately one million nephrons! Within the nephron, liquids are filtered from the blood, wastes removed, and excess ions and toxins moved into the filtrate. Water balance is regulated along the course of passage through the nephron. Then the modified filtrate passes through the collecting tubules of the nephrons and empties into the ureters, passing as urine to the bladder.
- Urine formation requires four steps. Study Figure 9.4, and note what occurs in each step.
- A feature of the nephron is the loop of Henle, where water is removed from the filtrate. Note that the filtrate travels down and back up the loop, which results in a **countercurrent** system and allows the kidney to form concentrated urine with minimal water loss.

Figure 9.4   Key functions of excretory systems

Hormonal circuits link kidney function, water balance, and blood pressure
(Biology, *11e: 44.5;* Focus, *2e: 32.5*)

▌ **Antidiuretic hormone (ADH)** is an important hormone in the regulation of water balance to maintain normal blood osmolarity. (A diuretic helps increase urine volume; *anti*diuretic hormone reduces urine volume.)

▌ What happens after a human sweats profusely? Blood osmolarity increases because water has been lost. This causes release of ADH. ADH makes the collecting ducts more permeable to water, so more water leaves the filtrate and is reabsorbed into the blood. Therefore, blood osmolarity is reduced. The urine is more concentrated, and water loss from the body is reduced. This is yet another example of a mechanism to maintain homeostasis.

Hormones and the Endocrine System

(Biology, *11e: Chapter 45;* Focus, *2e: Chapter 32*)

YOU MUST KNOW

- The endocrine system is one of two body systems for communication and regulation.
- How hormones are transported, bind to specific target cells, and trigger cellular responses.
- The secretion, target, action, and regulation of at least two hormones.
- An illustration of both positive and negative feedback in the regulation of homeostasis by hormones.

CONNECT WITH THE CURRICULUM FRAMEWORK

EK 3.D.2: Cells communicate with each other through direct contact with other cells or from a distance via chemical signaling. The endocrine system is one of three human systems that are explicitly included in the Curriculum Framework. The release of each hormone is regulated by a feedback system. You should select one hormone that is under positive regulation and one that is under negative regulation and be able to explain the feedback system for each one. You will find suggested examples in the last concept of this system on page 1006 as well as the example on p. 1005.

Hormones and other signaling molecules bind to target receptors, triggering specific response pathways **(Biology, *11e: 45.1;* Focus, *2e: 32.2*)**

▌ The **endocrine system** of an animal is the sum of all its hormone-secreting cells and tissues.

▌ **Endocrine glands** are *ductless* and secrete hormones directly into body fluids.

▌ **Hormones** are chemical signals that cause a response in *target cells*.

- **Positive and negative feedback** regulate most endocrine secretion.
- Here is a review of the two ways hormones initiate cellular responses. Recall that these mechanisms were covered in some detail earlier in Topic 2, The Cell.

  - *Water-soluble hormones* cannot pass through the hydrophobic plasma membrane but will bind to **Cell-surface receptors**. Cell-surface receptors bind the hormone and trigger a *signal transduction pathway*. A signal transduction pathway consists of a series of molecular events that initiate a response to the signal. *Example:* The binding of epinephrine to liver cells causes a cascade that leads to the conversion of glycogen into glucose.
  - *Lipid-soluble hormones* pass through the plasma membrane and bind to **Intracellular receptors**. The receptor-hormone complex then acts as a transcription factor, causing a change in gene expression. *Example:* Testosterone enters the cell and binds to its specific receptor; this complex then enters the nuclei of target cells, binds to the DNA, and stimulates transcription of a specific gene.

Feedback regulation and coordination with the nervous system are common in endocrine signaling (Biology, *11e: 45.2;* Focus, *2e: 32.2)*

- A feedback loop linking the response back to the initial stimulus is characteristic of hormone control pathways.

  - Regulation often involves **negative-feedback** loops, in which the response reduces the initial stimulus. By decreasing hormone signaling, negative-feedback loops prevent excessive pathway activity.
  - **Positive-feedback** loops reinforce a stimulus, leading to an even greater response. (More gets you more.)

- Hormones in the body can affect one tissue, a few tissues, or most of the tissues in the body (as with the sex hormones). Although all cells of the body may be exposed to the hormone, only those cells that express receptors to the hormone will respond. Therefore, one hormone can affect many different tissues in the body, with different responses in each cell type.

Endocrine glands respond to diverse stimuli in regulating homeostasis, development, and behavior (Biology, *11e: 45.3;* Focus, *2e: 32.2)*

- Let's take a look at the regulation of two specific hormones, one by positive feedback and one by negative feedback. Recall that you should be able to describe one example of each.
- The maintenance of blood calcium level shown in Figure 9.5 is an example of how homeostasis is maintained by *negative feedback*. Remember, in negative feedback, *more gets you less*.
- The regulation of oxytocin is an example of *positive feedback*. Oxytocin stimulates uterine contractions during childbirth and also stimulates production of prostaglandins by the placenta. Prostaglandins stimulate release of more oxytocin and more prostaglandins, stimulating more uterine contractions. Remember, in positive feedback, *more gets you more*.

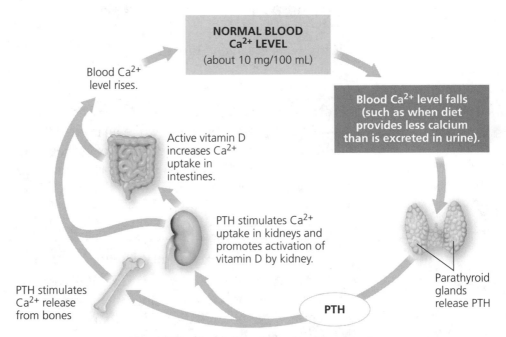

Figure 9.5   Regulation of blood calcium levels

Within the figure:

NORMAL BLOOD Ca²⁺ LEVEL (about 10 mg/100 mL)

Blood Ca²⁺ level rises.

Active vitamin D increases Ca²⁺ uptake in intestines.

PTH stimulates Ca²⁺ uptake in kidneys and promotes activation of vitamin D by kidney.

PTH stimulates Ca²⁺ release from bones

PTH

Blood Ca²⁺ level falls (such as when diet provides less calcium than is excreted in urine).

Parathyroid glands release PTH

ORGANIZE YOUR THOUGHTS

Now that you have reviewed the negative-feedback regulation of blood calcium, prepare your own figure to show the regulation of blood glucose by insulin and glucagon. (L.O. 3.35: The student is able to create representation(s) that depict how cell-to-cell communication occurs by direct contact or from a distance through chemical signaling.)

PRACTICE THE PRACTICE: Data Interpretation

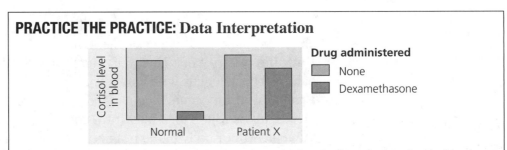

Glucocorticoids are secreted by the adrenal glands, but their release is stimulated by adrenocorticotropic hormone (ACTH), which the anterior pituitary produces. Chronically high levels of glucocorticoids can result in obesity, muscle weakness, and depression, a combination of symptoms called Cushing's syndrome. Excessive activity of either the pituitary or the adrenal gland can be the cause. To determine which gland has abnormal activity in a particular patient, doctors use the drug dexamethasone, a synthetic glucocorticoid that blocks ACTH release.

Based on the graph, identify which gland is affected in patient X and give the evidence to support your choice.

You can find the answer at the end of this topic, on page 267.

Animal Reproduction

(Biology, *11e: Chapter 46;* Focus, *2e: Chapter 36*)

WHAT'S IMPORTANT TO KNOW?

You are not expected to know the anatomy of the human reproductive system nor specific hormonal controls of reproduction. See the following list for material that is included in the framework explicitly and material being used as illustrative examples.

YOU MUST KNOW

- Advantages of asexual versus sexual reproduction.
- Various reproductive strategies in response to energy availability.
- Timing and coordination of reproduction may be triggered by environmental cues as well as pheromones.

Both asexual and sexual reproduction occur in the animal kingdom
(Biology, *11e: 46.1;* Focus, *2e: 36.1*)

- **Sexual reproduction** is the creation of offspring by the fusion of haploid gametes to form a zygote. The female gamete is the *ovum*, and the male gamete is the *sperm*.

- **Asexual reproduction** is reproduction in which all genes come from one parent; there is no fusion of egg and sperm. There are several modes of asexual reproduction.

  - **Fission** is the separation of a parent into two or more individuals of about the same size, as in sea anemones.
  - **Budding** occurs when new individuals arise from outgrowths of the parent. This happens with corals and hydras.
  - **Fragmentation** occurs when an individual breaks into several pieces, all of which then may form complete adults. *Regeneration*, the regrowth of body parts, is a necessary part of fragmentation. This mode of reproduction happens with starfish, sponges, and cnidarians
  - **Parthenogenesis** is the process in which a female produces eggs that develop *without* being fertilized. Depending on the species performing parthenogenesis, the offspring can be either haploid or diploid. For example, male bees are produced by parthenogenesis and are always haploid, whereas parthenogenic lizard species are diploid.

- Asexual reproduction has the advantage of production of more offspring identical to the parent. So why sex? Sex may result in beneficial gene combinations that arise through recombination that speed up adaptation in a changing environment. The shuffling of genes during sexual reproduction might allow a population to rid itself of sets of harmful genes more readily.

- There are variations in patterns of sexual reproduction. One is *hermaphrodism*, in which each individual has both male and female reproductive systems. In this case, any two individuals can mate. Another take on this pattern involves sex reversal, in which reproductive success is enhanced by changing sexes.
- Sexual cycles are often related to changing seasons; if seasonal temperature is an important cue, climate change may decrease reproductive success.
- The timing of reproductive behaviors is triggered by various cues, such as day length or resource availability. This will allow gametes to be produced by both males and females at the same time, increasing the probability of fertilization. Offspring will emerge when environmental conditions and food resources are most favorable.
- Global climate change has resulted in many examples of energy resources emerging earlier in the season, such as sprouting green plants and hatching insects. Species that depend on these resources for successful reproduction may not be ready for this early emergence, miss the resource, and suffer negative reproductive consequences resulting from a lack of energy.

Fertilization depends on mechanisms that bring together sperm and eggs of the same species (Biology, *11e: 46.2;* Focus, *2e: 36.1*)

- **Fertilization** is the union of sperm and egg.
- **External fertilization** occurs when eggs are shed by the female and fertilized by the male outside the female's body, usually in water. The release of gametes must be synchronous and often involves environmental cues or courtship behaviors. Species with external fertilization in general produce very large numbers of gametes.
- **Internal fertilization** occurs when sperm are deposited in the female reproductive tract and fertilization occurs within the tract. It is an adaptation that allows sperm to reach an egg even when the environment is dry. Fewer gametes and fewer zygotes are often produced.
- When fertilized eggs are protected by shells or within the female's body, fewer zygotes are produced.
- *Pheromones* are chemicals produced by members of one species that can influence the physiology and behavior of other members of the species. They are often important as sexual attractants and can trigger reproductive receptiveness.

Reproductive organs produce and transport gametes (Biology, *11e: 46.3;* Focus, *2e: 36.2*)

- **Spermatogenesis** is the production of mature sperm cells by meiosis in the testes.
- **Oogenesis** is the development of mature ova by meiosis in the ovaries. In humans, it begins during embryonic development. These egg cells are quiescent until puberty. From puberty onward, hormones periodically stimulate a follicle to grow and its egg cell to complete meiosis.
- Spermatogenesis differs from oogenesis in several ways:
  - Spermatogenesis produces four sperm cells in contrast to oogenesis, which produces a single egg.
  - Spermatogenesis begins at puberty and continues throughout a mature male's entire life; oogenesis ends with menopause.

■ Spermatogenesis is continuous after puberty, whereas oogenesis has long interruptions. Immature eggs form in the female embryo but do not complete their development until years, and often decades, later.

The interplay of tropic and sex hormones regulates mammalian reproduction (Biology, *11e: 46.4*; Focus, *2e: 36.3*)

> **TIP FROM THE READERS**
> The hormonal control of reproduction is rich in examples of feedback and illustrates how the circulation of hormones in the blood affects target tissues, making this a good process to understand.

■ In both male and female humans, the coordinated actions of hormones from the hypothalamus, anterior pituitary, and gonads govern reproduction.

■ Both males and females produce FSH and LH (follicle stimulating hormone and luteinizing hormone). FSH and LH stimulate cells in the ovaries and testes to produce the gametes as well as sex hormones, and high levels of these sex hormones will inhibit release of stimulating hormones from the hypothalamus and anterior pituitary—another example of negative-feedback control.

In placental mammals, an embryo develops fully within the mother's uterus (Biology, *11e: 46.5*; Focus, *2e: 36.4*)

■ **Human chorionic gonadotropin (HCG)** is a hormone secreted by the developing embryo that acts to maintain the uterine lining in early pregnancy. Its high level in the urine is used as the basis of a common early pregnancy test.

PRACTICE THE PRACTICE: Making Inferences from Data

Although you are not required to know the names and actions of the hormones involved in human reproduction, you could be given a diagram that shows their interactions and asked to interpret the figures. For the following exercise, we have selected two important figures for you to analyze.

1. In young women, the hormone estrogen is essential for normal sexual development. At puberty, estrogen triggers the development of female features, such as breasts and wider hips.

   Estrogen is a lipid-soluble steroid hormone. The following diagram shows the estrogen signaling process that normally functions in the body. Next to the diagram is a list of some possible causes for this young woman's delayed puberty.

   Based on Figure A, propose at least three reasons puberty may be delayed.

2. The patient's doctor decided to put the patient on estrogen therapy for five months. Supplemental estrogen would be expected to correct some

---

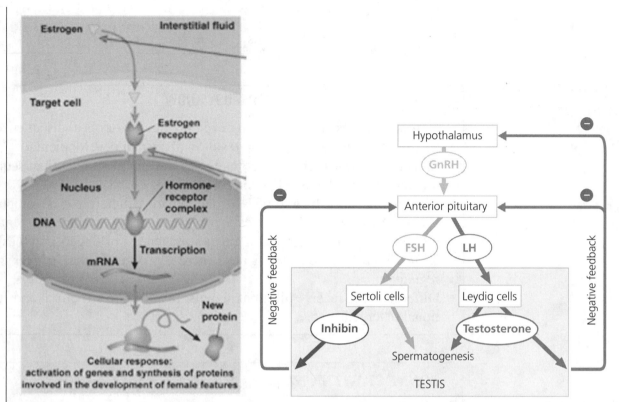

Figure A. Estrogen Signaling Pathway

Figure B. Hormonal control of the testes

of the potential problems in estrogen signaling, which you identified in question 1. This therapy would allow estrogen signaling to go forward.

Unfortunately, after five months, the patient still showed no signs of puberty. Based on this result, what could you eliminate as a potential cause of delayed puberty?

3. Recall that hormones bind to receptors in diverse tissues. Give three specific examples of tissues that can be expected to have estrogen receptors.

4. Although Figure A shows the estrogen signaling pathway, the pathway for testosterone signaling is identical. Use this information to explain why anabolic steroids result in increased muscle mass and strength.

5. In the production of testosterone, what are the signal, target cells, and response?

6. Explain how low testosterone levels can lead to reduced fertility.

7. Paradoxically, men who use anabolic steroids to enhance athletic performance have very high levels of testosterone but reduced fertility. Explain how this is possible.

You can find answers at the end of this topic, on page 267.

Animal Development

(Biology, *11e: Chapter 47*; Focus, *2e: Chapter 36*)

<table>
<tr><td>

YOU MUST KNOW

- Homeotic genes are involved in developmental patterns and sequences.
- Mutations in critical genes can result in abnormal development.
- Induction of transcription factors during development results in sequential gene expression and the correct timing of events.
- Genetic regulation by microRNAs plays an important role in development
- Programmed cell death (apoptosis) plays a role in normal development and differentiation (for example, in the morphogenesis of fingers and toes).
- Differentiation in development is a result of cues that trigger gene regulation.
- Different cells receive different signals, resulting in structural and functional divergence.

</td></tr>
</table>

CONNECT WITH THE CURRICULUM FRAMEWORK

Development involves complex interactions and communication between cells and is addressed in several parts of the Curriculum Framework. Keep the importance of timing and signaling in mind as you study development.

- ▮ Timing and coordination of specific events are necessary for the normal development of an organism, and these events are regulated by a variety of mechanisms. (EK 2.E.1) There are four LOs associated with this!
- ▮ Interactions between external stimuli and regulated gene expression result in specialization of cells, tissues, and organs. (EK 4.A.3)

Fertilization and cleavage initiate embryonic development
(Biology, *11e: 47.1*; Focus, *2e: 36.4*)

▮ Molecules and events at the egg surface play a crucial role in each step of fertilization.

- ▮ First, sperm dissolve or penetrate any protective layer surrounding the egg to reach the plasma membrane.
- ▮ Next, molecules on the sperm surface bind to receptors on the egg, helping ensure that a sperm of the same species fertilizes the egg.
- ▮ Finally, changes at the surface of the egg prevent polyspermy, the entry of multiple sperm nuclei into the egg. These changes include depolarization, much like what occurs in neuron transmission and removal of the sperm-binding receptors from the egg membrane.

▮ Across a range of animal species, embryonic development involves common stages that occur in a set order.

Morphogenesis in animals involves specific changes in cell shape, position, and survival (Biology, *11e: 47.2; Focus, 2e: 36.4*)

▌ **Morphogenesis** is the cellular and tissue-based process by which the embryo takes on form.

▌ Certain cells in the embryo are programmed to change shape or location. Others are programmed to die. A type of *programmed cell death* called **apoptosis** is a common feature of animal development. Familiar examples include the cells in the tail of a tadpole, which undergo apoptosis during frog metamorphosis, or the elimination of webbing between the digits in many birds and mammals.

Cytoplasmic determinants and inductive signals contribute to cell fate specification (Biology, *11e: 47.3*)

▌ Every diploid cell formed during an animal's development has the same genome. How then do cells acquire different fates? The patterns of development result from a combination of different **cytoplasmic determinants** and **inductive cell signals**. *Cytoplasmic determinants* are chemical signals such as mRNAs and transcription factors that may be parceled out unevenly in early cleavages. *Induction* is an interaction among cells that influences their fate, usually by causing changes in gene expression.

▌ Development is a sequence of events marked by cycles of signaling and differentiation. Cells in a developing embryo receive and respond to different signaling molecules that vary with their location within the embryo, and their developmental potential becomes more limited as development proceeds.

▌ Genetic transplantation experiments support the link between gene expression and normal development. For example, in a classic transplantation experiment, Spemann and Mangold determined that the dorsal lip of the blastopore is an "organizer" that induces a series of events that result in formation of the notochord and neural tube.

▌ **Totipotent cells** are capable of developing into all the different cell types of a given species. The cells of mammalian embryos may remain totipotent until the 16-cell stage but have a limited developmental potential from that point onward. Cells at this early stage that are totipotent are referred to as **stem cells**.

Neurons, Synapses, and Signaling

(Biology, *11e: Chapter 48; Focus, 2e: Chapter 37*)

YOU MUST KNOW

- The anatomy of a neuron.
- The role of active transport in establishing the membrane potential of a neuron.
- The mechanisms of impulse transmission in a neuron.
- How depolarization of the presynaptic cell leads to the release of neurotransmitters.
- The events at the synapse that allow a presynaptic neuron to communicate with the postsynaptic cell.

Neuron organization and structure reflect function in information transfer (Biology, *11e: 48.1; Focus, 2e: 37.1*)

▌ The **neuron** is the functional unit of the nervous system (Figure 9.6). It is composed of a **cell body**, which contains the nucleus and organelles; **dendrites**, which are cell extensions that receive incoming messages from other cells; and **axons**, which transmit messages to other cells.

▌ Many axons are covered by an insulating fatty **myelin sheath** produced by Schwann cells. This speeds the rate of impulse transmission.

▌ The **synapse** is a gap between one neuron and another neuron or muscle cell or gland.

▌ **Neurotransmitters** are chemical messengers released from vesicles in the **synaptic terminals** into the synapse. They will diffuse across the synapse and bind

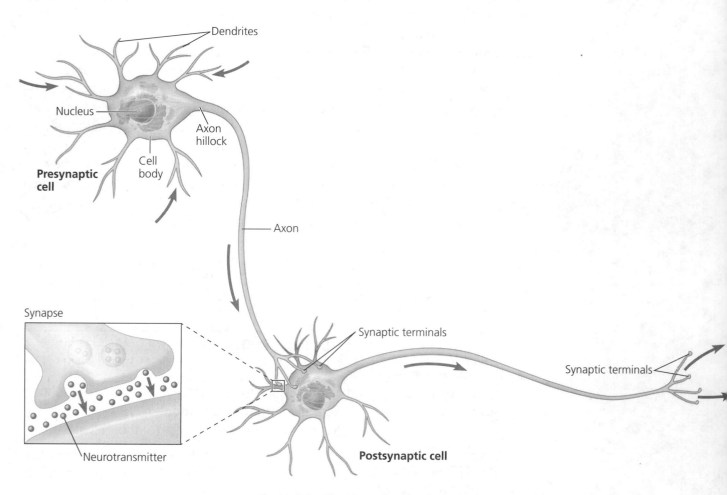

Figure 9.6   Structure of a vertebrate neuron

to receptors on the neuron, muscle fiber, or gland across the synapse, effecting a change in the second cell. *Examples:* acetylcholine, dopamine, and serotonin.

■ At the synapse, the transmitting neuron is the *presynaptic cell*; the neuron, muscle, or gland that receives the signal is the *postsynaptic cell.*

■ **Sensory receptors** collect information about the world outside the body as well as processes inside the body. *Examples* include the rods and cones of the eye, pressure receptors in the skin, chemoreceptors, and thermoreceptors.

■ There are specialized populations of neurons that handle each stage of information processing.

- **Sensory neurons** transmit information from the eyes and other sensors that detect stimuli to the brain or spinal cord for processing.
- **Interneurons** form local circuits that connect sensory and motor neurons or make local connections in the brain and spinal cord. They are responsible for the integration of sensory input.
- **Motor neurons** transmit signals to *effectors*, such as muscle cells and glands.

■ The **central nervous system (CNS)** consists of the brain and spinal cord, and the **peripheral nervous system (PNS)**, consists of the nerves that communicate motor and sensory signals throughout the rest of the body.

■ **Nerves** are bundles of neurons. A nerve can contain all motor neurons or all sensory neurons, or it can be mixed.

Ion pumps and ion channels establish the resting potential of a neuron (Biology, *11e: 48.2*; Focus, *2e: 37.2*)

■ **Membrane potential** describes the difference in electrical charge across a cell membrane.

■ The membrane potential of a nerve cell at rest is called its **resting potential**. It exists because of differences in the ionic composition of the extracellular and intracellular fluids across the plasma membrane.

■ The concentration of Na^+ is higher outside the cell, whereas the concentration of K^+ is higher inside the cell. This gradient is maintained by sodium-potassium pumps. (Refer to panel 1, Figure 9.7.)

■ Changes in the membrane potential of a neuron are what give rise to transmission of nerve impulses (action potentials). A stimulus changes the permeability of the membrane to Na^+, and Na^+ channels open. The membrane depolarizes as Na^+ enter the cell. This may result in an action potential.

Action potentials are the signals conducted by axons (Biology, *11e: 48.3*; Focus, *2e: 37.3*)

■ An **action potential** (nerve impulse) is an *all-or-none response* to depolarization of the membrane of the nerve cell. Carefully study Figure 9.7 to follow what happens in an action potential.

■ To generate an action potential, a certain level of depolarization must be achieved, known as the **threshold**.

■ **Saltatory conduction**, which is the jumping of the nerve impulse between *nodes of Ranvier* (areas on the axon not covered by the myelin sheath), speeds up the conduction of the nerve impulse.

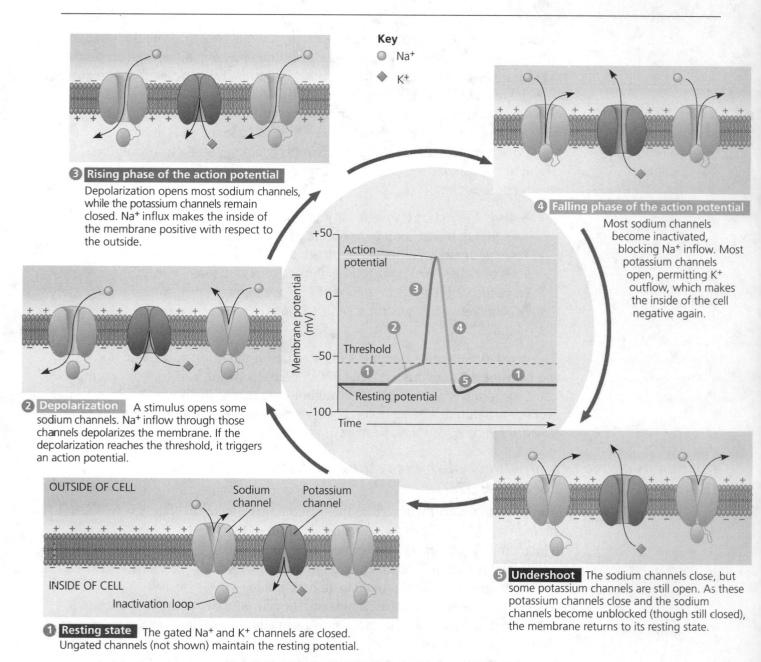

3 **Rising phase of the action potential**
Depolarization opens most sodium channels, while the potassium channels remain closed. Na⁺ influx makes the inside of the membrane positive with respect to the outside.

4 **Falling phase of the action potential**
Most sodium channels become inactivated, blocking Na⁺ inflow. Most potassium channels open, permitting K⁺ outflow, which makes the inside of the cell negative again.

2 **Depolarization** A stimulus opens some sodium channels. Na⁺ inflow through those channels depolarizes the membrane. If the depolarization reaches the threshold, it triggers an action potential.

Key
○ Na⁺
◆ K⁺

5 **Undershoot** The sodium channels close, but some potassium channels are still open. As these potassium channels close and the sodium channels become unblocked (though still closed), the membrane returns to its resting state.

1 **Resting state** The gated Na⁺ and K⁺ channels are closed. Ungated channels (not shown) maintain the resting potential.

Figure 9.7   Conduction of an action potential

Neurons communicate with other cells at synapses (Biology, *11e: 48.4;* Focus, *2e: 37.4*)

▌ When an action potential is generated in a neuron, it travels along the axon toward the synaptic terminals where the depolarization results in the release of neurotransmitters.

▌ Neurotransmitters are the chemical signals released by the first cell in the pathway, the *presynaptic cell*. They diffuse into the *synaptic cleft*, bind to receptors on the plasma membrane of the *postsynaptic cell*, and cause a response in the second cell.

▌ Study the steps involved in neurotransmitter release and impulse transmission in Figure 9.8. Cover the legend below the diagram, and explain each of the four steps illustrated.

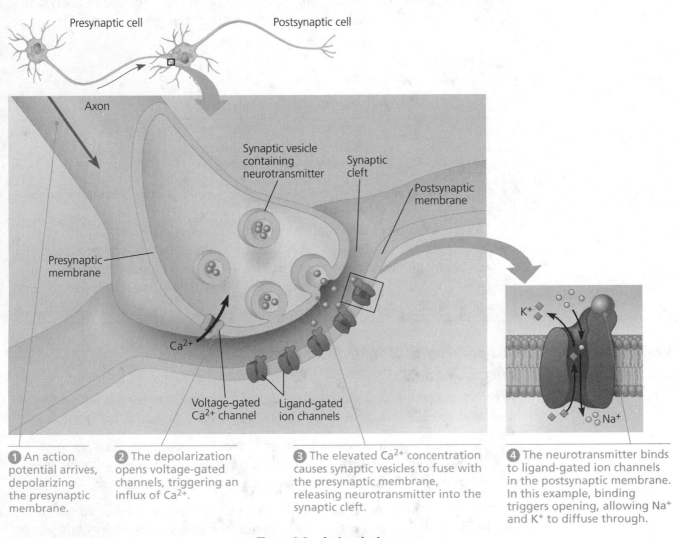

① An action potential arrives, depolarizing the presynaptic membrane.

② The depolarization opens voltage-gated channels, triggering an influx of Ca^{2+}.

③ The elevated Ca^{2+} concentration causes synaptic vesicles to fuse with the presynaptic membrane, releasing neurotransmitter into the synaptic cleft.

④ The neurotransmitter binds to ligand-gated ion channels in the postsynaptic membrane. In this example, binding triggers opening, allowing Na^+ and K^+ to diffuse through.

Figure 9.8   A chemical synapse

- There are two categories of neurotransmitters: *excitatory* and *inhibitory*. Excitatory neurotransmitters cause depolarization of the postsynaptic membrane, which brings the membrane potential closer to the threshold. This was illustrated in Figure 9.7. Inhibitory neurotransmitters cause hyperpolarization of the postsynaptic membrane, which moves the membrane potential further from the threshold.
- How are signals terminated? Neurotransmitters are removed from the synapse and signaling ends by one of two mechanisms: enzymes break down the neurotransmitter, or the neurotransmitter is recaptured into the presynaptic neuron and repackaged into synaptic vesicles.
- **Acetylcholine** is a very common neurotransmitter; it can be inhibitory or excitatory. It is released by motor neurons at the neuromuscular junction. Other common neurotransmitters are epinephrine, norepinephrine, dopamine, and serotonin.
- The acetylcholine (ACh) released by motor neurons leads to the depolarization of muscle fibers and their contraction. There are a couple of paralytic agents that affect this pathway and cause paralysis. The nerve gas sarin inhibits the enzyme acetylcholinesterase (AChe), which removes acetylcholine from the synapse. When this enzyme does not function, ACh builds up and results in paralysis. On the other hand, botulism toxin prevents the release of acetylcholine. Without ACh, muscle fibers cannot contract, resulting in paralysis.

Nervous Systems

(Biology, *11e: Chapter 49;* Focus, *2e: Chapter 38*)

YOU MUST KNOW

- The brain serves as a master neurological center for processing information and directing responses.
- Different regions of the brain have different functions.
- Structures and associated functions for animal brains are products of evolution, and increasing complexity follows evolutionary lines.
- How the vertebrate brain integrates information, which leads to an appropriate response.

Nervous systems consist of circuits of neurons and supporting cells
(Biology, *11e: 49.1;* Focus, *2e: 38.1*)

- A **reflex** is a simple automatic nerve circuit in response to a stimulus. Let's use a protective reflex, such as jerking your finger off a flame, as an example:

  - A *stimulus* is detected by a *receptor* in the skin, conveyed via a *sensory neuron* to an *interneuron* in the spinal cord, which synapses with a *motor neuron*, which will cause the *effector*, a muscle cell, to contract.

- Note that at its simplest level, conscious thought is not required in a reflex.
- Study Figure 9.9 as you review the organization of the nervous system.
- The **central nervous system (CNS)** is the brain and spinal cord.

Figure 9.9 Branches of the nervous system

▮ The **peripheral nervous system (PNS)** consists of paired cranial and spinal nerves and associated ganglia. It is divided into the following:

  ■ The *motor (somatic) nervous system*, which carries signals to skeletal muscles: It is a voluntary system.
  ■ The *autonomic nervous system*, which regulates the primarily automatic, visceral functions of smooth and cardiac muscles: This is an involuntary system. Its divisions are as follows:
  ■ The **sympathetic division**, which, when activated, causes the heart to beat faster and adrenaline to be secreted (with all its effects)
  ■ The **parasympathetic division**, which has the opposite effect when activated, slowing heartbeat and digestion

The vertebrate brain is regionally specialized (Biology, *11e: 49.2;* Focus, *2e: 38.2*)

> **STUDY TIP** Different regions of the brain have different functions. You are not expected to know each region and its function, but you should have a firm grasp of several as illustrative examples.

▮ The **brainstem** is made up of the medulla oblongata, pons, and midbrain. The brainstem controls homeostatic functions, such as breathing, swallowing, and digestion, and conducts sensory and motor signals between the spinal cord and higher brain centers (Figure 9.10).

▮ The **cerebellum** coordinates movement and balance. For example, hand-eye coordination is under control of the cerebellum.

▮ The **thalamus** is the main center through which sensory and motor information passes to and from the cerebrum.

▮ The **hypothalamus** regulates homeostasis; basic survival behaviors such as feeding, fighting, fleeing, and reproducing; and thermostat, appestat, thirst center, and circadian rhythms. Its neurosecretory cells secrete releasing and inhibiting hormones that affect release of some hormones from the anterior pituitary.

▮ The **cerebrum** has two hemispheres, each with a covering of gray matter over white matter. Information processing is centered here, and this region is particularly extensive in mammals.

Figure 9.10 The vertebrate brain

- The *cerebral cortex* controls voluntary movement and cognitive functions.
- The human cerebral cortex has four lobes, each with specialized functions. These have been mapped to precise areas. For example, we know that visual stimuli are processed at the back of the cerebrum, in the occipital lobe, and that hearing is localized in the temporal lobe.
- The *corpus callosum* is a thick band of axons that enables communication between the right and left cortices.

> **CONNECT WITH THE CURRICULUM FRAMEWORK**
>
> There are eight different objectives (LO 3.43–3.50) specific to the nervous system, so work hard on this area!

Sensory and Motor Mechanisms

(Biology, *11e: Chapter 50;* Focus, *2e: Chapters 38, 39*)

> **WHAT'S IMPORTANT TO KNOW?**
> Sensory and motor mechanisms are not an explicit topic of the Curriculum Framework, but your teacher may choose to introduce you to this material. This chapter contains information that may be the basis of both multiple-choice and essay questions. A general understanding of this section will help you be more confident in dealing with potential questions. Here are what we consider to be the main points of this chapter:
>
> - Different sensory receptors respond to various types of input.
> - Neurons communicate with muscle fibers to stimulate contraction.
> - Interaction of cellular structures leads to muscle contraction.

Sensory receptors transduce stimulus energy and transmit signals to the central nervous system (Biology, *11e: 50.1;* Focus, *2e: 38.4*)

- A sensory receptor is a sense organ or cell that detects stimuli. Different types respond to different inputs. For example, *photoreceptors* in the eye respond to light, *chemoreceptors* function in taste and smell, and *thermoreceptors* in the skin detect heat or cold.
- Other types of receptors include mechanoreceptors, which respond to physical stimuli, such as touch or vibration, and pain receptors.

■ **Reception** occurs when a receptor detects a stimulus. **Perception** occurs in the brain as this information is processed. As an example, when you view an optical illusion in which a figure seems to change, what is actually changing is your perception of the object.

The physical interaction of protein filaments is required for muscle function (Biology, *11e: 50.5; Focus, 2e: 39.1*)

■ **Skeletal muscle** is attached to bones and is responsible for bone movement. The muscle consists of long fibers, each of which is a single muscle cell.

■ Each muscle fiber is a bundle of **myofibrils**, which are composed of two kinds of myofilaments: **thin filaments** and **thick filaments**.

■ The thin filaments are composed of *actin* and a regulatory protein.
■ The thick filaments are composed of *myosin*.

■ The **sarcomere** is the basic contractile unit of the muscle. Study the sarcomere in Figure 9.11 as you read about the general action of a sarcomere.

Figure 9.11   Sections of a sarcomere

■ Notice that during **muscle contraction**, the length of the sarcomere is reduced. The actin filaments are fixed and slide over the myosin in such a way that their degree of overlap increases. This is known as the **sliding-filament model** of muscle contraction.

■ Use Figure 9.12 as you review what happens during depolarization of a muscle fiber and what leads to the movement of actin and myosin.

■ A **motor neuron** will cause a muscle fiber to contract when its depolarization causes the neurotransmitter *acetylcholine* to be released into the synapse of the *neuromuscular junction*.

■ As acetylcholine binds to receptors on the muscle fiber, ion channels open on the muscle cell membrane. This triggers an *action potential* (wave of depolarization) in the muscle cell.

■ The action potential spreads along **T tubules (transverse tubules)** to the **sarcoplasmic reticulum**.
■ This depolarization causes the sarcoplasmic reticulum to release **calcium ions**, and now actin and myosin can interact as myosin heads attach to the actin filaments after being phosphorylated by ATP.
■ The muscle contracts, with actin filaments sliding over myosin.

The electrical, chemical, and molecular events regulating skeletal muscle contraction are shown in a cutaway view of a muscle cell and in the enlarged diagram below. Action potentials (horizontal arrows) triggered by the motor neuron sweep across the muscle fiber and into it along the transverse (T) tubules, initiating the movements of calcium that regulate muscle activity.

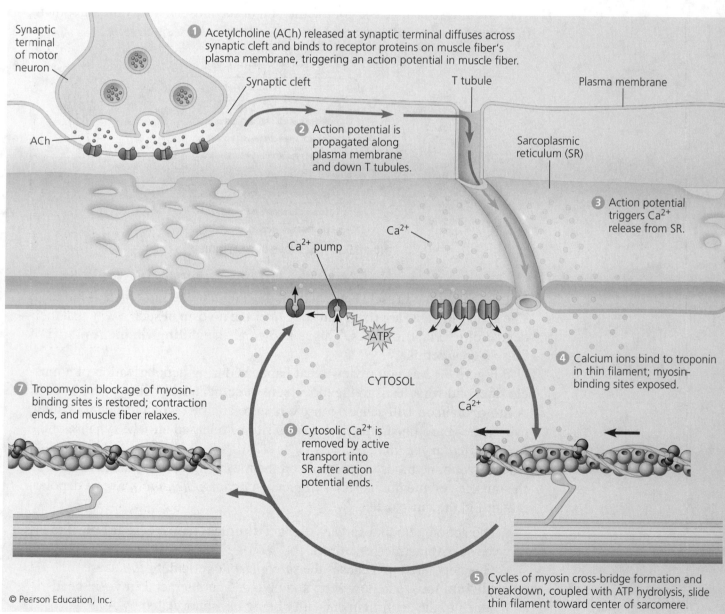

Figure 9.12   Myoneural junction and muscle contraction

Animal Behavior

(Biology, *11e: Chapter 51*; Focus, *2e: Chapter 39*)

YOU MUST KNOW

- How behaviors are the result of natural selection.
- Ways in which animals use signals to indicate dominance, find food, establish territory, and ensure reproductive success.
- How innate and learned behaviors increase survival and reproductive fitness.
- How organisms use communication to increase fitness.
- The role of altruism and inclusive fitness in kin selection.

Discrete Sensory Inputs Can Stimulate Both Simple and Complex Behaviors
(Biology, *11e: 51.1*; Focus, *2e: 39.3*)

▌ **Behavior** is what an animal does and how it does it. Behavior is a result of genetic and environmental factors, is essential for survival and reproduction, and is subject to natural selection over time.

▌ **Innate behaviors** are developmentally fixed. They are inherited unlearned behaviors. As you study the many types of behaviors, consider how each promotes survival of the individual.

▌ A **fixed action pattern (FAP)** is a sequence of unlearned acts that is largely unchangeable and usually carried to completion once it is initiated. Fixed action patterns are triggered by *sign stimuli*. A classic example of an FAP was noted by *Niko Tinbergen* in male stickleback fish, which attack red objects. The red object is the sign stimulus; the attack is the FAP.

▮ **Migration** is a complex behavior seen in a wide variety of animals. Animals may navigate by detecting the earth's magnetic field or using visual cues.

▮ **Circadian rhythms** are those that occur on a daily cycle. Other rhythms occur over longer periods and can be triggered by differing day lengths or lunar cycles.

▮ A **signal** is a stimulus that causes a change in the behavior of another individual and is the basis for animal communication. The following are examples of different types of signals:

▪ **Pheromones** are chemical signals that are emitted by members of a species that affect other members of the species. They often relate to reproductive behavior or serve as alarm signals.

▪ **Visual signals**, such as the warning flash of white of a mockingbird's wing or the mating display of a peacock fanning his tail feathers, transmit information to other members of the species.

▪ **Auditory signals**, such as the screech of a blue jay or song of a warbler, may communicate danger or species identity.

Learning establishes specific links between experience and behavior (Biology, *11e: 51.2*; Focus, *2e: 39.4*)

▮ **Learned behaviors** are behaviors that are modified based on specific experiences. (Recall that innate behaviors are inherited.)

▮ **Imprinting** is a combination of learned and innate components that are limited to a *sensitive period* in an organism's life and is generally irreversible. Konrad Lorenz demonstrated imprinting in greylag geese. When hatchlings spent their first few hours with him, they followed him as though he were their mother! Many bird species learn their song in a similar manner.

▮ **Associative learning** is the ability of many animals to associate one feature of their environment with another feature, such as associating certain stimuli or behaviors with reward or punishment.

▮ Twin studies in humans indicate that both environment and genetics contribute significantly to behaviors.

▮ Behavior can be directed by genes. For example, a single gene appears to control the courtship ritual in fruit flies.

Selection for individual survival and reproductive success can explain diverse behaviors (Biology, *11e: 51.3*; Focus, *2e: 39.5*)

▮ Keep in mind that behaviors are selected for because of the advantages they provide for survival and reproduction. Consider different methods for obtaining food, or foraging. What strategies provide the most calories for the effort to obtain the food?

▮ **The optimal foraging model** proposes that there is a compromise between the benefits of nutrition and the cost of obtaining food. This is why a lion does not feed on ants.

▌ **Mating systems** vary between species. The needs of the young are important constraints in the development of these systems. Systems include the following:

- ▪ **Promiscuous**, with no strong pair bonds
- ▪ **Monogamous**, with one male and one female
- ▪ **Polygamous**, with one individual mating with several others

▌ Continue to keep in mind the evolutionary advantage of a behavior. Which of these mating systems would be most advantageous to a species that produces helpless young that require food delivered to them?

Genetic analyses and the concept of inclusive fitness provide a basis for studying the evolution of behavior (Biology, *11e: 51.4;* Focus, *2e: 39.6*)

▌ **Altruism** occurs when animals behave in ways that reduce their individual fitness but increase the fitness of other individuals in the population. *Example:* A blue jay giving an alarm call attracts attention to its location.

▌ **Inclusive fitness** is the total effect an individual has on proliferating its genes by producing its own offspring and by providing aid that enables other close relatives to produce offspring. The natural selection that favors this kind of altruistic behavior by enhancing reproductive success of relatives is called **kin selection**.

▌ Just checking to see if you are really awake as you read all this! Here is one of our favorite quotes on the topic, from J. B. S. Haldane: "I would lay down my life for two brothers or eight cousins." Can you explain what this means?

Answer to PRACTICE THE PRACTICE: Data Interpretation, p. 249

The adrenal gland is affected. Its excessive activity (which typically results from a tumor) allows it to secrete cortisol even when ACTH release by the pituitary is suppressed. If the pituitary had been affected, suppression of ACTH release by dexamethasone would have decreased cortisol secretion by the healthy adrenal gland much more markedly.

Answer to PRACTICE THE PRACTICE: Making Inferences from Data, p. 252

1. The level of estrogen may be too low; the estrogen molecule may be structurally defective and not able to bind the receptor; the receptors may be defective and not able to bind the estrogen; there may be too few estrogen receptors; the estrogen receptors cannot enter the nucleus.
2. If the patient's estrogen levels had been too low, then giving her supplemental estrogen should have corrected her condition. Similarly, if her estrogen molecule had been defective, supplemental estrogen should have helped. This suggests that the issue is not with estrogen but with the patient's estrogen receptor.
3. This question can have numerous responses as long as the tissue is one that shows changes during puberty. Examples include the development of breasts, changes in the skeleton, development of axillary and pubic hair, maturation of the reproductive organs, increase in activity of sebaceous glands, and others.

4. The muscle cells have receptors for testosterone, which will act as a transcription factor to increase muscle mass.
5. The signal is LH, the target is Leydig cells in the testes, and the response is production of testosterone.
6. Because testosterone is required for spermatogenesis, low levels of it would result in decreased sperm production.
7. Testosterone inhibits the production of GnRH, LH, and FSH by negative feedback. Each of these is in the pathway that leads to spermatogenesis, so inhibiting any of these hormones will reduce fertility.

Answer to PRACTICE THE PRACTICE: Reading Information from a Diagram, p 259

1. The stimulus causes sodium channels to open and sodium ions to flow into the cell. The inside of the membrane becomes more positive (depolarized).
2. The membrane potential has gone from a resting state of about −75mV to approximately 40mv. The interior of the membrane is now positive with respect to the outside or depolarized. This is a result of the influx of sodium ions.
3. The resting potential is approximately −75mv. The threshold is approximately −45mv. (Be sure your response includes the correct sign and gives units!)
4. When the threshold is reached, an action potential or wave of depolarization will sweep down the axon toward the synapse.
5. Resting potential is restored as sodium ion channels close, so no more sodium ions enter the cell. Also, potassium ion channels open and potassium ions flow out. The inside of the cell becomes repolarized as the inside becomes more negative with respect to the outside.

Level 1: Knowledge/Comprehension Questions

The Level 1, Knowledge/Comprehension, questions review essential content knowledge but don't represent the type of question you will see on the AP exam. The Level 2, Application/Synthesis, questions are similar to those you will see on the exam.

1. During transmission across a typical chemical synapse,
   (A) the binding of neurotransmitters to receptors initiates exocytosis.
   (B) action potentials trigger chemical changes that make the synaptic vesicles fuse with each other.
   (C) vesicles containing neurotransmitters diffuse to the receiving cell's plasma membrane.
   (D) neurotransmitter molecules bind to receptors in the receiving cell's plasma membrane.

2. Once the threshold potential is reached after a neuron is stimulated, which of the following occurs?
   (A) The interior of the cell becomes negative with respect to the outside.
   (B) K^+ channels open.
   (C) Na^+ channels close.
   (D) An action potential is generated.

3. Barrier defenses are an important nonspecific arm of the immune system. All of the following are barrier defenses EXCEPT
   (A) skin.
   (B) phagocytes.
   (C) lysozyme in saliva.
   (D) mucous secretions.

4. An immune response to a specific antigen generates the production of which type of cell that launches an attack the next time that same antigen infects the body?
   (A) effector cells
   (B) memory cells
   (C) T cells
   (D) antibodies

5. Which of the following is released into the synaptic cleft by the presynaptic neuron and acts as a signaling molecule?
   (A) sodium ions
   (B) calcium ions
   (C) neurotransmitter
   (D) receptor proteins

6. What type of cell acts as an intermediary between humoral and cell-mediated immunity?
   (A) plasma cell
   (B) cytotoxic T cell
   (C) B cell
   (D) helper T cell

7. Embryonic development is a series of carefully coordinated events. Which of the following represents a correct sequence of development?
   1. A hollow blastula is changed into an embryo that has three tissue layers.
   2. Cytoplasmic determinants signal the development of right and left sides of the embryo.
   3. A neural tube is created by invagination of the ectoderm.
   4. Individual cells of the embryo divide but do not grow.

   (A) 2, 1, 4, 3
   (B) 4, 1, 2, 3
   (C) 4, 2, 1, 3
   (D) 1, 2, 4, 3

8. Which of these correctly describes the autonomic nervous system?
   (A) It integrates sensory inputs to the brain.
   (B) It carries signals to and from skeletal muscles.
   (C) It regulates the internal environment of the body.
   (D) It is part of the central nervous system.

9. Which part of this figure shows an active plasma B cell?

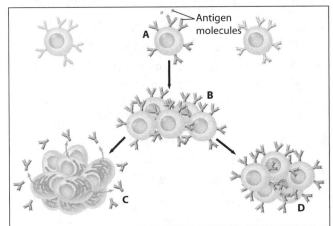

   (A) part A
   (B) part B
   (C) part C
   (D) part D

10. Which of the following represents a failure of a homeostatic mechanism?
    (A) activation of the thirst center after profuse sweating
    (B) production of insulin after eating a jelly donut
    (C) hypothermia after falling into a glacier-fed lake
    (D) skin flushing and sweating during exercise

Level 2: Application/Analysis/Synthesis Questions

After reading the paragraph, answer the questions that follow.

Under normal conditions, blood sugar levels are controlled within a narrow range by negative feedback. Two hormones are involved in maintaining blood sugar levels at the set point (about 90 mg of glucose/100 mL of blood). When blood sugar levels rise above the set point, the hormone insulin signals the liver to absorb the excess sugar. When blood sugar levels drop below the set point, the hormone glucagon signals the liver to release its stored glucose to the bloodstream. In type 1 diabetes, the body doesn't produce enough insulin, and insulin supplements are required.

1. Based on your understanding of homeostasis, for negative-feedback control of blood glucose levels to function properly
   (A) the control center for glucose must be somewhere in the digestive system.
   (B) there must be sensors that monitor blood glucose levels.
   (C) there must be several other hormones involved (in addition to insulin and glucagon).
   (D) the body must prevent glucose levels from changing even slightly.

2. If you hadn't eaten for several hours, how would your glucose levels be returned to the set point?
   (A) Insulin would be released to move glucose into cells and the liver.
   (B) Glucagon would be released to cause the liver to release glucose.
   (C) Pathways in cellular respiration would switch to using lipids and proteins for ATP production.
   (D) Insulin and glucagon would each be released to quickly return glucose levels to the set point.

3. An animal's inputs of energy and materials would exceed its outputs
   (A) if the animal is an endotherm, which must always take in more energy because of its high metabolic rate.
   (B) if it is actively foraging for food.
   (C) if it is growing and increasing its mass.
   (D) never; to maintain homeostasis, these energy and material budgets always balance.

4. Which statement best describes the difference in responses of effector B cells (plasma cells) and cytotoxic T cells?
   (A) B cells confer active immunity; cytotoxic T cells confer passive immunity.
   (B) B cells kill pathogens directly; cytotoxic T cells kill host cells.
   (C) B cells secrete antibodies against a pathogen; cytotoxic T cells kill pathogen-infected host cells.
   (D) B cells accomplish the cell-mediated response; cytotoxic T cells accomplish the humoral response.

5. Select the one description that is not a feature of the immune system.
   (A) An antibody has more than one antigen-binding site.
   (B) An antigen can cause different antibodies to be generated.
   (C) A pathogen may present more than one antigen.
   (D) A lymphocyte has receptors for multiple antigens.

After reading the paragraph, answer questions 6 and 7.

To protect U.S. soldiers serving overseas, each soldier receives vaccinations against several diseases, including smallpox, before deployment. Following intelligence about an imminent smallpox threat, the Army wants to ensure that soldiers stationed in war zones are fully protected from exposure to the disease, so all the soldiers in the threat zone are given a second vaccination against smallpox.

6. The first vaccination provides immunity because
   (A) a localized inflammatory response is initiated.
   (B) the vaccine contains manufactured antibodies against smallpox.
   (C) antigenic determinants in the vaccine activate B cells, which form plasma cells as well as memory cells.
   (D) the vaccine contains antibiotics and other drugs that kill the smallpox virus.

7. The second vaccination is beneficial because it
   (A) contains plasma cells that survive longer than 4 or 5 days.
   (B) stimulates production of a higher concentration of antibodies in the bloodstream.
   (C) requires two injections to stimulate antibody formation.
   (D) keeps previously produced plasma cells circulating in the bloodstream.

Figures A and B show two typical cell-signaling cascades. Use them to answer questions 8–10.

8. Which figure shows a water-soluble signaling molecule, and what is the evidence for this?
   (A) Figure A, because the signaling molecule results in a response within the cytoplasm.
   (B) Figure A, because the signaling molecule does not pass through the phospholipid bilayer.
   (C) Figure B, because the signaling molecule enters the cell to bind the receptor.
   (D) Figure B, because the activated receptor is able to enter the nucleus of the cell.

9. In Figure A, which molecule represents the receptor protein, and how does it function?
   (A) Molecule A is the receptor protein because it binds to a plasma membrane surface protein.
   (B) Molecule B is the receptor protein, and molecule A is the ligand that binds it.
   (C) Molecule C is the receptor protein, and it is lipid soluble.
   (D) Molecule D is the receptor protein and once activated initiates a response.

A

B

10. Which of the following correctly represents the events in Figure B?
    (A) In step 1, a signaling molecule binds a G protein-coupled receptor.
    (B) In step 2, the G protein-coupled receptor is activated.
    (C) In step 3, the bound receptor passes through the plasma membrane.
    (D) In step 4, the bound receptor functions as a transcription factor.

11. The following figure indicates several different neuron structures. Which statement correctly describes the function of the structure?

    (A) Structure C is produced by Schwann cells and increases the rate of impulse transmission.
    (B) Structure A releases a neurotransmitter when an action potential is generated.
    (C) Structure B is depolarized when calcium ions are released in this area.
    (D) Structure D initiates the action potential when depolarized.

12. Altruism is putting the well-being of another ahead of one's own. How could altruism persist in terms of natural selection?
    (A) Survival of other members of the species will maintain Hardy-Weinberg equilibrium.
    (B) It can result in the survival of the recipients of the behavior.
    (C) This is just one aspect of an important evolutionary principle, survival of the fittest.
    (D) If the altruistic member's behavior is directed toward a close relative, his genes will persist in the population.

After reading the paragraph, answer questions 13 and 14.

One commonly used insecticide contains a permanent acetylcholinesterase inhibitor. Acetylcholine is a neurotransmitter that stimulates skeletal muscle contraction. Acetylcholinesterase removes acetylcholine from the synapse after the signal is received. When insects are exposed to this insecticide, they will twitch for a brief period and then die. Exposure to high pesticide concentrations has a similar effect on humans and can also be caused by exposure to the nerve gas sarin and other chemical agents.

13. Why does the insecticide cause uncontrollable twitching in insects?
    (A) Acetylcholine is released, but the insecticide prevents it from diffusing across the synapse.
    (B) Acetylcholine is released, but the insecticide prevents it from binding to the receptor sites of the postsynaptic neurons.
    (C) The insecticide blocks the active site of acetylcholinesterase, making the enzyme nonfunctional.
    (D) The insecticide prevents acetylcholinesterase from being removed from the synapse.

14. Because pesticides affect humans in a manner similar to that of roaches, it would be valid to conclude that
    (A) acetylcholinesterase affects the DNA of all animals.
    (B) the mechanism of stimulating skeletal muscle contraction must be similar in humans and roaches.
    (C) pesticides are harmful to roaches but not to humans.
    (D) the terminal end of the axon releases acetylcholine in roaches but not in humans.

15. Which of these statements describes a feature that is common to all action potentials (nerve impulses) generated along a neuron?
    (A) An action potential causes the membrane of the neuron to hyperpolarize and then depolarize.
    (B) An action potential can undergo temporal and spatial summation.
    (C) Action potentials are triggered by a depolarization that reaches the threshold.
    (D) All action potentials move at the same speed along all axons.

16. When the action potential reaches the synaptic terminals, which event will occur next?
    (A) Voltage-gated calcium channels in the membrane open.
    (B) Synaptic vesicles fuse with the membrane.
    (C) The postsynaptic cell produces an action potential.
    (D) Ligand-gated ion channels open, allowing neurotransmitters to enter the synaptic cleft.

17. Why are action potentials usually conducted in only one direction?
    (A) The nodes of Ranvier can conduct potentials in only one direction.
    (B) The brief refractory period prevents reopening of voltage-gated Na^+ channels.
    (C) The axon hillock has a higher membrane potential than the terminals of the axon.
    (D) Voltage-gated channels for both Na^+ and K^+ open in only one direction.

After reading the paragraph, answer questions 18 and 19.

Salmon hatch in freshwater streams, swim to the open ocean where they spend several years and migrate thousands of miles, and then return to their home streams to spawn (reproduce) and die. A researcher is investigating how the salmon locate their original spawning area. The researcher will study salmon from two distant regions, Ketchikan and Cold Bay. Data from experiments suggest that more than one type of homing mechanism may be involved in this behavior. When salmon arrive at a river mouth from the open sea, they appear to use olfactory cues to find their home streams, but how do they find their way back to the correct spot along the coastline from the open ocean?

18. Which of the following experimental approaches might the researcher propose to test the hypothesis that geomagnetic factors (the influence of Earth's magnetic field) play a key role in the ability of salmon to find the proper location along the coast?
    (A) Trap adult salmon in Ketchikan, Alaska; transport them to a different location on the Alaska Peninsula, Cold Bay; and see if they can return to their home stream.
    (B) Hatch salmon from Ketchikan, Alaska; subject them to the geomagnetic characteristics of Cold Bay, Alaska; and then release them and see where they eventually return.
    (C) Collect hatchling salmon from Ketchikan, Alaska; release them into the ocean; and then see where they eventually return.
    (D) Hatch salmon from Ketchikan, Alaska; raise them in water from Cold Bay, Alaska; and then release them and see where they eventually return.

19. What type of behavior would explain the ability of the salmon to return to their home streams?
    (A) imprinting, which occurs when a behavior is learned during a critical period in early life
    (B) innate behavior, which is developmentally fixed
    (C) social learning, which is passed from one individual to another
    (D) habituation, which occurs when the same stimulus is applied numerous times

20. Which of the following describes an example of negative feedback?
    (A) the movement of sodium across a membrane through a transport protein and the movement of potassium in the opposite direction through the same transport protein
    (B) the pressure of the baby's head against the uterine wall during childbirth that stimulates uterine contractions, causing greater pressure against the uterine wall, which produces still more contractions
    (C) a population of bacteria in a petri dish that grows until it has used all its nutrients and then declines
    (D) a heating system in which the heat is turned off when the temperature exceeds a certain point and is turned on when the temperature falls below a certain point

Use the following graph to answer questions 21 and 22.

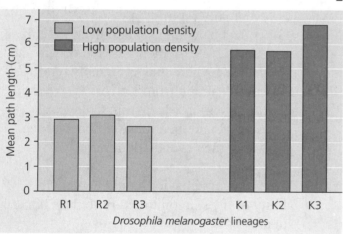

Drosophila melanogaster lineages

A study of *Drosophila melanogaster* examined one way foraging behavior might have evolved. Data from the study are summarized in the accompanying graph, which depicts the foraging distance of different populations. Variation in a gene called *forager* (*for*) dictates how far *D. melanogaster* larvae travel when foraging. On average, larvae carrying the *for^R* ("Rover") allele travel nearly twice as far while foraging as do larvae with the *for^s* ("sitter") allele. After many generations of living at low population density in the lab, *D. melanogaster* larvae (populations R1–R3)

followed foraging paths significantly shorter than those of *D. melanogaster* larvae that had lived at high density (populations K1–K3). Researchers hypothesized that natural selection was responsible for these results.

21. Which alternative hypothesis is ruled out by having three R and K lines, rather than one of each?
    (A) The difference between the R and K lines is the result of environmental differences in the food availability of their habitats.
    (B) The difference between the R and K lines arose through a random process such as genetic drift.
    (C) The difference between the R and K lines is the result of different *for* allele frequencies between the population groups.
    (D) The difference between the R and K lines arose through gene flow.

22. Both alleles of the *forager* gene are present in natural populations of *D. melanogaster*. Which of the following provides an explanation for interpreting evolutionary change in behavior in a colony of *D. melanogaster* under crowded conditions?
    (A) There will be an increase in *for^s* ("sitter") allele as short trips save energy while providing sufficient food.
    (B) There will be an increase in *for^R* ("Rover") allele as long trips allow the larvae to extend beyond areas of depleted food.
    (C) The alleles for foraging will remain in Hardy-Weinberg equilibrium at the roughly 2 *for^R* : 1 *for^s* ratio, as indicated in the graph.
    (D) An increase in *for^R* can be expected as the colony will be crowded, an environmental signal to *D. melanogaster* for the need to increase foraging range.

Use the graph of the two phases of the adaptive immune response to answer questions 23–25.

© Pearson Education, Inc.

23. What is the most reasonable explanation for the solid line peak (around day 40)?
    (A) The peak of the secondary immune response to antigen Y is a result of increased antibody production from memory B cells.
    (B) The peak of the secondary immune response to antigen X is a result of increased antibody production from memory B cells.
    (C) The peak of the primary immune response to antigen Y is the result of increased production of antibodies from cytotoxic T cells.

(D) The peak of the secondary immune response to antigen X is the result of interactions between helper T cells and cytotoxic T cells.

24. Which of the statements is supported by the graph?
    (A) The primary and secondary immune responses are equal.
    (B) The primary immune response occurs more quickly but is a weaker response.
    (C) The secondary immune response is stronger than the primary immune response.
    (D) The answer cannot be determined from the graph.

25. A third exposure to antigen X will produce an even stronger immune response than the second exposure did.
    (A) This statement is supported by the graph.
    (B) This statement is not supported by the graph.
    (C) This statement cannot be determined from the graph.
    (D) The graph supports the statement that the third exposure to antigen X will be equal to exposures one and two.

Grid-In Questions

These questions call for a numerical response.

1. At this moment your heart is pumping about 70 mLs of blood per heartbeat, and your heart is beating at a rate of 72 beats per minute. How many liters of blood will you pump in the next hour? (Answer to the nearest tenth.)

2. The partial pressure of a gas is the pressure exerted by a particular gas in a mixture of gases. For example, at sea level the pressure of the atmosphere, a mixture of gases, is 760 mm Hg. Oxygen makes up 21% of the mixture, so the partial pressure of oxygen is (760 × 0.21 = 159.6 mm Hg). A mountain climber is about to summit a small peak with an atmospheric pressure of 510 mm Hg. What is the difference to the nearest tenth in the partial pressure of oxygen at sea level compared with the mountain peak?

3.

© Pearson Education, Inc.

If an action potential lasts from the beginning of the rising phase to the point of maximal undershoot (on this graph, 2.3 msec), what is the maximum frequency at which a neuron could fire action potentials in one second? Note that time on the x-axis is given in milliseconds (msec). Assume that the neuron can fire only one action potential at a time and that the refractory period following the action potential is negligible.

Free-Response Question

1. *Natural selection favors behaviors that increase survival and successful reproduction. For each of the following types of behaviors, describe an example in nature, and justify how this behavior is adaptive.*

   (a) innate behavior
   (b) learned behavior
   (c) cooperative behavior
   (d) chemical signals

Ecology

An Introduction to Ecology and the Biosphere
(Biology, *11e: Chapter 52; Focus, 2e: Chapter 40*)

YOU MUST KNOW

- The role of abiotic factors in the formation of biomes.
- How biotic and abiotic factors affect the distribution of biomes.
- How changes in these factors may alter ecosystems.
- Global climate change is occurring and affects the distribution of organisms.

Earth's climate varies by latitude and season and is changing rapidly (Biology, *11e: 52.1; Focus, 2e: 40.1*)

▮ **Ecology** is the scientific study of the interactions between organisms and the environment.

- ▪ These interactions are organized in a hierarchy from the individual organism to the entire planet. (*See Figure 52.2*, Biology, *11e, or Figure 40.2*, Focus, *2e*.)

▮ **Climate** is the long-term prevailing weather conditions in a given area. Four key components of climate are temperature, precipitation, sunlight, and wind. Climate patterns can be described in terms of two scales: *macroclimate* and *microclimate*.

- ▪ **Macroclimate patterns** work at the global, regional, or local level.
- ▪ The changing angle of the sun over the year, bodies of water, and mountains exert seasonal, regional, and local effects on the **macroclimate**.
- ▪ **Microclimate** is determined by fine-scale variations such as sunlight and temperature differences under a log compared with the surrounding forest floor.
- ▪ **Climate change** is a directional change to the global climate that lasts three decades or more (as opposed to short-term changes in the weather).

  - ▪ Increasing carbon dioxide and other greenhouse gas concentrations are warming Earth, wind and precipitation patterns are shifting, and extreme weather events are occurring more frequently.

- Changes in climate can alter the population sizes or distribution of many species. Some species will not be able to shift their ranges quickly enough to survive.

The distribution of terrestrial biomes is controlled by climate and disturbance (Biology, *11e: 52.2*; Focus, *2e: 40.1*)

- **Biomes** are the major types of ecosystems that occupy very broad geographic regions.
- The importance of climate, especially precipitation and temperature, are reflected in the climograph for the major biomes of North America featured in Figure 10.1.

Figure 10.1   Climograph for some major biomes in North America

> **STUDY TIP** Why are some biomes rich in species abundance? Why is productivity higher in some ecosystems? You will not be expected to know the names of specific biomes, but you may be expected to predict and justify how alteration of a factor such as moisture, light, or soil nutrients would impact the system. Always look for the big picture! Ask *why? What if?* (Species abundance is related to primary productivity, which provides energy resources, and numerous niches. Productivity is higher in ecosystems that have abundant light energy, warmer temperatures, and longer growing seasons).

- **Desert** is marked by sparse rainfall, and desert plants and animals are adapted to conserve and store water. Temperature (either hot or cold) can be extreme.
- **Chaparral** is dominated by dense, spiny, evergreen shrubs and fire-adapted plants. It includes coastal areas with mild, rainy winters and long, hot, dry summers.

- **Temperate grassland** is marked by seasonal drought with occasional fires and by large grazing mammals. All these factors prevent the significant growth of trees. Grassland soil is rich in nutrients, making these areas good for agriculture.
- **Temperate broadleaf forest** is marked by dense stands of deciduous trees that require sufficient moisture. These forests are stratified: The top layer contains one or two strata of trees; beneath that are shrubs; and under that is an herbaceous stratum. **Canopy** refers to the upper layers of trees in a forest. In fall, most trees drop their leaves, many mammals enter hibernation, and many birds migrate to warmer regions.
- Northern **coniferous forest** (also called the *taiga*) is dominated by cone-bearing trees such as pine, spruce, and fir. Distribution is in a large band across northern North America and Eurasia to the edge of the arctic tundra. Winters are cold, and summers are cool and moderate. This is the largest terrestrial biome.
- **Tundra** is marked by permafrost (a permanently frozen layer of soil), very cold temperatures, high winds, and little rainfall. Tundra supports no trees or tall plants. It accounts for about 20% of Earth's terrestrial surface.
- **Tropical rain forest** has pronounced vertical stratification. The canopy is so dense that little light breaks through. These forests are marked by epiphytes, which are plants that grow on other plants instead of in soil. Rainfall varies by season but averages 200 to 400 cm annually. Biodiversity in this biome is greater than in all other terrestrial biomes.

> **TIP FROM THE READERS**
> What biome do you live in? Focus on your biome as an illustrative example. Know the typical species found there and reasons for their distribution.

Aquatic biomes are diverse and dynamic systems that cover most of Earth (Biology, *11e: 52.3*; Focus, *2e: 40.2*)

- **Aquatic biomes** make up the largest part of the biosphere because water covers roughly 75% of Earth's surface. These biomes are classified into **freshwater biomes** and **marine biomes**. These biomes are described in Figure 52.15, *Biology*, 11e, and Figure 40.9, *Focus*, 2e.
- Most aquatic biomes display vertical stratification. For example, the **photic zone** includes the upper layer of water, in which there is enough light for photosynthesis to occur; whereas the **aphotic zone** is characterized by very low light penetration.
- **Freshwater biomes** include lakes, wetlands, streams, and rivers.

  - **Estuaries** are areas where freshwater streams or rivers merge with the ocean. Salinity varies spatially and with the rise and fall of the tides.

- *Marine biomes* include intertidal, pelagic, benthic zones and **coral reefs**. Coral reefs are among the most productive ecosystems on Earth.

Interactions between organisms and the environment limit the distribution of species (Biology, *11e: 52.4;* Focus, *2e: 40.3*)

▎ Species distributions are a consequence of both ecological factors and evolutionary history. Dispersal of a species may be limited by evolutionary history combined with geographic factors (e.g., kangaroos being found only in Australia), but biotic and abiotic factors also limit distribution.

   ▪ **Biotic factors** include interactions with other species through predation and herbivory, parasites, pathogens, and competing organisms.
   ▪ The **abiotic components** of an environment are the nonliving, chemical, and physical components. Some important abiotic factors include temperature, water, oxygen, salinity, sunlight, and soil.

Population Ecology

(Biology, *11e: Chapter 53;* Focus, *2e: Chapter 40*)

<table>
<tr><td align="center">**YOU MUST KNOW**</td></tr>
</table>

- How density, dispersion, and demographics can describe a population.
- The differences between exponential and logistic models of population growth.
- How to apply mathematical models to predict changes in population growth rates or size.
- How density-dependent and density-independent factors can control population growth.
- Interactions between populations affect the distributions and abundance of populations. (EK 4.B.3)
- How a change in matter or energy will affect the population or community. (LO 4.16)
- The effect of age distributions and fecundity on human populations as presented in age-structure pyramids.

Biotic and abiotic factors affect population density, dispersion, and demographics (Biology, *11e: 53.1;* Focus, *2e: 40.4*)

▎ A **population** is a group of individuals of a single species living in the same general area. **Population ecology** explores how biotic and abiotic factors influence the density, distribution, size, and age structure of populations.

▎ Three fundamental characteristics of the organisms in a population are the following:

   ▪ **Density** is the number of individuals per unit area or volume. The density of a population increases by births or immigration and decreases by deaths or emigration.

- **Dispersion** is the pattern of spacing among individuals within the boundaries of the population.

    - The most common pattern of dispersion is *clumped*, with individuals in patches, usually around a required resource. *Example:* cottonwood trees along a stream in the arid Southwest.
    - A *uniform* or evenly spaced dispersion pattern is often the result of antagonistic interactions. Animals that defend territories often show a uniform pattern. Some plants secrete chemicals that inhibit growth of nearby individuals that could compete for resources. *Example:* red-winged blackbirds aggressively defending territories during mating season.
    - *Random* dispersion shows unpredictable spacing. It occurs in the absence of strong attractions or repulsions among individuals or where resources are relatively constant across an area.

- **Demography** is the study of vital statistics of a population, especially birth, death, and migration rates. A graphic way to show birth and death rates in a population is a survivorship curve. Three types of survivorship curves are shown in Figure 10.2.

    - **Type I** shows low death rates during early life and midlife; then the death rate increases sharply in older age groups. This pattern is typical for large organisms with long life spans.
    - **Type II** shows a constant death rate over the organism's life span. Often, these organisms are heavily preyed upon, so individuals die before reaching old age.
    - **Type III** shows very high early death rates—then a flat rate for the few surviving until reaching older age groups. Many bird species show a high death rate for the first year—then a slowing for the remainder of their life span.

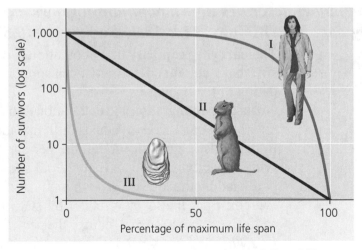

Figure 10.2   Survivorship curves: types I, II, and III

The exponential model describes population growth in an idealized, unlimited environment (Biology, *11e: 53.2; Focus, 2e: 40.5*)

▮ **Exponential population** growth refers to population growth under ideal conditions. Figure 10.3 shows a graph of population growth as predicted by the exponential model. Any species, regardless of its life history, is capable of exponential growth if resources are abundant.

▮ Exponential population growth is shown by the equation $dN/dt = r_{max}N$. In this equation dN is the size of the population at a particular instant in time; dt is the time interval involved in the calculation; r_{max} is the maximum per-capita rate of increase for the species under study; N is the population size.

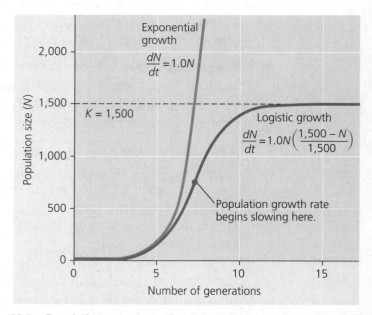

Figure 10.3   Population growth predicted by the exponential and logistic model

The logistic model describes how a population grows more slowly as it nears its carrying capacity (Biology, *11e: 53.3; Focus, 2e: 40.5*)

▮ The **carrying capacity** of a population is defined as the maximum population size that a certain environment can support at a particular time with no degradation of the habitat.

▮ Not taking immigration and emigration into consideration, a population's growth rate (per-capita increase) equals birth rate minus death rate: $dN/dt = B - D$.

▮ In the **logistic growth model**, the per-capita rate of increase declines as carrying capacity is reached. Figure 10.3 shows a graph of population growth as predicted by the logistic growth model.

▮ We construct the logistic model by starting with the exponential model and adding an expression that reduces the per-capita rate of increase as N approaches K: $dN/dt = r_{max}N (K - N)/K$. In this formula, the new term is $(K - N)/K$, where K is the carrying capacity and N remains the population estimate. Study the mathematical relationship between K and N in the formula.

PRACTICE THE PRACTICE: Apply a Formula to Calculate Population Growth Rate

Rate and Growth	
Rate $$\frac{dY}{dt}$$	dY = amount of change dt = change in time
Population Growth $$\frac{dN}{dt} = B - D$$	B = birth rate D = death rate
Exponential Growth $$\frac{dN}{dt} = r_{max}N$$	N = population size
Logistic Growth $$\frac{dN}{dt} = r_{max}N\left(\frac{K - N}{K}\right)$$	K = carrying capacity r_{max} = maximum per capita growth rate of population

This figure shows the ecology formulas that you should be able to use. These formulas are from the AP Biology Equations and Formulas page (p. 358). Try these problems for practice.

1. If r_{max} = 1.0 and carrying capacity (K) = 1,500, calculate the population growth rate (logistic growth), where population size (N) = 1,600. Explain what is happening to the population in this case.

2. Calculate the population growth rate, where the population size (N) = 1,200. Explain what is happening to the population in this case.

3. If r_{max} is doubled, predict how the population growth rate will change. Now calculate the population growth rate for problem 2 when r_{max} is doubled.

4. What would the value of the expression $(K - N)/K$ be if $K = N$? What growth would you predict for the population?

You can find answers at the end of this topic, on page 296.

Life history traits are products of natural selection
(Biology, *11e: 53.4;* Focus, *2e: 40.6*)

▌ Traits that affect an organism's schedule of reproduction and survival make up its **life history**. Life histories include three components, which answer the following questions about reproductive strategies:

- ▪ How early in the life cycle does reproduction begin?
- ▪ How often does the organism reproduce? Some organisms save their resources for one big reproductive event (*big-bang reproduction*), whereas others produce offspring in *repeated reproduction*.
- ▪ How many offspring are there per reproductive event?

- Life history traits are evolutionary outcomes—*not* conscious decisions by organisms. There are trade-offs between high rates of reproduction and percentages of surviving offspring.
- Selection of life history traits that are sensitive to population density and carrying capacity is referred to as **K-selection**. *K*-selection operates in populations living close to the density imposed by the carrying capacity. By contrast, selection for traits that maximize reproductive success in uncrowded environments is called **r-selection**.

  - The logistic growth model is sometimes associated with *K*-selection, whereas the exponential growth model is often associated with *r*-selection. Both *K*-selection and *r*-selection are two ends of a continuum of life history strategies.
  - The white rhinoceros demonstrates *K*-selection, and mice demonstrate *r*-selection strategies. Which strategy is most likely to result in an endangered species when faced with an event that eliminates 90% of the population?

Density-dependent factors regulate population growth
(Biology, *11e: 53.5;* Focus, *2e: 40.6*)

- When a death rate does not change with an increase in population density, it is said to be **density independent**. Natural disasters are examples of density-independent factors.
- A death rate that rises as population density rises and a birth rate that falls as population density rises are **density-dependent factors**. Examples of the major factors that reduce birth rates or increase death rates include the following:

  - *Competition for resources:* As population density increases, competition for resources intensifies. This might include competition for food, space, or essential nutrients.
  - *Territoriality:* Available space for territories or nesting may be limited, thus controlling the population.
  - *Disease:* Increasing densities allow for easier transmission of diseases.
  - *Predation:* As prey populations increase, predators may find the prey more easily.

  Density-dependent factors regulate population size by negative feedback.

- All populations exhibit some size fluctuations. Many populations undergo regular boom-and-bust population cycles that are influenced by complex interactions between biotic and abiotic factors.

The human population is no longer growing exponentially but is still increasing rapidly (Biology, *11e: 53.6;* Focus, *2.e: 43.5*)

▍ The exponential growth model in Figure 10.3 approximates the population explosion of humans over the last four centuries. Although the human population is still growing, the rate of growth began to slow in the 1960s. The annual growth rate peaked at 2.2% in 1962 but had dropped to 1.1% by 2014.

▍ One reason for falling human population growth is demographic transition. **Demographic transition** occurs when a population goes from high birth rates and high death rates to low birth rates and low death rates. Demographic transition may regularly take 150 years to complete. Death rates usually fall first, as a result of increased medical care and sanitation; however, birth rates take much longer to fall, thus delaying transition.

▍ **Age-structure pyramids** show the relative number of individuals of each age in a population and can be used to predict and explain many demographic patterns. Study Figure 10.4. Why is Afghanistan poised for rapid growth? Why might economic growth in Italy be predicted to slow?

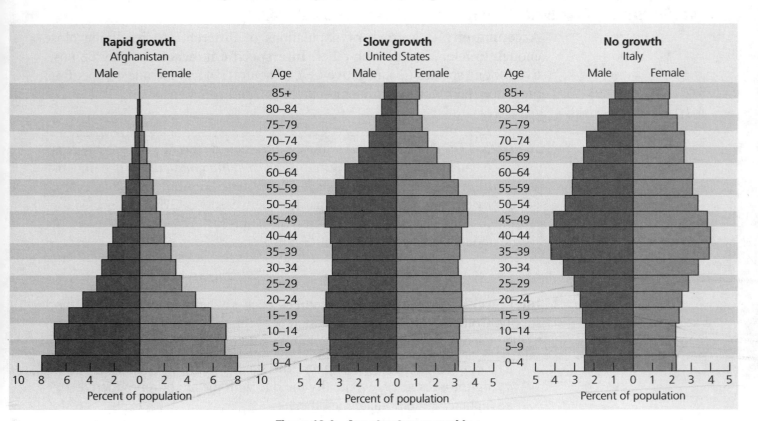

Figure 10.4   Age structure pyramids

▍ The global carrying capacity for humans is not known. A concept termed the **ecological footprint** refers to the total land and water area needed for all the resources a person consumes in a population. Currently, 1.7 hectares per person is considered sustainable. A typical person in the United States has a footprint of 8 hectares.

Community Ecology

(Biology, 11e: Chapter 54; Focus, 2e: Chapter 41)

YOU MUST KNOW

- The concept of a niche and how it is affected by competition.
- The role of competitive exclusion in interspecific competition.
- The symbiotic relationships of parasitism, mutualism, and commensalism.
- Species diversity has two components: species richness and relative abundance.
- The impact of keystone species on community structure.
- The difference between primary and secondary succession.

Community interactions are classified by whether they help, harm, or have no effect on the species involved (Biology, *11e: 54.1*; Focus, *2e: 41.1*)

▌ A **community** is a group of populations of different species living close enough to interact with each other. **Interspecific interactions** may be positive for one species (+), negative (−), or neutral (0) and include competition, predation, herbivory, parasitism, mutualism, and commensalism.

> **STUDY TIP** The prefix *inter-* means between different groups, whereas *intra-* means within the same group. *Intraspecific competition* is competition within the same species—such as two males fighting over a territory. *Interspecific competition* is competition between two different species for resources such as food. Pay attention to the prefix! You could be asked to write about either type of competition in an essay.

▌ **Interspecific competition** for resources occurs when resources are in short supply. Competition is a −/− interaction between the species involved. Central to the idea of competition and community structure are these two concepts:

▪ The **competitive exclusion principle** states that when two species are vying for a resource, eventually the one with the slight reproductive advantage will eliminate the other.

▪ An organism's **ecological niche** is the sum total of biotic and abiotic resources that the species uses in its environment. A species' **fundamental niche**, the niche potentially occupied by the species, is often different from the **realized niche**, the portion of the fundamental niche the species actually occupies. The classic study of barnacle species in your text (see Inquiry Figure 54.3 in *Biology*, 11e, or Figure 41.3 in *Focus*, 2e) is worth reviewing to help you understand niche types and competitive exclusion.

- **Predation** is a +/− interaction between two species in which one species (the **predator**) eats the other species (the **prey**). Animals display a variety of defensive adaptations from predation, including the following:

    - **Cryptic coloration**, in which the animal is camouflaged by its coloring.
    - **Aposematic**, or **warning, coloration**, in which a poisonous animal is brightly colored as a warning to other animals.
    - **Batesian mimicry**, referring to a situation in which a harmless species has evolved to mimic the coloration of an unpalatable or harmful species. In **Müllerian mimicry**, two bad-tasting species resemble each other, ostensibly so that predators will learn to avoid them equally.

- **Herbivory** is also a +/− interaction in which an herbivore eats part of a plant or alga. It is advantageous for an animal to be able to distinguish toxic from nontoxic plants. A plant's main protective devices are chemical toxins, spines, and thorns.
- **Parasitism** is a +/− interaction in which the parasite derives its nourishment from its **host**. Parasites may have a significant effect on the survival, reproduction, and density of their host population. Would you support the position that parasitism is a form of predation?
- **Mutualism** is an interspecific interaction that benefits both species (+/+). Both pollinators and flowering plants benefit from their relationship.
- **Commensalism** benefits one of the species but neither harms nor helps the other species. A fern growing in the shade of another plant could be an example of a commensal relationship.

CONNECT WITH THE CURRICULUM FRAMEWORK

- How do specific interactions between individuals or populations affect species distribution and abundance? (EK 4.B.3)
- How do human and global natural events affect ecosystem distribution? (EK 4.B.4)

Diversity and trophic structure characterize biological communities (Biology, *11e: 54.2*; Focus, *2e: 41.2*)

- **Species diversity** measures the number of different species in a community (species richness) *and* the relative abundance of each species. A community with an even species abundance is more diverse than one in which one or two species are abundant and the others are rare.
- Communities that are more diverse generally have greater productivity and are more stable than those that are less diverse.
- The **trophic structure** of a community refers to the feeding relationships among the organisms. **Trophic levels** are the links in the trophic structure of a community.

- Energy is transferred upward in a food chain—from the plants and other autotrophs (**primary producers**) through herbivores (**primary consumers**) to carnivores (**secondary, tertiary, and quaternary consumers**). This transfer of energy from one trophic level to another is referred to as a **food chain. Food webs** consist of two or more food chains linked together.
- Energy is lost at each transfer in a food chain; only about 10% is transferred up to the next level. Therefore, food chains are relatively short.
- For a food chain that consists of grasses → rabbits → hawk, what percentage of the energy is available to the hawk? (The answer is only 1%.)
- **Dominant species** in a community have the highest **biomass** (the sum weight of all the members of a population) or are the most abundant.
- **Keystone species** exert control on the community structure by their important ecological niche. They are not usually the most abundant, but they occupy pivotal ecological roles. When they are removed, the ecosystem often collapses. Notice in Figure 10.5 (and Inquiry Figure 54.18 in *Biology*, 11e, or Figure 41.15 in *Focus*, 2e) the impact of the keystone predator *Pisaster* (a sea star) on the diversity of species present in a tidal pool.

Figure 10.5   Impact of keystone predator on species diversity

Disturbance influences species diversity and composition (Biology, *11e: 54.3;* Focus, *2e: 41.3*)

- A disturbance—storm, fire, flood, drought, or human activity—changes a community by removing organisms or changing resource availability. Disturbance is not necessarily bad for a community.
- The **intermediate disturbance hypothesis** states that moderate levels of disturbance create conditions that foster greater species diversity than do low or high levels of disturbance.
- **Ecological succession** refers to transitions in species composition in a certain area over ecological time.

  - In **primary succession**, plants and animals gradually invade a region that was virtually lifeless, where soil has not yet formed. The gradual colonization of a newly formed volcanic island is an example.

- **Secondary succession** occurs when an existing community has been cleared by a disturbance that leaves the soil intact. An abandoned farm will show secondary succession as it starts with the soil intact.

Biogeographic factors affect community diversity
(Biology, *11e: 54.4*; Focus, *2e: 41.4*)

- Two biogeographic contributions are especially important in community diversity:

  - **The latitude of the community:** Plant and animal life is generally more abundant and diverse in the tropics and becomes less so moving toward the poles.
  - **The area of the community:** If all other factors are held equal, the larger the geographic area of a community, the more species it has.

- Because of their isolation and limited size, islands are natural laboratories for studying biogeographic factors. This idea also pertains to "islands" surrounded by land, such as national parks surrounded by development.
- The **island biogeography model** is primarily influenced by two factors:

  - Rates of immigration and extinction are influenced primarily by the *size* of the island and the *distance* of the island from the mainland. The greater the size of the island, the higher *immigration* rates will be and the lower the rates of *extinction*.
  - As the distance from the mainland increases, the rate of *immigration* falls, whereas *extinction* rates increase.
  - This model predicts that species richness increases with island size; it can be useful in predicting the effects of habitat loss on species diversity.

Pathogens alter community structure locally and globally
(Biology, *11e: 54.5*; Focus, *2e: 41.5*)

- When disease-causing microorganisms (referred to as pathogens) are introduced into new habitats, they can have disastrous effects because new host populations have not had a chance to become resistant to the pathogen through natural selection.
- There are numerous examples of introduced pathogens and their ability to drastically alter entire ecosystems, including the chestnut blight fungus that killed the most abundant tree species in the Eastern forests and the white-band disease that is killing the corals of the Caribbean. The list is seemingly endless. Controlling these pathogens requires an understanding of complex ecological interactions.
- Human activities transport pathogens around the world at unprecedented rates.

Ecosystems and Energy

(Biology, 11e: Chapter 55; Focus, 2e: Chapter 42)

YOU MUST KNOW

- How energy flows through the ecosystem.
- The difference between gross primary productivity and net primary productivity.
- The carbon and nitrogen biogeochemical cycles.
- How biogeochemical cycles affect individual organisms, populations, and ecosystems.
- Energy does not cycle but is lost at each trophic level. A constant input is required. Nutrients do cycle.

CONNECT WITH THE CURRICULUM FRAMEWORK

There are many LOs that relate to ecology. Some emphasize the role of environmental factors on phenotypes and natural selection. Other LOs focus on the movement of matter and energy through ecosystems. Pay attention to this as you work through this section.

■ Be able to use a representation to illustrate the movement of matter or energy through an ecosystem. (LO 4.15) Study Figures 10.6 and 10.7 carefully!
■ Be able to predict the effects of a change of matter or energy availability in an ecosystem. (LO 4.16)

Physical laws govern energy flow and chemical cycling in ecosystems
(Biology, 11e: 55.1; Focus, 2e: 42.1)

▌ An **ecosystem** is the sum of all the organisms living within its boundaries (biotic community) and all the abiotic factors with which they interact. Ecosystem ecology involves two unique processes: *energy flow* and *chemical cycling*.

▌ The flow of energy can be traced through the feeding or trophic levels in food chains and food webs. *Energy cannot be recycled*; therefore, energy must be constantly supplied to an ecosystem—in most cases by the sun.

   ■ The first law of thermodynamics states that energy cannot be created or destroyed but only transferred and transformed. What role do producers such as plants play in an ecosystem? Plants convert solar energy to chemical energy. The amount of solar energy converted (not created) sets the energy budget for the ecosystem.

   ■ An implication of the second law of thermodynamics is that energy conversions are inefficient. Some energy is always lost as heat. As energy moves through food chains, much of the energy is lost as heat to the ecosystem.

- **Primary producers** in an ecosystem are the **autotrophs** ("self-feeders"). They support all other organisms in the ecosystem.
- Organisms that are in trophic levels above primary producers cannot make their own food and are therefore consumers or **heterotrophs** ("other-feeders").
- *Herbivores* eat primary producers and are called **primary consumers**.
- *Carnivores* that eat herbivores are called **secondary consumers**, whereas carnivores that eat secondary consumers are termed **tertiary consumers**.
- **Detritivores**, or **decomposers**, are consumers that get their energy from *detritus*, which is nonliving organic material such as the remains of dead organisms, feces, dead leaves, and wood. Detritivores convert organic materials from all trophic levels to inorganic compounds that can be used by producers. In this way, nutrients cycle through ecosystems.

Energy and other limiting factors control primary production in ecosystems (Biology, *11e: 55.2;* Focus, *2e: 42.2*)

- The amount of light energy converted to chemical energy by autotrophs is an ecosystem's **primary production**. The amount of all photosynthetic production sets the spending limit for the energy budget of the entire ecosystem.

  - Total primary production in an ecosystem is known as that system's **gross primary production (GPP)**.
  - GPP is not the amount of energy available to consumers, however. Some of the fuel molecules made by the producers must be used by the producers as fuel for their own cellular respiration. **Net primary production (NPP)** is equal to gross primary production minus the energy used by the primary producers for their "autotrophic respiration" (R_a):

$$NPP = GPP - R_a$$

  - *Primary production* in aquatic ecosystems is affected primarily by light availability and nutrient availability. In the photic zone, light—and therefore photosynthesis—decreases with depth.
  - In aquatic ecosystems, nutrients limit primary productivity more than light. The nutrient most often limiting marine production is either nitrogen or phosphorus.
  - Temperature and moisture are the key factors controlling primary production in terrestrial ecosystems. A measure of the amount of water transpired by plants and evaporated from the landscape, termed **evapotranspiration**, combines both key terrestrial factors.
  - Productivity and energy transfer are addressed in Investigation 10, Energy Dynamics, beginning on page 340. Even if you did not do this investigation, working through the material presented there would help your understanding of productivity.

Energy transfer between trophic levels is typically only 10% efficient (Biology, *11e: 55.3;* Focus, *2e: 42.3*)

▌ Energy is lost at each trophic level as heat is consumed in life process such as movement and reproduction.

▌ The loss of energy from trophic level to trophic level is one of the factors that keeps food chains so short. In general, approximately 10% of available energy is transferred to the next trophic level.

▌ If 10% of energy is transferred from primary producer to primary consumer to secondary consumer, only 1% of the net primary production (10% of 10%) is available to secondary consumers.

▌ *Ecological pyramids* can give insight into food chains. Try to sketch and explain each of these: a *biomass pyramid,* an *energy pyramid*, and a *number pyramid*. A biomass pyramid and a number pyramid can be inverted. It should be clear that an energy pyramid can never be inverted.

Biological and geochemical processes cycle nutrients and water in ecosystems (Biology, *11e: 55.4;* Focus, *2e: 42.4*)

▌ **Biogeochemical cycles** are nutrient cycles that involve both biotic and abiotic components. Understanding these cycles allows scientists to trace how nutrients flow through ecosystems and how humans may have altered the flow.

▌ The **carbon cycle** has historically been a close balance between the amount of CO_2 removed from ecosystems by photosynthesis and the amount added by cellular respiration. The burning of fossil fuels and wood has added significant amounts of additional CO_2 to the atmosphere. Examine Figure 10.6 to see the generalized flow of carbon while also considering the effects of CO_2 on global warming.

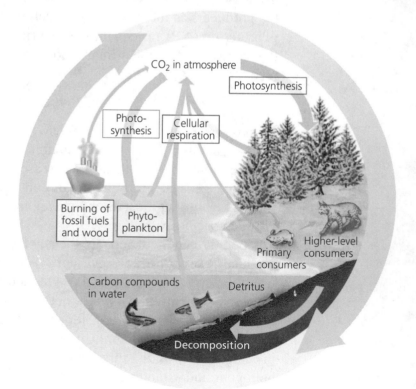

Figure 10.6   The carbon cycle

■ The **nitrogen cycle** moves nitrogen from the atmosphere through the living world. Nitrogen is a common limiting factor for plant growth, making its movement through ecosystems especially important. Note the important role of bacteria in the nitrogen cycle as you study Figure 10.7.

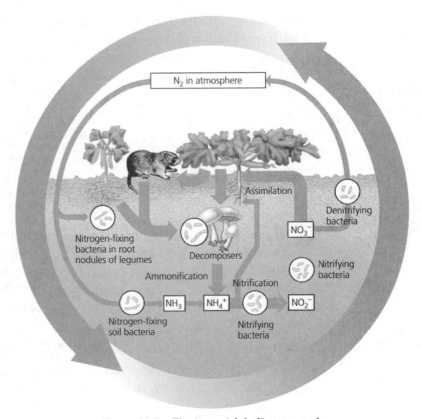

Figure 10.7   The terrestrial nitrogen cycle

■ Most of Earth's nitrogen is in the form of N_2, which is unusable by plants. The major pathway for nitrogen to enter an ecosystem is **nitrogen fixation**, the conversion of N_2 by bacteria to forms that plants can use. Earlier we described this relationship between legumes (plants) and the bacterium *Rhizobium* as an example of mutualism.

■ **Nitrification** is the process by which ammonium (NH_4^+) is oxidized to nitrite and then nitrate (NO_3^-) by bacteria. Two inorganic nitrogen forms can be absorbed by plants: nitrates and ammonium.

■ **Denitrification** by bacteria releases nitrogen into the atmosphere.

■ Other important nutrient cycles to review are the water and phosphorus cycles.

> **TIP FROM THE READERS**
> Work through Figures 10.6 and 10.7. You need to be able to explain how a change in the amount of nitrogen, carbon dioxide, or another factor would affect an ecosystem. To understand the impact of acid rain, fertilizer runoff, or global warming, you need to understand these cycles!

Restoration ecologists help return degraded ecosystems to a more natural state (Biology, *11e: 55.5;* Focus, *2e: 42.5*)

▌ **Bioremediation** is the use of organisms, usually prokaryotes, fungi, or plants, to detoxify polluted ecosystems. Bioremediation has helped restore areas degraded by mining or to remove oil or radioactive elements.

▌ **Bioaugmentation** is the introduction of desirable species such as nitrogen fixers to add essential nutrients.

Conservation Biology and Global Change

(Biology, *11e: Chapter 56;* Focus, *2e: Chapter 43*)

> **YOU MUST KNOW**
>
> • The value of biodiversity and the major human threats to it.
> • How human actions are changing the Earth.
> • How to predict consequences on both local and global ecosystems of specific human activities. (LO 45.20)

Human activities threaten Earth's biodiversity (Biology, *11e: 56.1;* Focus, *2e: 43.1*)

▌ **Biodiversity**—short for biological diversity—can be considered at three main levels: genetic diversity in a population, species diversity, and ecosystem diversity.

▌ Why is biodiversity important?

1. More diverse ecosystems are more stable and able to resist threats.
2. Numerous important drugs have been derived from plant, fungi and bacterial species.
3. Genetic diversity makes it more likely that a species will be able to escape extinction if a new pathogen emerges.

▌ Four major threats to biodiversity are habitat loss, introduced species, overharvesting, and global change.

▌ **Acid precipitation** was one of the first types of global change to cause concern. It is defined as rain, snow, or fog with a pH less than 5.2. The burning of wood and fossil fuels releases sulfur oxides and nitrogen oxides into the atmosphere. These oxides react with water, forming sulfuric acid and nitric acid.

Population conservation focuses on population size, genetic diversity, and critical habitat (Biology, *11e: 56.2;* Focus, *2e: 43.2*)

▌ When a population drops below a minimum viable population (MVP) size, its loss of genetic variation resulting from nonrandom mating and genetic drift can trap it in an *extinction vortex*. One key factor is the loss of the genetic variation necessary to enable evolutionary responses to environmental change, such as the appearance of new strains of pathogens.

Landscape and regional conservation help sustain biodiversity (Biology, *11e: 56.3;* Focus, *2e: 43.3*)

▌ The structure of a landscape can strongly influence biodiversity. As *habitat fragmentation* increases and edges become more extensive, biodiversity tends to decrease. *Movement corridors* can promote dispersal and help sustain populations.

▌ A **biodiversity hot spot** is a relatively small area with an exceptional concentration of endemic species and a large number of endangered and threatened species. Biodiversity hot spots are also hot spots of extinction and thus prime candidates for protection.

Earth is changing rapidly as a result of human actions (Biology, *11e: 56.4;* Focus, *2e: 43.4*)

▌ Nutrient cycling is altered by human activities, particularly agriculture. For example, soil nitrogen is often depleted by crops. Fertilizers and livestock activities can cause excess nitrogen to enter aquatic ecosystems, contaminating water supplies, killing fish, and fueling algal blooms.

▌ In **biological magnification**, toxins that cannot be broken down biologically by normal chemical means become more concentrated in successive trophic levels of a food web, so they magnify in concentration as they move through the food chain. Mercury, lead, and DDT are examples of toxins that severely affect top-level carnivores.

▌ Pharmaceuticals are another group of toxins that are of growing concern. Over-the-counter and prescription drugs, sex steroids, antibiotics, and growth-promoting drugs used in agriculture are all found today in water supplies and fresh-water ecosystems.

▌ The **greenhouse effect** refers to the absorption of heat Earth experiences because of certain atmospheric gases. Carbon dioxide and water vapor intercept and absorb much reflected infrared radiation, re-reflecting some back toward Earth.

 ▪ As a result of deforestation and the burning of fossil fuels, CO_2 levels have been steadily increasing over the past 150 years. This rise in CO_2 levels contributes to the greenhouse effect and is one aspect of **climate change**, a directional change to the global climate that lasts for three decades or more.

▌ The ecosystems where the climate has changed the most are those in the far north. As snow and ice melt and uncover darker, more absorptive surfaces, these systems reflect less radiation back to the atmosphere and warm further. Rising temperatures have caused some Arctic regions to switch from being a CO_2 *sink* to a CO_2 *source*. These are worrisome examples of positive feedback.

■ Another human impact on the Earth is the depletion of atmospheric ozone (O_3). The **ozone layer** reduces the amount of UV radiation penetration from the sun through the atmosphere. Chlorine-containing compounds used by humans are eroding the ozone layer, allowing more DNA-damaging UV radiation to penetrate to the surface of the Earth.

Answers to PRACTICE THE PRACTICE: Apply a Formula to Calculate Population Growth Rate, p. 283.

1. With a population size (N) of 1,600,

$$\frac{dN}{dt} = r_{max}N\frac{(K - N)}{K} = \frac{1(1,600)(1,500 - 1,600)}{1,500}$$

and the population "growth" rate is -107 individuals per year. The population is shrinking because the population size is greater than the carrying capacity of the environment.

2. With a population size (N) of 1,200,

$$\frac{1(1,200)(1,500 - 1,200)}{1,500}$$

and the population growth rate is 240 individuals per year. This population is growing because its population size (N) is below carrying capacity (K).

3. If r_{max} is doubled, the population growth rate would also double.

$$\frac{2(1,200)(1,500 - 1,200)}{1,500}$$

and the population growth rate would be 480 individuals/year, so the population would quickly exceed carrying capacity in this case.

4. The value of $(K - N)/K$ would be 0 if $K = N$, and the population would no longer grow. This implies that when a population reaches carrying capacity, there are no longer excess resources to support further growth.

Level 1: Knowledge/Comprehension Questions

The Level 1, Knowledge/Comprehension, questions review essential content knowledge but don't represent the type of question you will see on the AP exam. The Level 2, Application/Synthesis questions, are similar to those you will see on the exam.

1. Which of the following is a correct description of ozone in the upper atmosphere?
   (A) It is composed of O_2.
   (B) It limits the amount of radiation available for photosynthesis.
   (C) It is thinning, partially as a result of widespread use of certain chlorine-containing compounds.
   (D) It is a result of widespread burning of fossil fuels.

2. The carrying capacity of a population is defined as
   (A) the amount of time the parents in the population spend rearing and nurturing their offspring.
   (B) the maximum population size that a certain environment can support at a particular time.
   (C) the amount of vegetation that a certain geographic area can support.
   (D) the number of different types of species a biome can support.

Directions: Questions 3–6 consist of four lettered choices followed by a list of numbered phrases or sentences. For each numbered phrase or sentence, select the one choice that is most closely related to it. Each choice may be used once, more than once, or not at all.

Questions 3–6
   (A) temperate grassland
   (B) tropical forest
   (C) tundra
   (D) desert

3. Characterized by permafrost and few large plants

4. Characterized by epiphytes, a significant canopy, and abundant rainfall

5. Characterized by occasional fires, nutrient-rich soil, and large grazing animals

6. Characterized by sparse rainfall and extreme daily temperature fluctuations

7. A bacterial colony that exists in an environment displaying ideal conditions will display which of the following growth patterns?
   (A) logistic growth
   (B) intrinsic growth
   (C) demographic growth
   (D) exponential growth

8. Which of the following interspecific interactions represents a form of interaction different from the others?
   (A) a tick on a human
   (B) deer browsing on shrubs
   (C) a honeybee and apple blossoms
   (D) a deadly bacterium and its host

9. When one species was removed from a tide pool, the species richness became significantly reduced. The removed species was probably
   (A) the species with the greatest biomass.
   (B) a potent parasite.
   (C) the species with the highest relative abundance.
   (D) a keystone species.

10. Which of the following would not be a density-dependent factor limiting a population's growth?
   (A) increased predation by a predator
   (B) a limited number of available nesting sites
   (C) a stress syndrome that alters hormone levels
   (D) a very early fall frost

11. There are many reasons the human population is increasing so rapidly. Select the one factor that does not significantly affect this growth rate.
    (A) Technology has increased our carrying capacity.
    (B) The death rate has greatly decreased since the Industrial Revolution.
    (C) The age structure of many countries is highly skewed toward younger ages.
    (D) Fertility rates in many developing countries are above the 2.1 children per female replacement level.

12. A Type I survivorship curve is level at first, with a rapid increase in mortality in old age. This type of curve is
    (A) typical of many invertebrates that produce large numbers of offspring.
    (B) typical of large mammals.
    (C) found most often in *r*-selected populations, which have a rapid rate of reproduction.
    (D) almost never found in nature.

13. The process in which CO_2 in the atmosphere intercepts and absorbs reflected infrared radiation and re-reflects it back to Earth is known as
    (A) global warming.
    (B) ozone depletion.
    (C) the greenhouse effect.
    (D) biological magnification.

14. A species' specific use of the biotic and abiotic factors in an environment is collectively called the species'
    (A) habitat.
    (B) trophic level.
    (C) ecological niche.
    (D) partition.

15. The dominant species in a community is the one that
    (A) has the greatest number of genes per individual.
    (B) is at the top of the food chain.
    (C) has the largest biomass.
    (D) eats all other members of the community.

16. A fire cleared a large area of forest in Yellowstone National Park in the 1980s. When the first plants pioneered this burned area, this was an example of
    (A) primary succession.
    (B) secondary succession.
    (C) biological evolution.
    (D) a keystone species.

Level 2: Application/Analysis/Synthesis Questions

After reading the paragraph, answer questions 1 and 2.

The largest estuary in the United States is the Chesapeake Bay, which extends through six states. The bay is one of the most productive natural areas in the world. It is home to thousands of plants and animals, including many commercially important species. The water of the bay is relatively shallow. Many areas are no more than 10 feet deep, with an average depth of 30 feet. Light penetrates the shallow water and supports the submerged plants that provide food and shelter for the many species living in the bay ecosystem. However, like many estuaries, the bay receives large amounts of fertilizer runoff from farms, lawns, and wastewater treatment facilities. This runoff introduces large amounts of nutrients.

1. Which of the following is the most probable sequence of events when fertilizer runoff reaches the bay?
   (A) submerged vegetation increases ➔ more food for fish and shellfish ➔ fish and shellfish populations increase
   (B) phytoplankton population increases ➔ more food for fish and shellfish ➔ fish and shellfish populations increase
   (C) phytoplankton population increases ➔ sunlight blocked to submerged vegetation ➔ submerged vegetation dies ➔ fish and shellfish populations decrease
   (D) submerged vegetation decreases ➔ fish and shellfish feed on decaying plants ➔ phytoplankton feed on fish and shellfish ➔ commercial fisheries decline

2. Which of the following pairs of nutrients would have the greatest effect on growth of phytoplankton?
   (A) carbon and hydrogen
   (B) oxygen and carbon dioxide
   (C) nitrogen and phosphorus
   (D) calcium and water

Use the graph below to answer questions 3 and 4.

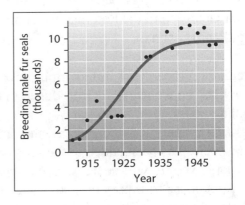

3. According to this graph of the population growth of fur seals, in what year did the population first reach its carrying capacity?
   (A) 1925
   (B) 1930
   (C) 1940
   (D) 1950

4. The formula $dN/dt = r_{max}N(K - N)/K$ describes the pattern of growth for the graph. Which of the following is true concerning the formula and the part of the graph that describes 1945?
   (A) $K = N$
   (B) $r_{max}N$
   (C) The variable K is constantly changing.
   (D) $(K - N)/K = 9{,}000$

After reading the paragraphs, answer questions 5 and 6.

Introduced species are a problem all over the world, and there are many examples in the United States. Several years ago, a fisherman caught a northern snakehead fish in a pond in Crofton, Maryland (a suburb of Washington, DC). Snakeheads are a favorite food of immigrants from China, and live fish can frequently be found in Asian markets. It's suspected that the fish in the Crofton pond were purchased locally and then intentionally released.

Snakeheads are top predators, and 90% of the northern snakeheads' diet consists of other fishes. The northern snakehead can breathe out of water and travel short distances (about 100 feet) across land. They also reproduce rapidly. Females can lay more than 100,000 eggs per year. Juveniles have also been identified in the Potomac River and other rivers in Pennsylvania.

5. Predict the most likely effect on biodiversity when snakeheads are introduced into an aquatic ecosystem.
   (A) Biodiversity will increase because another species has been added to the ecosystem.
   (B) Biodiversity will decrease because the snakehead will prey on native species.
   (C) Biodiversity will remain the same because local species will prey on the snakeheads and limit their reproduction.
   (D) Biodiversity will decrease because the snakeheads will feed heavily on producer species.

6. Based on the characteristics of the snakehead described, which of the following is most likely to be a productive strategy to reduce the spread of this species?
   (A) Extend the fishing season for prey fishes.
   (B) Introduce a natural predator to feed on juvenile snakeheads.
   (C) Introduce a fungus that prevents fish eggs from hatching.
   (D) Introduce algae and photosynthetic bacteria to reduce nutrient levels in the water.

Use the population pyramid for Nigeria to answer questions 7 and 8.

7. The age-structure data for Nigeria show that the country has many more individuals under the age of 15 than over the age of 40. What does this imply about the future population of Nigeria?
   (A) The population will probably remain stable.
   (B) The population will probably decrease.
   (C) The population will probably grow rapidly.
   (D) The number of older people will probably increase rapidly.

8. Based on the age structure of the country, which of the following situations would be most likely over the next 20 years?
   (A) strong economic gains stimulated by population growth
   (B) an increased demand for resources based on population growth
   (C) a decreased demand for medical services resulting from the small number of elderly citizens
   (D) a decline in housing prices based on lack of demand

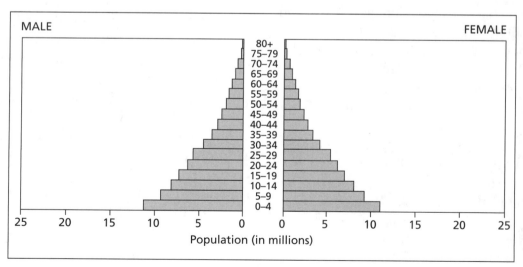

Population Pyramid for Nigeria, 2007

From U.S. Census Bureau International Data Base, 2007

9. Which statement best describes energy transfer in a food web?
(A) Energy is transferred to consumers, which convert it to nitrogen compounds and use it to synthesize amino acids.
(B) Energy from producers is converted into oxygen and transferred to consumers.
(C) Energy from the sun is stored in green plants and transferred to consumers.
(D) Energy moves from autotrophs to heterotrophs to decomposers, which convert it to a form producers can use again.

10. In ocean kelp forests, kelp perch are preyed upon by kelp bass. The graph shows proportional mortality rates for kelp perch as a function of density. Which statement is a logical conclusion based on the data?

(A) Fluctuations in kelp perch density are a result of normal population cycles.
(B) A negative feedback loop regulates the kelp perch population size.
(C) The equilibrium density for the population of kelp perch can be calculated.
(D) Higher predation levels lead to healthier kelp perch populations over time.

11. The graph shows the relationship of lamb production to population size of a naturally occurring population of Soay sheep on Hirta Island. Which of the following statements is the most likely explanation of the pattern observed in these data?

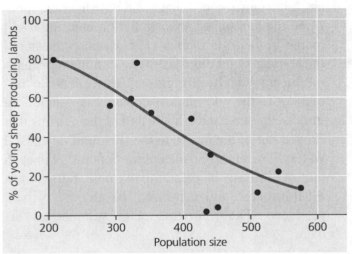

(A) Density-independent factors such as drought and fire are the most likely factors to cause these changes in population size.
(B) As population size increases on the island, the rate of reproduction goes down, which may be a result of increased competition for resources.
(C) The lower rate of reproduction occurs as the female sheep become older.
(D) As population size on the island increases, fewer sheep are bred to maintain carrying capacity.

As the population size on the island increases, fewer sheep are bred in order to maintain carrying capacity. Use the reading and data table to answer questions 12–16.

In a classic experiment, John Teal studied the flow of energy through the producers, consumers, and detritivores in a salt marsh. Teal measured the amount of solar radiation entering a salt marsh in Georgia over a year. He also measured the aboveground biomass of the dominant primary producers, which were grasses, as well as the biomass of the dominant consumers—including insects, spiders, and crabs—and of the detritus that flowed out of the marsh to the surrounding coastal waters. To determine the amount of energy in each unit of biomass, he dried the biomass, burned it in a calorimeter, and measured the amount of heat produced. The following chart summarizes his data.

Form of Energy	$kcal/(m^2 \cdot yr)$
Solar radiation	600,000
Gross grass production	34,580
Net grass production	6,585
Gross insect production	305
Net insect production	81
Detritus leaving marsh	3,671

Data from J. M. Teal, Energy flow in the salt marsh ecosystem of Georgia, *Ecology* 43:614–624 (1962).

12. What percentage of the solar energy that reaches the marsh is incorporated into gross primary production?
    (A) 1.1%
    (B) 5.8%
    (C) 10.3%
    (D) 17.4%

13. What percentage of the solar energy that reaches the marsh is incorporated into net primary production?
    (A) 0.01%
    (B) 0.2%
    (C) 1.1%
    (D) 12.3%

14. How much energy is lost by primary producers as respiration in this ecosystem?
    (A) 3,921 $kcal/(m^2 \cdot yr)$
    (B) 6,585 $kcal/(m^2 \cdot yr)$
    (C) 13,735 $kcal/(m^2 \cdot yr)$
    (D) 27,995 $kcal/(m^2 \cdot yr)$

15. If all of the detritus leaving the marsh is plant material, what percentage of all net primary production leaves the marsh as detritus each year?
    (A) 8%
    (B) 20%
    (C) 43%
    (D) 53%

16. The data from the energy flow in a saltwater ecosystem supports which of the following statements?
    (A) The progressive loss of energy along the food web explains why most food webs include only four or five trophic levels.
    (B) The movement of energy through the food web explains why most food webs contain more top-level carnivores than primary consumers.
    (C) The efficient cycling of energy through a food web explains the abundance of species on Earth.
    (D) The high level of energy transfer between all trophic levels in a food web accounts for the large biomass of the saltwater ecosystem.

Grid-In Questions

The following questions require a numerical response.

1. A population of 20 bobcats was introduced onto a barrier island to help control the large rodent population. The bobcat population's birth rate is 0.48 bobcats/year per capita, and the death rate is 0.21 bobcats/year per capita. Given the initial bobcat population, predict the population size after two years on the island. (Round to the nearest whole number.)

2. Ecologists often cannot count all the individuals in a population. In such cases, they use the mark-recapture method to estimate population size. An ecologist wished to estimate the population of white-footed deer mice in an old field. On her first trapping, she caught 142 mice and marked each one with a harmless dye on the back of its head. Two weeks later, she conducted her second trapping; she caught 133 mice of which 41 were marked with the dye[1]. Use the formula

$$N = sn/x$$

where N = population size estimate, s = number of mice marked in the first trapping, n = number of mice caught in the second trapping, and x = the number of mice that were marked in the second trapping. What is the population estimate of the white-footed deer mouse? (Round your answer to the nearest whole number.)

Free-Response Question

1. *All of the organisms in a community are interrelated by the abiotic and biotic resources they use in the course of their lives.*

   (a) **Explain** the flow of energy among a hawk, a mouse, and a plant in a particular ecosystem.
   (b) Select **two** examples of the impact of human population growth on abiotic components of the environment. For each example, *explain* how a change in the abiotic component will affect the biotic component of the biosphere.

---

[1] In the second trapping no new mice are marked.

Part III

The Laboratory

AP Biology is designed to be equivalent to a two-semester college course, and laboratory experience must be included in all AP Biology courses. The College Board has published a collection of suggested investigations with the expectation that all students will complete eight major investigations during the course. Of these, two should come from topics included in each Big Idea. Many of the investigations may be ongoing projects or require several days for completion. Your teacher may select from many possible investigations, so the labs you do may be different from the ones we present here. Your success in the course does not hinge on completion of a particular lab, but rather on your mastery of the underlying Science Practices.

Our students find that a review of the laboratory exercises is an excellent way to study many of the core concepts of their AP Biology course. A great resource for your review is LabBench, available at http://www.phschool.com/science/biology_place/labbench/. Although it accompanies the "classic" lab manual, there is a wealth of information about some labs that your teacher may choose to use as starting points for investigations. At LabBench you will find exercises that take you through 12 basic college labs, along with sample questions to test your understanding. *We recommend strongly that you use this resource!*

Inquiry-Based Investigations

In laboratory, your teacher will engage you in inquiry labs in which you do not have step-by-step instruction. Rather, you will select your own question, develop a hypothesis, determine your own procedure for data collection, and analyze your results. During the course of the year, work in the laboratory will help you gain skill in the science practices. Here are some tasks that you should be able to do:

- Design a plan for collecting data to answer a scientific question using adequate controls
- Predict the results you expect
- Evaluate an experiment to describe variables that were not controlled and theorize about how those variables might have affected the outcome of the experiment
- Analyze data to identify patterns or relationships
- Construct appropriate graphs based on collected data
- Use graphs to formulate conclusions or make predictions
- Summarize patterns shown by data
- Identify outliers in a data set; propose an explanation for the outliers and a rationale for dealing with them
- Identify possible sources of error in an experimental procedure or data set
- Use mathematics to solve problems, analyze data, and make predictions

---

CONNECT WITH THE CURRICULUM FRAMEWORK

Now would be a good time to turn to page 314 to review the Science Practices. Note that all the tasks above use these practices. These are skills you learn by doing, so keep them in mind as you review each investigation.

TIP FROM THE READERS

Being able to conceive, design, and execute your inquiry investigation is important, but you can also develop important skills by reviewing published data and interpreting it. In the Campbell textbooks, you will find the Inquiry Figures and Scientific Skills Exercises to be very valuable. (These items also are in the online resource *Mastering Biology*.) If you work through these figures and answer the associated questions you will find it much easier to handle similar questions on the AP Exam.

BIG IDEA 1: Investigation 1, Artificial Selection

Overview of the Lab

▌ In this investigation, you will study the effect of artificial selection in Fast Plants, although your teacher might select any organism with a fairly short life cycle, such as fruit flies. You and your classmates will observe a range of traits, such as height of plant at first flower, number of trichomes (hairs) on the leaf petioles, or leaf color, and select the individual plants that are at one extreme for this trait. These plants will serve as the parents for the next generation of plants, and you will discard the rest.

YOU MUST KNOW

- Selection alters allelic frequency and can result in the shift of a phenotypic character within a population over time.
- A technique to investigate selection as a mechanism of evolution.
- How to apply mathematical methods to data to predict what will happen to the population in the future.
- Quantitative methods to determine whether populations are significantly different, and appropriate use of error bars, graph type, and statistical tests.

SCIENCE PRACTICES: CAN YOU . . .

- Design a plan for collecting data that will investigate the effect of selection on a population?
- Analyze data to identify patterns and relationships?
- Use data to predict what will happen to a population in the future, based on models of types of selection? (LO 1.22)

Hints and Review

▌ You will measure or quantify the trait for the first generation and then do the same for their offspring. If there are enough measurements, data often show a normal or bell-shaped distribution for the first generation.

▌ The data collected for each generation can be used to generate a histogram. Future generations may show the effect of directional selection.

▌ Go back to page 169 (see Topic 6) to review the modes of selection.

Questions

The following data are from an artificial selection experiment with Fast Plants.

Height (in cm) at First Flower Generation 1	Height (in cm) at First Flower Generation 2
8.2	9.6
7.3	9.3
9.2	8.8
8.1	6.4
8.0	8.9
7.8	8.8
7.9	8.2
9.1	7.9
6.2	8.7
8.9	8.8

1. What is the mean height of the plants in the first generation to the nearest tenth?

2. What is the mode of plant height in the second generation to the nearest tenth?

3. To the nearest tenth, what is the percentage increase in height of plants in the second generation?

4. What procedure would be the most useful to test the effect of selection for height at first flowering on the mean height of the plants?
   (A) Select plants for breeding that are closest to the average height of the population.
   (B) Use the entire population for breeding, but increase the amount of fertilizer and light.
   (C) Select seeds from only those plants whose height exceeds the mean for the generation.
   (D) Randomly select five plants for breeding.

PRACTICE THE PRACTICE: Graphical Analysis of Data

A researcher wanted to evaluate three plant samples from a single population based on their mean heights. The following chart summarizes the data.

	Sample I	Sample II	Sample III
Mean height of plants (cm)	6.5	8.9	9.0
Standard error of the mean (SEM) (cm)	0.3	0.2	0.3

1. Prepare a graph of the data in the table. Include error bars to indicate _+/− 2 SEM.

2. Are the samples within expected height variation for the population? Explain your evaluation of the data using **Claim/Evidence/Reasoning**.
   You can find answers in Part V, Answers and Explanations, page 436.

BIG IDEA 1: Investigation 2, Mathematical Modeling: Hardy-Weinberg

▌ This investigation has you manipulate a computer spreadsheet to build a mathematical model to investigate the relationship between changing allelic frequencies in a population and evolution. The investigation helps develop an understanding of the Hardy-Weinberg equation, increase expertise with a spreadsheet program, and build a model to answer questions posed by the data. The skills you develop from creating the spreadsheet model and using it will be invaluable throughout many of your college courses.

YOU MUST KNOW

- The Hardy-Weinberg equation and be able to use it to determine the frequency of alleles in a population.
- Conditions for maintaining Hardy-Weinberg equilibrium.
- How genetic drift, natural selection, and the heterozygote advantage affect Hardy-Weinberg equilibrium.

SCIENCE PRACTICES: CAN YOU . . .

- Use a data set to reflect a change in the genetic makeup of a population over time, and apply mathematical methods to investigate the cause(s) and effect(s) of this change?
- Apply mathematical methods to data from a real or simulated population to predict how the genetic composition of a population may change due to natural selection, genetic drift, gene flow, or other factors?
- Evaluate data-based evidence that describes evolutionary changes in the genetic makeup of a population over time?
- Use data from mathematical models based on the Hardy-Weinberg equilibrium to analyze genetic drift and the effect of selection in the evolution of specific populations?
- Justify how data from mathematical models based on the Hardy-Weinberg equation can be used to analyze genetic drift and the effects of selection in the evolution of specific populations?
- Describe a model that represents evolution within a population?
- Evaluate data sets that illustrate evolution as an ongoing process?

Hints and Review

▌ The **Hardy-Weinberg Law of Genetic Equilibrium** provides a mathematical model for studying evolutionary changes in allelic frequency within a population. It predicts that the frequency of alleles and genotypes in a population will remain constant from generation to generation if the population is stable and in genetic equilibrium.

> **Five conditions are necessary for a population to remain at Hardy-Weinberg equilibrium:**
>
> 1. No mutation
> 2. Random mating
> 3. No natural selection
> 4. Extremely large population size (no genetic drift)
> 5. No gene flow (emigration, immigration, transfer of pollen, etc.)

▎ **No mutations**—The gene pool is modified if mutations alter alleles or if entire genes are deleted or duplicated. Mutations are so rare that a mutation alone does not change allelic frequency, but natural selection may make a mutation more common in a population over time. This is evolution.

▎ **Random mating**—If individuals tend to mate within a subset of the population, such as with their near neighbors or close relatives (inbreeding), random mixing of gametes does not occur. In a population at equilibrium, mating must be random.

▎ **No natural selection**—Allele frequencies can change when individuals with different genotypes differ in their survival or reproductive success. If selection occurs, those alleles that are selected for will become more common. For example, if resistance to a particular herbicide allows weeds to live in an environment that has been sprayed with that herbicide, the allele for resistance may become more frequent in the population.

▎ **Extremely large population size**—A large breeding population helps ensure that chance alone does not disrupt genetic equilibrium. In a small population, only a few copies of a certain allele may exist. If for some chance reason the organisms with that allele do not reproduce successfully, the allelic frequency will change. This random, nonselective change is what happens in **genetic drift**.

▎ **No gene flow**—No new alleles can come into the population, and no alleles can be lost. Both immigration and emigration can alter allelic frequency. To estimate the frequency of alleles in a population, we can use the Hardy-Weinberg equation.

▎ Let's go back to the idea of modeling to make predictions about what will happen to allelic frequencies in a population. Here are two questions to consider:

1. *Why aren't negative recessive alleles eliminated?* Negative recessive alleles are seldom eliminated because selection acts on phenotypes and the recessive alleles are "hidden" in the heterozygotes.

2. *Why do certain negative alleles, such as the one for sickle-cell anemia, persist at relatively high levels in certain populations?* The allele for sickle-cell anemia (*s*) conveys protection against malaria in individuals who are heterozygous (*Ss*)—called the *heterozygote advantage*. Individuals who lack this allele (*SS*) have normal hemoglobin but are susceptible to malaria. Although individuals who are *ss* may die from the consequences of the anemia, the negative allele persists in populations under pressure from malarial infection because the heterozygotes are less likely to die of malaria.

PRACTICE THE PRACTICE: Using Mathematics to Calculate Allelic Frequency

Need help? Turn back to page 167; a box contains an explanation of the use of the Hardy-Weinberg equation. It has all the information you need to calculate allelic frequencies when there are two different alleles.

Sample Problem #1:

Consider a population of pigs where B = tan pigs and b = black pigs. We can use the Hardy-Weinberg equation to determine the percentage of the pig population that is heterozygous for tan coat and arrive at the frequency of the two coat-color alleles.

1. Calculate q^2.

Count the individuals that are homozygous recessive in the illustration. Calculate the percentage of the total population they represent. This is q^2.

Answer: Four of the sixteen individuals show the recessive phenotype, so the correct answer is 25% or 0.25.

2. Find q.

Take the square root of q^2 to obtain q, the frequency of the recessive allele.

Answer: $q = 0.5$

3. Find p.

The sum of the frequencies of both alleles = 100%, $p + q = 1$. You know q, so what is p, the frequency of the dominant allele?

Answer: $p = 1 - q$, so $p = 0.5$

4. Find $2pq$.

The frequency of the heterozygotes is represented by $2pq$. This gives you the percentage of the population that is heterozygous.

Answer: $2pq = 2(0.5)(0.5) = 0.5$, so 50% of the population is heterozygous.

Sample Problem #2:

In a certain population of 1,000 fruit flies, 360 have red eyes, whereas the remainder have sepia eyes. The sepia eye trait is recessive to red eyes. How many individuals would you expect to be homozygous for red eye color?

Hint: The first step is always to calculate q! Start by determining the number of fruit flies that are homozygous recessive ($= q^2$).

Answer: You should expect 40 to be homozygous dominant.

Calculations:

q^2 for this population is $640/1,000 = 0.64$

$q = \sqrt{0.64} = 0.8$

$p = 1 - q = 1 - 0.8 = 0.2$

The homozygous dominant frequency $= p^2 = (0.2)(0.2) = 0.04$

Therefore, you can expect 4% of 1,000, or 40 individuals, to be homozygous dominant.

TIP FROM THE READERS

There are a couple confusing things about these problems. Here's what to watch for:

1. If you are given the number of individuals showing the dominant trait, this is *not* p^2 because it includes heterozygotes. However, you can use it to determine q^2 and from that get a value for q. When you use the H-W equation to calculate allelic frequency, always determine the value of q first!

2. You may get a problem in which you are told the frequency of an allele. You are being directly given p or q! Genotypic frequencies, such as the 25% of the pigs that were black, represent q^2. To find the allelic frequency of q requires taking the square root. Be sure to read carefully to determine if you are given allelic or genotypic frequencies in problems!

Questions

1. If the frequency of two alleles in a gene pool is 90% A and 10% a, what is the frequency of individuals in the population with the genotype Aa?
   (A) 0.81
   (B) 0.09
   (C) 0.18
   (D) 0.01

2. If a population experiences no migration, is very large, has no mutations, has random mating, there is no selection, which of the following would you predict?
   (A) The population will evolve but much more slowly than normal.
   (B) The makeup of the population's gene pool will remain virtually the same as long as these conditions hold.
   (C) The composition of the population's gene pool will change slowly in a predictable manner.
   (D) Dominant alleles in the population's gene pool will slowly increase in frequency, whereas recessive alleles will decrease.

3. In a population that is in Hardy-Weinberg equilibrium, the frequency of the homozygous recessive genotype is 0.09. What is the frequency of individuals that are homozygous for the dominant allele?
   (A) 0.7
   (B) 0.21
   (C) 0.42
   (D) 0.49

BIG IDEA 1: Investigation 3, Comparing DNA Sequences to Understand Evolutionary Relationships with BLAST

Overview of the Lab

In this investigation, you will be introduced to one of the tools of bioinformatics, BLAST, which stands for Basic Local Alignment Search Tool. When a DNA sequence is uploaded to BLAST, entire genomic libraries are searched for identical or similar sequences in a matter of seconds. The purpose of this lab is to have you use some of the tools of bioinformatics while becoming adept in making and interpreting cladograms or phylogenetic trees. First, you place a newly discovered fossil species onto an existing cladogram using information from a photograph. Then, to confirm your placement, you will use BLAST to compare several genes and use the information to refine your cladogram.

YOU MUST KNOW

- Computer programs have sophisticated ways of measuring and representing relatedness among organisms.
- How to use similarities in gene or amino acid sequences to determine evolutionary relationships.
- Phylogenetic trees graphically represent ancestral groups and their descendants, and it is possible to draw these by using many types of evidence, including morphology, DNA, and protein sequences.

SCIENCE PRACTICES: CAN YOU . . .

- Use a data set in conjunction with a phylogenetic tree or cladogram to determine evolutionary history and speciation? (LO 1.18)
- Create a phylogenetic tree that correctly represents evolutionary history and speciation from a provided data set? (LO 1.19)

Hints and Review

- The BLAST website allows you to input either DNA or amino acid/protein sequences to search for species that show similarities. You are able to set the parameters for a search and can compare species.
- Cladograms can represent the same information in many ways. Think of them as mobiles hanging from a ceiling and rotating; you will begin to see how it is possible to show the same relationship in different ways.
- All cladograms show *nodes* that represent a point of divergence from a *common ancestor* of each branch.

Questions

1. Suppose that species 1 and species 2 have similar appearances but very divergent gene sequences and that species 2 and species 3 have very different appearances but similar gene sequences. Which statement best reflects their relationships?

   (A) Species 1, 2, and 3 are all closely related because they share either a similar appearance or a similar gene sequence.

   (B) Species 1 and 2 are most closely related because their similar appearance indicates convergent evolution.

   (C) Species 2 and 3 are most closely related because of their genetic similarity.

   (D) Species 1 and 2 are most closely related because they share a common ancestor with species 3.

2. Three of the following trees describe the same phylogenetic relationships among taxa A, B, C, and D. Which tree shows a different phylogeny?

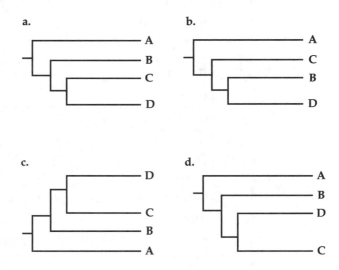

3. Which of the following approaches would allow a biologist studying the evolution of four similar species of birds to choose the best phylogenetic tree from all possible phylogenies?

   (A) Choose the simplest tree that is based on physical appearances.

   (B) From a comparison of DNA sequences, choose the tree that requires the smallest number of evolutionary events.

(C) Choose the tree that has the most evolutionary changes because this would be the most likely explanation for how these very similar birds evolved into four distinct species.

(D) Determine which species can interbreed; those that can interbreed evolved from a common ancestor most recently.

4. When cytochrome *c* molecules are compared, yeasts and molds are found to differ by approximately 46 amino acids per 100 residues (amino acids in the protein); insects and vertebrates are found to differ by 29 amino acids per 100 residues. What can you conclude from these data?

(A) You can conclude very little, unless you compare the DNA sequences for the cytochrome *c* genes.

(B) Insects and vertebrates diverged from a common ancestor more recently than did yeasts and molds.

(C) Yeasts and molds diverged from a common ancestor more recently than did insects and vertebrates.

(D) The evolution of cytochrome *c* occurred more rapidly in yeasts and molds than in insects and vertebrates.

PRACTICE THE PRACTICE: Using Traits to Construct a Cladogram

The table below shows three key events in the evolution of plants: the development of vascular tissue, flowers, and seeds. Presence of this character in the group is indicated by a +; absence of the character is indicated by a 0.

Plant Group	Vascular Tissue	Flowers	Seeds
Mosses	0	0	0
Gymnosperms	+	0	+
Angiosperms	+	+	+
Ferns	+	0	0

1. Construct a cladogram to show the correct relationship among these plant groups.

2. What character does the common ancestor of both ferns and angiosperms have?

3. What character does only the common ancestor of gymnosperms and angiosperms have?

4. Use a small dark circle labeled "a" to indicate the location of the common ancestor of mosses and ferns, and a small dark circle labeled "b" to indicate the location of the common ancestor of ferns, angiosperms and gymnosperms.

You can find answers in Part V, Answers and Explanations, page 437.

BIG IDEA 2: Investigation 4, Diffusion and Osmosis

Overview of the Lab

In Part I, you will create cell models with agar cubes and use them to calculate surface-area-to-volume ratios and make predictions about the rate of diffusion. In Part II, dialysis tubing, which is selectively permeable, is used to create cell models to investigate questions about movement of molecules across the membrane. In Part III, living tissue is used to observe and understand osmosis in cells.

YOU MUST KNOW

- Factors that affect diffusion across the membrane.
- How water potential is measured and its relationship to solute concentration and pressure potential of a solution.
- Water moves from a region where water potential is high to a region where water potential is low.
- The relationship of molarity to osmotic concentration.
- How to determine the osmotic concentration of a solution from experimental data.

SCIENCE PRACTICES: CAN YOU . . .

- Design an experiment to measure the rate of osmosis in a model system?
- Analyze data and make predictions about molecular movement through cellular membranes?
- Connect the concepts of diffusion and osmosis to the structure of the membrane and molarity?
- Use the principles of water potential to predict and justify the movement of water into plant tissue?
- Calculate surface-area-to-volume ratios to predict which cell might eliminate wastes or procure nutrients faster? (LO 2.6)

Hints and Review

▌ The first part of this investigation involves calculating the surface area and volume of several sizes of agar cubes, which serve as models of cells. The cubes are prepared in such a way that you can observe a color change in them over time. This will demonstrate that the distance the material diffuses into the cubes is the same regardless of the size but that the percentage of the total cube volume penetrated goes down drastically as the cubes get larger.

▌ Because cells exchange materials with their environment by diffusion, the investigation demonstrates that smaller cells have more favorable surface-area-to-volume ratios.

▌ Refer to the AP Biology Equations and Formulas page to be sure you can calculate surface area and volume. (See page 358.) There is a practice problem on the sample test.

- Get a firm fix on the terminology! This is one topic where you will not get any credit if you understand the concept but garble the vocabulary. Let's add some more terms.

- **Osmosis** is the movement of water from a region of high concentration to a region of low concentration through a selectively permeable membrane.

- In **dynamic equilibrium**, molecules are in motion, but there is no net change in concentration.

- Study Figure 4.1 to review some important terms.

- In Figure 4.1a, the two solutions are equal in their solute concentrations. We say that they are **isotonic** to each other.

Figure 4.1 Diffusion across a selectively permeable membrane

- In Figure 4.1b, the solution in the bag contains less solute than the solution in the beaker. The solution in the bag is **hypotonic** (lower solute concentration) to the solution in the beaker. The solution in the beaker is **hypertonic** (higher solute concentration) to the one in the bag. Water will move from the hypotonic solution into the hypertonic solution.

- You must have a solid knowledge of the principles of diffusion to understand this lab, but what many students find most difficult in this laboratory is the concept of water potential. Here's a quick review:

- **Remember this:** *Water moves from a region where water potential is high to a region where water potential is low.* Think of water potential as potential energy, and you will understand why this is so.

- **Water potential** (Ψ) involves *two* components: solute potential (Ψ_S) and pressure potential (Ψ_P).

- In this laboratory we use bars as the unit of measure for water potential; 1 bar = approximately 1 atmosphere.

- **Solute potential (Ψ_S)** results from the presence of solutes. An increase in solute concentration will cause solute potential to decrease. (Ψ_S becomes more negative.) Adding solute, therefore, lowers the water potential.

- **Pressure potential (Ψ_P)** is zero in an open container. When a solution is enclosed by a rigid cell wall, the movement of water into the cell will exert pressure on the cell wall and the pressure potential (Ψ_P) will increase. This increase in pressure within the cell will raise the water potential.

- The water potential of pure water in an open container is zero because there is no solute, and the pressure in the container is zero.

- A dehydrated potato slice does *not* have high water potential. Its water potential is low, and if placed in distilled water (which has high water potential), water will move into the potato cells.

Figure 4.2 will help you understand the relationships of water potential, solute potential, and pressure potential.

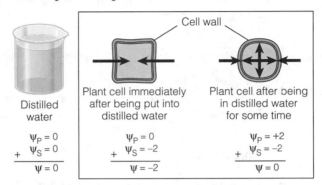

Figure 4.2   Water potential in a plant cell

Calculating Water Potential and Solute Potential

- Water potential is calculated using the following formula:

$$\Psi = \Psi_P + \Psi_S$$

Water potential (Ψ) = pressure potential (Ψ_P) + solute potential (Ψ_S)

- If you know the solute concentration, you can calculate solute potential (Ψ_S) using the following formula: $\Psi_S = -iCRT$
where
i = The number of particles the molecule will make in water; for NaCl this would be 2; for sucrose or glucose, this number is 1
C = Molar concentration (from your experimental data)
R = Pressure constant = 0.0831 liter bar/mole K
T = Temperature in degrees Kelvin = 273 + °C of solution

- These formulas and values for T and R are also on the AP Biology Equations and Formulas page. (See page 358.)

- What if you don't know the molarity? One way to determine it is to take a sample of the cells and drop them into solutions of known molarity. In this lab, we use cores taken from potatoes. If you obtain the following results, what is the molarity of the potato cores? (See Figure 4.3)

Figure 4.3   Percent change in mass of potato cores in various sucrose solutions

- The correct answer is approximately 0.35 M. This is determined by seeing at what molarity on the graph the cores neither gain nor lose mass. This is where the line crosses the *x*-axis.

- Now that the molarity of the potato is known, if the temperature of the solution is known you can calculate the solute potential using the formula $\Psi_S = -iCRT$.

> **TIP FROM THE READERS**
> This fundamental topic will definitely be tested on the exam. Be sure you understand this material! If you feel you need more practice, go to the web to *LabBench, Lab 1* (http://www.phschool.com/science/biology_place/labbench/).

Questions

1. In beaker b, shown in Figure 4.4, what is the water potential of the distilled water in the beaker and of the beet core?

Figure 4.4   Water potential practice problem

   (A) water potential in the beaker = 0; water potential in the beet core = 0
   (B) water potential in the beaker = 0; water potential in the beet core = −0.2
   (C) water potential in the beaker = 0; water potential in the beet core = 0.2
   (D) water potential in the beaker cannot be calculated; water potential in the beet core = 0.2

2. Which of the following statements is true for the diagrams in Figure 4.4?
   (A) The beet core in beaker a is at equilibrium with the surrounding water.
   (B) The beet core in beaker b will lose water to the surrounding environment.
   (C) The beet core in beaker b would be more turgid than the beet core in beaker a.
   (D) The beet core in beaker a is likely to gain so much water that its cells will rupture.

3. Calculate the solute potential of the potato cores in Figure 4.3. The temperature is 21°C.

   Express your answer in bars, rounded to the nearest one-hundredth.

BIG IDEA 2: Investigation 5, Photosynthesis

Overview of the Lab

▌ What factors affect the rate of photosynthesis in living leaves? In the first part of this lab, you will learn a procedure to measure the rate of photosynthesis. There are several methods for this. Your teacher may elect to use the floating disk procedure to indirectly measure the rate of oxygen production or a DPIP reduction method or probes interfaced with computers.

▌ In the second part, you will design and conduct an investigation of one factor that affects the rate of photosynthesis.

YOU MUST KNOW

- The equation for photosynthesis and understand the process of photosynthesis.
- The relationship between light wavelength or intensity and photosynthetic rate.
- The anatomy of a typical leaf and how the structures interact in photosynthesis.
- How to determine the rate of photosynthesis.

SCIENCE PRACTICES: CAN YOU . . .

- Measure the rate of photosynthesis using a technique that gives consistent results?
- Apply mathematical routines to calculate the rate of photosynthesis?
- Apply the concepts you have learned in the investigation to describe relationships of cell structure and function?
- Describe strategies for capture, storage, and use of free energy by plants?

Hints and Review

▌ In photosynthesis, plant cells convert light energy into chemical energy that is stored in sugars and other organic compounds.

The equation for photosynthesis is
$$6\,H_2O + 6\,CO_2 \rightarrow C_6H_{12}O_6 + 6\,O_2$$

■ There are several ways you could measure the rate of photosynthesis. One would be to measure the rate of oxygen production. In the floating disk procedure, you would submerge leaf disks and then measure how long it takes for enough oxygen to be produced to float the disks. Another method involves using the reduction of DPIP by electrons from chlorophyll that are excited when exposed to light.

■ You should be able to explain the chemical and physiological basis for the technique you use to measure the rate of photosynthesis.

1. In the floating disk procedure, a vacuum is created to remove accumulated gases from the air spaces in the leaf, which will cause the leaf disk to sink when placed in water. Because photosynthesis produces oxygen, most of these gas molecules are oxygen; when the disk is exposed to bright light, it will float again as oxygen is generated.

2. In the DPIP reduction technique, you disrupt the chloroplast membrane by tossing the plant material in a blender. When exposed to light, the electrons in chlorophyll will be boosted to higher energy levels, but the electron acceptors embedded in the thylakoid membranes are not able to function. These high-energy electrons from chlorophyll will be picked up by DPIP, a chemical that is readily reduced. When oxidized, DPIP is deep blue. When reduced, it becomes colorless. It is possible to measure the rate of color change with a spectrophotometer.

■ With a technique that will measure the rate of photosynthesis, such as DPIP reduction or oxygen accumulation, you can design an experiment to test a variable such as exposure to different light intensities (vary the distance from a bulb or vary the wattage of the bulb) or exposure to different wavelengths of light (use colored cellophanes or filters).

■ If you removed the gases in leaf disks and placed the disks in water near a bright light source, they would never rise! Can you explain this based on the equation for photosynthesis? There is so little CO_2 in water that photosynthesis can barely proceed. You should now be able to explain why the floating disk procedure requires the addition of baking soda to the water.

Questions

1. If a student uses the DPIP technique described above, which of the following statements best describes the role of DPIP?
   (A) It mimics the action of chlorophyll by absorbing light energy.
   (B) It serves as an electron donor and blocks the formation of NADPH.
   (C) It is an electron acceptor and is reduced by electrons from chlorophyll.
   (D) It is bleached in the presence of light and can be used to measure light levels.

2. Some students were not able to get many data points when using the DPIP technique because the solution went from blue to colorless in only 5 minutes when they used chloroplasts exposed to light. What modification to the experiment do you think would be most likely to provide better results?
   (A) Double the volume of chloroplasts used.
   (B) Double the volume of DPIP so that the solution has a lower initial transmittance.
   (C) Boil the chloroplast to further disrupt the thylakoid membrane.
   (D) Select a different plant material and blend it more thoroughly.

3. If a student performed this experiment using DPIP that was initially deep blue and got a flat line when graphing the data (showing very little change in color over time), which of these would be a plausible explanation?
   (A) The rate of photosynthesis was very high.
   (B) The intensity of light may have been too great for a reaction to occur.
   (C) The chlorophyll was damaged and could not respond to light.
   (D) The DPIP was already reduced when the experiment began.

4. A student used the floating disk technique to measure the rate of photosynthesis. After 20 minutes under a bright light, none of the disks had floated. Based on your understanding of photosynthesis, which of the following might be a reasonable explanation for this?
   (A) Not all green plant material does photosynthesis when exposed to light.
   (B) There was no source of carbon dioxide.
   (C) A source of oxygen was not available.
   (D) There was no water available for photosynthesis.

BIG IDEA 2: Investigation 6, Cellular Respiration

Overview of the Lab

In this experiment, you will learn how to use a respirometer to measure the rate of cellular respiration. With the respirometer as the research instrument, it is now possible to design an experiment to test the effect of a single variable on the rate of respiration.

YOU MUST KNOW

- The equation for cellular respiration.
- The components of a respirometer and how it works.
- The gas laws that affect volume changes within the respirometer.
- The relationship between movement of water in a respirometer and cellular respiration.
- The effect of temperature or increased metabolic activity on respiration.
- How to calculate the rate of respiration.

SCIENCE PRACTICES: CAN YOU ...

- Propose a question about some aspect of cellular respiration that could be investigated using available materials?
- Design an experiment to answer a question about cellular respiration including suitable controls?
- Analyze your data and use appropriate mathematical routines to describe your results?
- Provide evidence to justify a claim such as "dormant seeds respire at a low rate"?

The equation for cellular respiration is

$$C_6H_{12}O_6 + 6\ O_2 \rightarrow 6\ H_2O + 6\ CO_2 + \text{Energy}$$

Hints and Review

▌ How can you measure the rate of cellular respiration? When you study the equation for cellular respiration, you will see that there are at least three ways:

1. Measure the amount of glucose consumed.
2. Measure the amount of oxygen consumed.
3. Measure the amount of carbon dioxide produced.

▌ In this experiment, you will use either gas probes or *respirometers* to measure the amount of oxygen consumed.

▌ A **respirometer** is an air-tight chamber except for one opening for gases to enter or leave. Potassium hydroxide (KOH) is used to soak a cotton ball and will combine with the CO_2 produced by the organism you are using. A solid precipitate forms in the following reaction:

$$CO_2 + 2KOH \rightarrow K_2CO_3 + H_2O$$

Because CO_2 and O_2 are produced and consumed in equal amounts, any changes in the sealed container (assuming temperature and pressure remain constant) will be caused by a change in gas volume due to cellular respiration. As O_2 is consumed in respiration and CO_2 removed as a solid precipitate, pressure within the respirometer decreases and water enters the pipette. Study Figure 6.1 to see the components of a respirometer.

Figure 6.1 Components of a respirometer

Although no single experimental organism is prescribed in this lab, many students will use some sort of seeds or small invertebrates such as mealworms. We will describe ideas related to seeds or invertebrates, although your experimental organism may differ.

A seed contains an embryo plant and a food supply surrounded by a seed coat.

Germinating (sprouting) seeds will show a higher rate of respiration than the *nongerminating* seeds because metabolic activity is increased. However, these dry, nongerminating seeds are not dead but **dormant**. They can be stored for years and, when soaked in water, will germinate.

As you investigate, consider the size and metabolic activity of the organism you have selected and its rate of cellular respiration. Your knowledge of metabolism should lead you to see that more active or endothermic organisms require more energy and therefore have higher rates of respiration.

In most cases, chemical reactions occur more slowly at lower temperatures, so seeds or ectotherms that are chilled will show a lower rate of O_2 consumption.

A vial of glass beads alone might act as a *control* for this experiment. The control will compensate for any change in pressure or temperature.

Students are often confused by the difference between a *control* (the glass beads in this experiment) and *factors that are held constant*. In this experiment, you will hold constant factors such as the volumes within the containers, the number of peas or mealworms, and the temperature of the water for each experimental group.

- Figure 6.2 shows a graph of typical results from an experiment. What is the question being tested? (You will find the answer to this question at the end of this investigation.)

- You must be able to calculate the rate of these reactions. If you need to review how to do this, you can find a lesson on calculating rate in Investigation 13, Enzyme Activity.

Figure 6.2   Effect of temperature on respiration rate

TIP FROM THE READERS

Students often become confused about the effect of cold on the rate of respiration. You may know that there is more O_2 in colder water, but the presence of more O_2 is *not* the reason organisms respire more slowly when chilled! In general, within a normal physiological range for the organism, **the rate of metabolism is directly related to the temperature of the organism,** whether it is a pea seed, a cricket, or a goldfish.

Questions

1. What is the rate of oxygen consumption in germinating corn at 12°C, as shown in Figure 6.2?
   (A) 0.08 mL/min
   (B) 0.04 mL/min
   (C) 0.8 mL/min
   (D) 0.6 mL/min

2. Using Figure 6.2, which of the following is a reasonable claim based on the data?
   (A) The amount of oxygen consumed by germinating corn at 22°C is approximately twice the amount of oxygen consumed by germinating corn at 12°C.
   (B) The rate of oxygen consumption is the same in both germinating and nongerminating corn during the initial time period from 0 to 5 minutes.
   (C) The rate of oxygen consumption in the germinating corn at 12°C at 10 minutes is 0.4 mL O_2/minute.
   (D) The rate of oxygen consumption is higher for nongerminating corn at 12°C than at 22°C.

3. Which of the following conclusions is supported by the data shown on the graph in Figure 6.2?
   (A) The rate of respiration is higher in nongerminating seeds than in germinating seeds.
   (B) Nongerminating seeds are not alive and show no difference in rate of respiration at different temperatures.
   (C) The rate of respiration in the germinating seeds would have been higher if the experiment had been conducted in sunlight.
   (D) The rate of respiration increases as the temperature increases in both germinating and nongerminating seeds.

4. What is the role of KOH in a respirometer?
   (A) It serves as an electron donor to promote cellular respiration.
   (B) As KOH breaks down, it releases the oxygen needed for cellular respiration.
   (C) It serves as a temporary energy source for the respiring organism.
   (D) It binds with carbon dioxide to form a solid, removing CO_2 from the respirometer and allowing water to move into the respirometer.

Answer to question about Figure 6.2: Actually, the graph should suggest to you that two different questions were tested: 1. What is the effect of germination versus non-germination on cellular respiration? 2. What is the effect of temperature on cellular respiration?

BIG IDEA 3: Investigation 7, Cell Division: Mitosis and Meiosis

This laboratory involves five parts:

1. Modeling Mitosis

Beads, pipe cleaners, or other materials help model the events of the cell cycle, including chromosome duplication and movement.

2. Effects of Environment on Mitosis

You will plan an experiment using root squashes made from onion roots to investigate the effect of a protein (lectin), known to increase the rate of mitosis in the roots. You will then use Chi-square analysis to statistically analyze the data you have collected.

3. Loss of Cell Cycle Control in Cancer

HeLa cells and the Philadelphia chromosome demonstrate how genetic changes can lead to a loss of cell cycle control and cancer.

4. Modeling Meiosis

Model the events of meiosis, including independent assortment and crossing over, to demonstrate increased genetic variation. You will also demonstrate nondisjunction and explain its relationship to genetic disorders.

5. Meiosis and Crossing Over in *Sordaria*

In this part, you will observe crossover events in meiosis of a fungus and calculate map distance.

YOU MUST KNOW

- The events of mitosis and meiosis in plant and animal cells.
- How mitosis and meiosis differ.
- How normal cells and cancer cells differ from each other.
- What may go wrong during the cell cycle in cancer cells.
- The roles of segregation, independent assortment, and crossing over in generating genetic variation.
- How to calculate map distance from experimental data.
- How to evaluate experimental results using Chi-square analysis.

SCIENCE PRACTICES: CAN YOU . . .

- Make predictions about natural phenomena occurring in the cell cycle? (LO 3.7)
- Describe the events that occur in the cell cycle? (LO 3.8)
- Represent the connection between meiosis and increased genetic diversity? (LO 3.10)
- Use the mathematical routine of Chi-square analysis appropriately?

Part 1 and Part 5. Modeling Mitosis and Meiosis

Go back to Topic 2 to review mitosis and the cell cycle. Go to Topic 4 to review the important elements of meiosis. Although you have had this process described in class numerous times by this point in your high school career, we find that students struggle to model the process. Buy a cheap sack of colored pipe cleaners and try this:

1. Assemble two pairs of homologous chromosomes. (How did you represent the maternal and paternal chromosomes?)
2. Use them to model a cell in metaphase of mitosis.
3. Model metaphase I of meiosis.
4. Model metaphase II of meiosis.
5. Model crossing over. When does it occur?
6. When do the cells become haploid? Show it with your model.

This activity is deceptive: It seems easy but is surprisingly difficult! Work with a study partner and check with your teacher.

Part 2: Effects of Environment on Mitosis

▌ To investigate the effect of a chemical believed to affect the rate of cell division, you need to grow some of the plants in a medium with this chemical and another group in water as a control. You could then determine the effect on cell division by comparing the number of cells actively dividing in each treatment.

▌ Randomly select and count 250 cells in both the control and experimental groups. Record those that are in any stage of mitosis (prophase, metaphase, anaphase, or telophase) as well as the cells in interphase in both groups. Sample data are shown in Table 7.1.

	Cells in Interphase	Cells in Mitosis	Total # Cells
Control group	202	48	250
Experimental group	186	64	250

Table 7.1   Onion root tip cell phase data

▌ Actual data will not have such even numbers, but this will make it easier to illustrate what needs to be done. Based on the data, can you now conclude that your treatment increased the rate of cell division? Not yet! In science, you will need to use statistical methods to support such a conclusion. Chi-square analysis would be an appropriate test to apply here. If this is new information for you, proceed to the lesson that begins on page 354, Statistical Analysis, and work through the information provided there. Then come back here.

▌ Using the data from Table 7.1, do a Chi-square analysis to complete the following table. State the null hypothesis being tested. The solution to this chart is in the Answers and Explanations for this investigation on page 439.

Null Hypothesis:

	Observed (o)	Expected (e)	$(o - e)^2/e$
Interphase cells			
Mitosis cells			
Total			
		$X^2 =$	
Degrees of Freedom = $\qquad$ p value = $\qquad$ critical value =			
Accept or reject the null hypothesis?			
Explanation:			

Part 5: Meiosis and Crossing Over in Sordaria

▌ When the growing filaments of two haploid strains of *Sordaria* that produce spores of different colors meet, fertilization occurs and zygotes form. Figure 7.1 shows spore formation in *Sordaria*.

▌ Meiosis occurs within fruiting bodies to form four haploid *ascospores,* spores contained in *asci* (special sacs).

▌ One mitotic division then doubles the number of ascospores to eight.

▌ The number of **map units** between two genes is calculated by determining the percentage of recombinants that result from crossing over. The greater the frequency of crossing over, the greater the map distance.

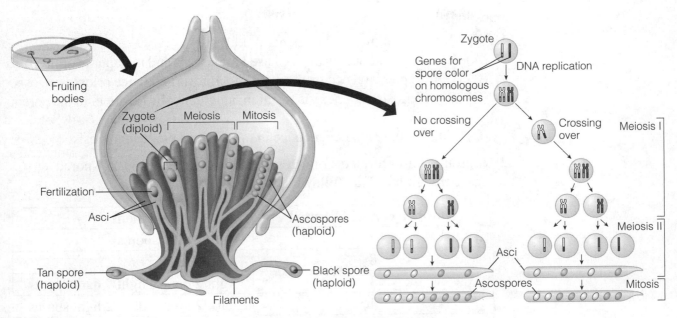

Figure 7.1   Crossing over in *Sordaria*

▌ Calculate the percentage of crossovers by dividing the number of crossover asci (these are the ones with spores arranged 2:2:2:2 or 2:4:2, as you see in Figure 7.2) by the total number of asci × 100.

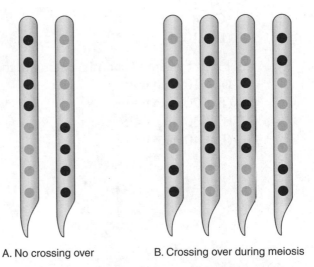

A. No crossing over   B. Crossing over during meiosis

Figure 7.2   Possible arrangements of ascospores

▌ To calculate the map distance, divide the percentage of crossover asci by 2. The percentage of crossover asci is divided by 2 because only half of the spores in each ascus are the result of crossing over.

Questions

1. Which of the following statements is correct?
   (A) Crossing over occurs in prophase I of meiosis and metaphase of mitosis.
   (B) DNA replication occurs once prior to mitosis and twice prior to meiosis.
   (C) Both mitosis and meiosis result in daughter cells identical to the parent cells.
   (D) Nuclear division occurs once in mitosis and twice in meiosis.

2. A group of asci formed from crossing light-spored with dark-spored *Sordaria* produced the following results:

Number of Asci Counted	Spore Arrangement
7	4 light/4 dark spores
8	4 dark/4 light spores
3	2 light/2 dark/2 light/2 dark spores
4	2 dark/2 light/2 dark/2 light spores
1	2 dark/4 light/2 dark spores
2	2 light/4 dark/2 light spores

How many of these asci contain a spore arrangement that resulted from crossing over?
   (A) 3
   (B) 7
   (C) 8
   (D) 10

3. From this small sample, calculate the map distance between the genes.
   (A) 10 map units
   (B) 20 map units
   (C) 30 map units
   (D) 40 map units

BIG IDEA 3: Investigation 8, Biotechnology: Bacterial Transformation

Overview of the Lab

You will use antibiotic-resistant plasmids to transform *Escherichia coli*. You will introduce a plasmid containing a gene for resistance to the antibiotic ampicillin into a strain of *E. coli* that ampicillin kills. If the susceptible bacteria incorporate the foreign DNA, they will become ampicillin resistant. You will then apply mathematical routines to calculate transformation efficiency. Finally, laboratory teams may design and conduct an investigation to study transformation in more depth.

YOU MUST KNOW

- The principles of bacterial transformation, including how plasmids are engineered and taken up by cells.
- Factors that affect transformation efficiency.
- How to verify and screen for transformed cells.
- Bacterial transformation is a type of horizontal gene transfer and increases genetic variation.

SCIENCE PRACTICES: CAN YOU . . .

- Justify the claim that humans manipulate heritable genetic information by identifying and describing at least two commonly used technologies? (LO. 3.4)
- Calculate transformation efficiency and express the results in scientific notation?
- Predict and justify how a change in the basic protocol for bacterial transformation would affect transformation efficiency?

Key Concepts of Bacterial Transformation

- Genetic **transformation** occurs when a host organism takes in foreign DNA and expresses the foreign gene.
- Bacterial cells have a single main chromosome and circular DNA molecules called plasmids, which carry genetic information. All of the genes required for basic survival and reproduction are on the single chromosome.
- **Plasmids** are circular pieces of DNA that exist outside the main bacterial chromosome and carry their own genes for specialized functions, including resistance to specific drugs. In genetic engineering, plasmids are one means used to introduce foreign genes into a bacterial cell. To understand how this might work, consider the plasmid in Figure 8.1.

Figure 8.1 Plasmid with ampicillin-resistant gene

▌ Plasmids have the *amp*^R gene, which confers resistance to the antibiotic ampicillin. *E. coli* cells containing this plasmid, termed **"+amp^R"** cells, can survive and form colonies on LB agar that has been supplemented with ampicillin.

▌ In contrast, cells lacking the amp^R plasmid, termed **"−amp^R"** cells, are sensitive to the antibiotic, which kills them. An ampicillin-sensitive cell (−amp^R) can be transformed to an ampicillin-resistant (+amp^R) cell by its uptake of a foreign plasmid containing the *amp*^R gene.

▌ **Competent cells** are cells that are most likely to take up extracellular DNA. Competent cells are in logarithmic growth, and chemical conditions are modified to induce the uptake of DNA. Study Figure 8.2 to review the lab procedure used to prepare competent cells and get them to take up the amp^R plasmids.

Figure 8.2 Procedure for bacterial transformation with amp plasmids

▌ Study Figure 8.3. It shows the expected results in this experiment.

▌ If there is no ampicillin in the agar, *E. coli* will cover the plate with so many cells it is called a "lawn" of cells (Plates A and C).

▌ Only transformed cells can grow on agar with ampicillin. Because only some of the cells exposed to the amp^R plasmids will actually take the plasmids in, only some cells will transform. Thus, you will see only individual colonies on the plate (Plate D).

Control 1 No amp^R
plasmids added

Control 2 No amp^R
plasmids added

Experimental tube 1
amp^R plasmids added

Experimental tube 2
amp^R plasmids added

| A | B | C | D |

No ampicillin
in growth medium

Ampicillin
in growth medium

No ampicillin
in growth medium

Ampicillin
in growth medium

Figure 8.3   Sample transformation lab

▮ If none of the sensitive *E. coli* cells has been transformed, nothing will grow on the agar with ampicillin (Plate B).

▮ **Restriction enzymes** or endonucleases are bacterial enzymes that will cut DNA at specific DNA sequences known as **recognition sites**. Often the enzymes cut the DNA so that the ends are single-stranded "sticky ends." A **gene of interest** (such as antibiotic resistance) can be introduced into a plasmid using restriction enzymes as described next.

▮ Introducing a gene of interest into bacteria:

1. Both the gene of interest and the plasmid are cut with the *same* restriction enzyme, so they have the same sticky ends.

2. DNA ligase is used to anneal and seal the sticky ends.

3. The recipient cells are transformed with the engineered plasmid.

4. Colonies carrying the plasmid are isolated.

▮ How do we know that transformation has been successful? The plasmid is constructed so that the gene of interest is linked to one of the following genes.

1. Use a **selection gene**, such as for antibiotic resistance. Only those cells that have incorporated the plasmid will have antibiotic resistance.

2. Use a **reporter gene** such as GFP (green fluorescent protein). Transformed cells will glow!

▮ **Transformation efficiency** is the number of transformed cells per microgram of the plasmid. High transformation efficiencies require cells that are in log phase of growth, suspended in ice-cold calcium chloride, have a rapid heat shock (this makes the membrane more permeable to the plasmid), and plasmids that are not too large. Each of these conditions could be manipulated to determine their effect on transformation.

Questions

In a molecular biology laboratory, a student obtained competent *E. coli* cells and used a common transformation procedure to induce the uptake of plasmid DNA with a gene for resistance to the antibiotic kanamycin. The results shown in Figure 8.4 were obtained.

Plate I.
LB agar
+kan plasmid

Plate II.
LB agar with kanamycin
+kan plasmid

Plate III.
LB agar
no plasmid added

Plate IV.
LB agar with kanamycin
no plasmid added

Figure 8.4   Transformation results

1. On which petri dish do only transformed cells grow?
   (A) Plate I
   (B) Plate II
   (C) Plate III
   (D) Plate IV

2. Which of the plates is used as a control to show that nontransformed *E. coli* will not grow in the presence of kanamycin?
   (A) Plate I
   (B) Plate II
   (C) Plate III
   (D) Plate IV

3. If a student wants to verify that transformation has occurred, which of the following procedures should she use?
   (A) Spread cells from Plate I onto a plate with LB agar; incubate.
   (B) Spread cells from Plate II onto a plate with LB agar; incubate.
   (C) Repeat the initial spread of $-kan^R$ cells onto Plate IV to eliminate possible experimental error.
   (D) Spread cells from Plate II onto a plate with LB agar with kanamycin; incubate.

4. During the course of an *E. coli* transformation laboratory, a student forgets to mark the culture tube that received the kanamycin-resistant plasmids. The student proceeds with the laboratory because he thinks that he will be able to determine from his results which culture tube contained cells that may have undergone transformation. Which plate would be most likely to indicate transformed cells?
   (A) a plate with a lawn of cells growing on LB agar with kanamycin
   (B) a plate with a lawn of cells growing on LB agar without kanamycin
   (C) a plate with 100 colonies growing on LB agar with kanamycin
   (D) a plate with 100 colonies growing on LB agar without kanamycin

BIG IDEA 3: Investigation 9, Biotechnology: Restriction Enzyme Analysis of DNA

Overview of the Lab

You will use restriction endonucleases and gel electrophoresis to create and analyze genetic fingerprints. You will use the results of electrophoresis to prepare a standard curve and estimate fragment sizes of an unknown sample.

YOU MUST KNOW

- The function of restriction enzymes and their role in genetic engineering.
- How gel electrophoresis separates DNA fragments.
- How to use a standard curve to determine the size of unknown DNA fragments.

SCIENCE PRACTICES: CAN YOU . . .

- Apply mathematical routines to construct a graph of DNA fragments of known size?
- Use a standard curve to determine the size of unknown DNA fragments?
- Use the results of gel electrophoresis to map the restriction sites of a bacterial plasmid?

Key Concepts of Restriction Enzyme Cleavage of DNA and Gel Electrophoresis

▌ **Gel electrophoresis** is a procedure that separates molecules based on their rate of movement through a gel under the influence of an electrical field.

▌ The direction of movement is affected by the charge of the molecules, and the rate of movement is affected by their size and shape, the density of the gel, and the strength of the electrical field.

▌ DNA is a negatively charged molecule, so it will move toward the positive pole of the gel when a current is applied. When DNA has been cut by restriction enzymes, the different-sized fragments will migrate at different rates. Because the smallest fragments move more easily through the gel, they will migrate the farthest during the time the current is on. Keep in mind that the length of each fragment is measured in number of DNA base pairs.

▌ You may use restriction enzymes to create your own DNA fragments or use fragments that are commercially prepared. In one lab we often purchase, students receive three samples of DNA obtained from the bacteriophage lambda. One sample is uncut DNA, one is incubated with the restriction enzyme *Hind*III, and one is incubated with *Eco*RI. The fragments of DNA are separated by electrophoresis, stained for visualization, and then analyzed.

■ After the DNA samples are loaded into wells in the gel, electricity is applied. The DNA fragments will migrate.

1. *DNA is negatively charged and will migrate toward the positive pole.*

2. *Smaller fragments of DNA will migrate faster than larger fragments.*

■ DNA is not visible to the naked eye. To visualize the DNA, it is necessary to add a dye, such as methylene blue, that will bind to it.

■ Each fragment of DNA is a particular number of nucleotides, or base pairs, long. When researchers want to determine the size of DNA fragments produced with particular restriction enzymes, they run the unknown DNA alongside DNA with known fragment sizes. The known DNA acts as a **marker** and is used to help determine the unknown fragment sizes.

■ Figure 9.1 shows the results of electrophoresis. In this case, semilog paper has been used to plot the results of the *Hind*III digest. Because its fragment sizes are known, this is the *standard curve*. It can now be used to determine the other fragment sizes from the DNA I and DNA II samples by interpolation.

■ In the commercial lab just described, *Hind*III is the marker and is used to prepare the standard curve. The standard curve is used to determine the fragment sizes in the *Eco*RI digest.

Figure 9.1   Using results of electrophoresis to determine fragment sizes for an unknown sample

Questions

1. How many base pairs is the fragment circled in Figure 9.1?
   (A) 350
   (B) 22
   (C) 2,200
   (D) 3,500

2. Which of the following statements is correct?
   (A) Longer DNA fragments migrate farther than shorter fragments.
   (B) Migration distance is inversely proportional to the fragment size.
   (C) Positively charged DNA migrates more rapidly than negatively charged DNA.
   (D) Uncut DNA migrates farther than DNA cut with restriction enzymes.

Here is a plasmid with restriction sites for *Bam*HI and *Eco*RI. Several restriction digests were done using these two enzymes either alone or in combination. Use Figure 9.2 to answer questions 3 and 4. **Hint:** Begin by determining the number and size of the fragments produced with each enzyme; "kb" stands for kilobases, or thousands of base pairs.

Figure 9.2   Plasmid with restriction sites for *Bam*HI and *Eco*RI

3. Which lane shows a digest with *Bam*HI only?
   (A) I
   (B) II
   (C) III
   (D) IV

4. Which lane shows a digest with both *Bam*HI and *Eco*RI?
   (A) II
   (B) III
   (C) IV
   (D) V

BIG IDEA 4: Investigation 10, Energy Dynamics

Overview of the Lab

Primary productivity is a measure of the amount of light energy converted to chemical energy in the form of organic compounds during a given period and sets the energy budget of an ecosystem. Energy flows constantly through an ecosystem. This investigation has you look at energy flow from plants (the producers) to the insects (consumers) that feed on them. This is done by measuring the biomass of the producers and then of the consumers.

YOU MUST KNOW

- The difference between gross and net productivity and how to measure them.
- Energy does not cycle; only matter cycles.
- The relationship between photosynthesis and respiration and how these processes relate to energy flow, NPP, and ecosystem energy dynamics.
- How to measure productivity to investigate a question about energy capture and flow in an ecosystem.

SCIENCE PRACTICES: CAN YOU . . .

- Plan and implement data collection strategies to answer a question about energy flow in an ecosystem?
- Analyze data to identify patterns or relationships?
- Refine your observations and measurements and evaluate the evidence provided by the data?

Hints and Review

> You must have a firm grip on the summary equations for both cellular respiration and photosynthesis to understand energy flow.

Photosynthesis

$$6\ CO_2 + 6\ H_2O + \text{Light energy} \rightarrow C_6H_{12}O_6 + 6\ O_2$$

Cellular Respiration

$$C_6H_{12}O_6 + 6\ O_2 \rightarrow 6\ CO_2 + 6\ H_2O + \text{Energy}$$

- **Primary productivity** is a term used to describe the rate at which plants and other photosynthetic organisms produce organic compounds in an ecosystem. There are two aspects of primary productivity:
  - **Gross primary productivity (GPP)** = the entire photosynthetic production of organic compounds in an ecosystem over a unit of time.
  - **Net primary productivity (NPP)** = the organic materials that remain after photosynthetic organisms in the ecosystem have used some of these compounds for their cellular energy needs (cellular respiration).
  - Net primary productivity is determined by subtracting the energy lost by cellular respiration from gross primary productivity, or NPP = GPP − Cellular respiration.
- Refer to the equation for photosynthesis. Because GPP is the result of photosynthesis, it can be measured in three ways:
  1. the amount of carbon dioxide used,
  2. the rate of oxygen production, or
  3. the rate of sugar formation = amount of biomass.
- In an aquatic ecosystem, you could measure the amount of dissolved oxygen to determine the rate of photosynthesis and determine productivity.
- This investigation has two parts to help you understand the essentials of productivity and energy flow. The following section describes each of these parts.

Part I : Estimating Net Primary Productivity of Fast Plants

- In a terrestrial ecosystem productivity is determined by finding the biomass, which indirectly measures the rate of carbon fixation in sugar formation.
- **Biomass** is the weight of organic material produced. To determine biomass, it is necessary to dry the material so that water is not included in the measure.
- The plant material will need to be dried; references can give you a reasonable approximation of the conversion factor to use to determine the kcals of energy. Because the plant material you measure has been doing both photosynthesis as well as respiration, you are determining *net*, not gross, productivity.

Part II: Estimating Energy Flow between Producers and Consumers

- In this part of the lab, you will use a consumer (cabbage butterfly larvae) and a producer (brussels sprouts or another food source for the consumers).
- You will determine the wet mass of the larva before and after you allow the larvae to feed for three days. Their change in mass reflects energy gained from the food they ate.
- From the wet mass of the larvae, you will use published data to approximate the dry biomass. But wait! These little guys are pushing out the waste as fast as they eat, so you must also collect and weigh it! This waste is called *frass*. When you combine both weights and consult published data, you should be able to calculate the energy represented by the increased mass of the larvae and their frass.

■ Compare the energy estimate for the plant material (NPP) and for the consumers. What conclusions can you formulate about energy transfers and energy efficiency between trophic levels?

■ According to the second law of thermodynamics, energy transfer is never 100% efficient. Most textbooks cite an energy transfer of only 10% between trophic levels. What other sources of energy consumption are not accounted for using this artificial ecosystem?

Questions

1. Figure 10.1 shows productivity in an aquatic environment, determined by the amount of oxygen produced.

Figure 10.1   Gross and Net Productivity at Varying Light Intensities

At what light intensity do you expect there to be no net productivity?
(A) any intensity below 100%
(B) only at intensities of 0% and 2%
(C) any intensity below 10%
(D) any intensity above 25%

2. What does "net productivity" mean, and how do you calculate it?
   (A) Net productivity is a measure of the organic products of photosynthesis that accumulate after cellular respiration. You calculate net productivity by subtracting the energy consumed in respiration from the total energy captured in photosynthesis.
   (B) Net productivity is a measure of the amount of respiration in a test area. You calculate net productivity by subtracting the amount of waste produced by the consumers from their biomass.
   (C) Net productivity is the total amount of carbon fixed. You calculate net productivity by determining the biomass of all producers in the test area over a unit of time.
   (D) Net productivity is the amount of energy available to the secondary consumers. You calculate net productivity by determining the biomass of the primary consumers.

3. Consider the following two ecosystems located at the same latitude, and choose the best description.

Ecosystem A	Ecosystem B
266 sunny days/year	183 sunny days/year
282 frost-free days/year	125 frost-free days/year
25" rain/year	36" rain/year

(A) Ecosystem A would be expected to have less species diversity because it has abundant light and a long growing season.

(B) Ecosystem B would have greater species diversity because it receives more water annually.

(C) Ecosystem A would be expected to have the highest gross primary productivity because it has more sunny days and a longer growing season.

(D) Ecosystem B would be expected to have the highest net primary productivity because it has longer days, allowing time for more photosynthesis.

BIG IDEA 4: Laboratory 11, Transpiration

Overview of the Lab

Transpiration is the major mechanism that drives the movement of water through a plant. In the first section of the laboratory, you will calculate leaf surface area and use this measurement to determine the average number of stomata per square millimeter of leaf. The investigation then focuses on learning a technique to measure the rate of transpiration, such as using a potometer or the whole-plant method. This knowledge will enable you to design an experiment to answer a question about a factor that influences the rate of transpiration.

YOU MUST KNOW

- The function of stomata in gas exchange in plants. What enters? What leaves?
- The role of water potential and transpiration in the movement of water from roots to leaves.
- The effects of various environmental conditions on the rate of transpiration.

SCIENCE PRACTICES: CAN YOU . . .

- Predict and justify whether a plant cell will give or lose water based on water potential?
- Create and annotate a diagram to show what would happen to grass planted near a road that has been salted in winter, including water potential in your representation?

Hints and Review

▌ Review **hydrogen bonding** (see Topic 1, Chapter 3)! In water, a hydrogen bond is a weak bond between the hydrogen of one water molecule and the oxygen of another, and it accounts for the unique properties of water, including adhesion and cohesion.

▌ Water enters a plant through the root hairs, passes through the tissues of the root into the xylem, and travels up through the xylem vessels into the leaves.

▌ **Transpiration** is the evaporation of water from the leaves through the stomata. It is the major force that pulls the water up through the plant.

▌ Study Figure 11.1 to see this process. When water enters the roots, hydrogen bonds link each water molecule to the next one (*cohesion*), so the molecules of water are pulled up the thin xylem vessels like beads on a string. The water molecules also cling to the thin walls of the xylem cells (*adhesion*). The water moves up the plant, enters the leaves, moves into air spaces in the leaf, and then evaporates (transpires) through the *stomata* (singular, *stoma*).

Figure 11.1   Leaf anatomy showing movement of water molecules

▌ **Stomata** are the pores in the epidermis of a leaf. There are hundreds of stomata in the epidermis of a leaf, mostly located in the lower epidermis. This reduces water loss because the lower surface receives less solar radiation than the upper surface. Each stoma allows the carbon dioxide necessary for photosynthesis to enter, while water evaporates through each one in transpiration.

▌ **Guard cells** are cells surrounding each stoma. They help regulate the rate of transpiration by opening and closing the stomata. To understand how they function, study the following figures. As you look at the figures, keep in mind that an increase in solute concentration lowers the water potential of the solution and that water moves from a region with higher water potential to a region of lower water potential.

▌ Notice that in Figure 11.2a the guard cells are turgid, or swollen, and the stomatal opening is large. This turgidity is caused by the accumulation of K^+ (potassium ions) in the guard cells. As K^+ levels increase in the guard cells, the water potential of the guard cells drops, and water enters the guard cells.

11.2a   Open Stomata   **11.2b   Closed Stomata**

▌ In Figure 11.2b, the guard cells have lost water, which causes the cells to become flaccid and the stomatal opening to close. This may occur when the plant has lost an excessive amount of water. In addition, it generally occurs daily as light levels drop and the use of CO_2 in photosynthesis decreases.

❶ Assemble 4 potometers.

Plant cutting
Air-tight seal
Water-filled tube
Calibrated pipette
Potometer

❷ Place each potometer in a different environment: room conditions, mist, wind, and bright light.

a. Control: room conditions　　b. Mist　　c. Wind　　d. Bright light

❸ Measure water loss in each potometer every 3 minutes for 30 minutes.

00:00　　30:00

Figure 11.3　Procedure for transpiration lab (potometer method)

▌ A leaf needs carbon dioxide and water for photosynthesis. For carbon dioxide to enter, the stomata on the surface of the leaf must be open. Transpiration draws water from the roots into the leaf mesophyll. However, the plant must not lose so much water during transpiration that it wilts. The plant must strike a balance between conserving water and bringing in sufficient amounts of CO_2 for photosynthesis.

▌ One way to measure water loss from a plant is to use a *potometer*, a device that measures the rate at which a plant draws up water. Because the plant draws up water as it loses it by transpiration, you are able to measure the rate of transpiration. The basic elements of a potometer are shown in Figure 11.3, step 1. They are

  ▌ a plant cutting,

  ▌ a calibrated pipette to measure water loss,

  ▌ a length of clear plastic tubing, and

  ▌ an airtight seal between the plant and the water-filled tubing.

Figure 11.3 shows a typical setup to investigate a variety of environmental effects on the rate of transpiration. Based on your knowledge of transpiration developed in this investigation, can you answer the following questions? (The answers are below on this page.)

1. What are some factors that you would need to hold constant for a valid *control*?
2. Predict the rate of transpiration in the plant that has been misted and placed in a plastic bag, compared with the control, and justify your prediction.
3. Predict the rate of transpiration in the plant in front of the fan, compared with the control, and justify your prediction.
4. Predict the rate of transpiration in bright light, compared with the control, and justify your prediction.
5. Why is the bright light being shone through a tub filled with water?

Questions

1. All of the following enhance water transport in terrestrial plants EXCEPT
   (A) hydrogen bonds linking water molecules.
   (B) capillary action due to adhesion of water molecules to the walls of xylem.
   (C) evaporation of water from the leaves.
   (D) K^+ being transported out of the guard cells.

2. Under conditions of bright light, in which part of a transpiring plant would water potential be lowest?
   (A) xylem vessels in the leaves
   (B) xylem vessels in the roots
   (C) root hairs
   (D) the spongy mesophyll of the leaves

Answers to PRACTICE THE PRACTICE: Engage in Scientific Questioning, above

1. In order for the *control* to be valid, you should consider using the same type of plant, have the same relative amount of leaf surface, have the water in all potometers at the same temperature, and place the control and experimental plant cuttings in virtually identical conditions with the exception of the single factor you are testing.
2. The plant cutting inside the plastic bag is in a situation of *high humidity*. Because of high water potential in the area surrounding the leaves, the rate of transpiration will be low.
3. The potometer with the *fan* shows increased water loss compared with the control. The reason is that the air movement results in greater evaporation, lowering water potential outside the plant surface, resulting in a higher rate of water loss or transpiration.
4. The potometer in *bright light* generally shows a higher rate of water loss, indicating more photosynthesis than the control.
5. A bright light produces heat, which operates as another variable. The water-filled container is a heat sink and will minimize the effect of heat on the plant.

BIG IDEA 4: Investigation 12, Fruit Fly Behavior

Overview of the Lab

▌ In this lab you will explore behaviors in an invertebrate and design an experiment to answer a question about behavior. Animals exhibit a variety of behaviors, both learned and innate, that promote their survival and reproductive success in a variety of ways. In this investigation, you will make detailed observations of an organism's behavior and design a controlled experiment to test a hypothesis about a specific case of animal behavior.

▌ If you use the 2012 "AP Investigations" manual, your experimental organisms may be fruit flies (as in the title of the investigation). It is equally possible that your teacher may select another species to use, such as mealworms or pill bugs.

YOU MUST KNOW

- Behaviors are regulated by various mechanisms and are acted on by natural selection.
- Descriptions of various animal behaviors, such as orientation behavior, geotaxis, phototaxis, chemotaxis, and how the behavior is adaptive.

SCIENCE PRACTICES: CAN YOU . . .

- Design a plan for collecting data to show how a particular species is affected by biotic or abiotic interactions?
- Analyze data collected to identify possible patterns and relationships between an organism or species and a biotic or an abiotic factor?
- Apply mathematical routines, such as statistical analysis, to evaluate data?

Hints and Review

▌ In this lab you will make detailed observations and learn about some interesting animal behaviors. Because the topic is so broad and there are so many local organisms and possibilities for your teacher to choose from, we will only make a few comments about animal behavior. This lab presents a wonderful opportunity to teach experimental design, so this is where we focus our discussion.

- Refer to the Introduction of this book for hints about writing the lab essay. At the conclusion of this course, you should have conducted a number of investigations where you have asked your own question and developed a procedure to investigate your hypothesis. You should now be able to design a controlled experiment to test a single variable, record data in a logical manner, and present your conclusions.

- There are hundreds of species of fruit flies—so how do members of the same species find each other and signal willingness to mate? Each species has evolved a complex series of behaviors that appear to be genetically programmed. Students who do Lab 11 in the 2001 AP Biology Lab Manual investigate this behavior in *Drosophila melanogaster.*

- How do fruit flies find their food sources? orient to gravity? orient to light? Investigation 12 (Fruit Fly Behavior) encourages a look at a number of behaviors in fruit flies and directs you in the preparation of a choice chamber.

- A common behavior experiment involves observing how pill bugs respond to their environment. In this experiment, students place pill bugs in a choice chamber—half in the side lined with dry filter paper and the other half in the side lined with wet filter paper. Pill bugs are crustaceans, so they respire through gills and generally live in a moist habitat. Because of this, most students hypothesize that more pill bugs will be found in the moist chamber. This is often what occurs but not always!

- This brings us to an important consideration: If a student prepares a single-choice chamber, the exercise is not a controlled experiment. Could there be more light at one end of the choice chamber? more activity and vibration? a chemical residue on one side? Any of these conditions and more could possibly influence the organism's behavior. Without a control, it is very risky to state a conclusion. What's needed is a **controlled experiment**.

> *TIP FROM THE READERS*
> Even if you did not do this investigation, we recommend you carefully study the suggestions about experimental design found in the following box. It reviews practices followed all year long and applies to virtually any inquiry lab you might do!

- A controlled experiment begins with a *hypothesis*—a proposed solution for the problem being investigated. A hypothesis is often written as an IF, THEN statement that predicts the outcome we might expect if our data supports the hypothesis. A hypothesis should not only predict results but must also be testable.

- In a controlled experiment, *all variables are held constant,* except the one being tested or manipulated. For instance, if the goal is to test response to wet versus dry conditions, the light, temperature, chemicals in the filter paper or on the dish surface, and movement of the table must all remain constant. In addition, all the experimental organisms must be of the same approximate age, size, and state of health. It is not enough to say that you will hold all variables constant; you must be explicit in your explanation of how you will do this.

- To be meaningful, the experiment must include a *large sample size* to be representative of a general condition.

- The *results must be measurable!* Are you going to count, measure, or find the mass? You must devise some way to quantify the results.

- Several *repetitions (or replicates)* of the experiment must be done. Like a large sample size, having several repetitions lets you verify your result.

- Before you design an experiment, it may be useful to *search the literature* to learn what has already been done and to help develop ideas for a reasonable study.

- Finally, *statistical analysis of your data* (such as the Chi-square test at the end of this topic) should be done to validate experimental results.

Questions

1. A student wanted to study the effect of nitrogen fertilizer on plant growth, so she took two similar plants and set them on a windowsill for a two-week observation period. She watered each plant the same amount, but she gave one a small dose of fertilizer with each watering. She collected data by counting the total number of new leaves on each plant and measuring the height of each plant in centimeters. Which of the following is a significant flaw in this experimental setup?
   (A) There is no variable factor.
   (B) There is no control.
   (C) There is no repetition.
   (D) Measurable results cannot be expected.

2. Students placed five pill bugs on the dry side of a choice chamber and five pill bugs on the wet side. The students collected data on the number on each side every 30 seconds for 10 minutes. After 6 minutes, eight or nine pill bugs were continually on the wet side of the chamber, and several were under the filter paper. Which of the following is *not* a reasonable conclusion from these results?
   (A) It takes the pill bugs several minutes to explore their surroundings and select a preferred habitat.
   (B) Pill bugs prefer a moist environment.
   (C) Pill bugs may find chemicals in dry filter paper irritating.
   (D) Pill bugs demonstrate no significant habitat preference.

3. If a student wanted to determine whether pill bugs prefer a moist or a dry environment, what would be a good first step in looking at the data?
   (A) Total the number of pill bugs on the dry side throughout the entire experiment and compare this with the number on the wet side throughout the experiment.
   (B) After waiting 5 minutes for the pill bugs to acclimate, count the number of pill bugs on the dry side every 30 seconds for 5 minutes and determine the total number on the dry side. Do the same for the wet side, and compare the data.
   (C) Compare the number of pill bugs on the dry side at the end of 10 minutes with the number of pill bugs on the wet side at the end of 10 minutes.
   (D) Divide the number of pill bugs on the dry side throughout the experiment by the number on the wet side throughout the experiment.

4. Which of the following hypotheses is stated best?
   (A) If pill bugs are allowed free movement, then more will be found in a moist environment than in a dry environment.
   (B) If pill bugs like a moist environment, then they will move to the wet side of a choice chamber.
   (C) If an experiment with pill bugs is run for 10 minutes, then more pill bugs will be found in the most favorable environment.
   (D) Pill bugs are found in moist habitats, so I predict that more will be found where it is wet.

BIG IDEA 4: Investigation 13, Enzyme Activity

▌ This experiment investigates the enzymatic activity of peroxidase. In Procedure 1, you will learn how to measure the activity of peroxidase; in Procedure 2, you will investigate the effect of varying pH on enzyme activity. The investigation then requires the design of an experiment to determine the effect of a selected variable on enzyme activity.

▌ Your teacher might choose to use another enzyme-substrate system, so the tips that follow will be generalized for any enzyme.

YOU MUST KNOW

- Enzymes are proteins, so their final conformation is affected by the interactions between their R-groups.
- The shape of an enzyme and its active site determine its activity.
- How factors such as temperature, pH, and enzyme concentration affect the rate of an enzyme reaction.

SCIENCE PRACTICES: CAN YOU . . .

- Design a controlled experiment to measure the activity of a specific enzyme under varying conditions?
- Use mathematical routines to calculate the rate of a reaction from a graph or data chart?
- Predict and justify how changing an environmental factor such as temperature or pH would alter an enzyme's activity?

Hints and Review

▌ Enzymes are large globular proteins. Much of their three-dimensional shape is the result of interactions between the R (variable) groups of their amino acids. Anything that changes these interactions will change the shape of the enzyme and therefore alter the rate of reaction. The *active site* is the portion of the enzyme that will interact with the substrate.

▌ Remember: *Change the shape, change the function!*

▌ Enzyme activity is affected by pH and temperature because these variables affect the 3-D shape of the enzyme. Extremes of pH and temperature result in *denaturation*, when the 3-D shape is so altered that the enzyme can no longer function.

▌ Enzymes are not denatured by cold, but the rate of reaction is decreased as temperature decreases.

Figure 13.1   Enzyme activity over time

Enzyme Action Over Time

We can calculate the rate of an enzymatic reaction by measuring, over time, either the disappearance of substrate (as in our catalase example) or the appearance of product (as in Figure 13.1). For example, on the graph, what is the rate, in moles per second, over the interval from 0 to 10 seconds?

$$\text{Rate} = \frac{\Delta y}{\Delta x}$$

For this example, the rate would be

$$\frac{7 \text{ moles} - 0 \text{ moles}}{(10 \text{ seconds} - 0 \text{ seconds})} = \frac{7}{10}$$
$$= 0.7 \text{ moles/second}$$

▎ Note that the slope of the graph is steepest during the *initial* time period; this is when the rate of a reaction is greatest and occurs because the substrate is most abundant, allowing for more enzyme–substrate collisions. The rate of the reaction decreases as substrate is consumed and the slope of the graph flattens.

▎ What is the rate for this same reaction between 40 and 60 seconds? (It is 0.) You should be able to explain this.

Questions

1. In order to keep the rate of reaction constant over the entire time course, which of the following should you do?
   (A) Add more enzyme.
   (B) Gradually increase the temperature after 60 seconds.
   (C) Add more substrate.
   (D) Add H_2SO_4 after 60 seconds.

2. To determine the rate of enzyme activity, you do an experiment in which you mix enzyme and substrate together for 30 seconds, 60 seconds, 90 seconds, and 120 seconds. After the specified times, you add H_2SO_4 (sulfuric acid) to the reaction chamber to halt the reaction. What is the role of H_2SO_4 in this experiment?
   (A) It is the substrate on which the enzyme acts.
   (B) It denatures the enzyme by altering the active site.
   (C) It accelerates the reaction between enzyme and substrate.
   (D) It blocks the active site of the enzyme.

Statistical Analysis: Chi-Square Analysis of Data

Overview of Chi-Square

It is not sufficient to say, "My data looks really good!" or "The results were very close to what I expected." In science, we impose rigorous tests to support the validity of results. One of these tests is Chi-square analysis. Here is a short review of how to do this test and at the same time check your knowledge of genetic ratios expected with different crosses.

> ### YOU MUST KNOW
>
> - What is meant by "degrees of freedom," "critical value," "probability value," and "null hypothesis".
> - How to do Chi-square analysis of data and explain your results.

Chi-Square Analysis of Data

Red-eyed fruit flies mate and produce the offspring shown on the right hand side of the following table. What was the genetic make-up of these red-eyed flies? **Explain** your conclusion. (Remember, this means you are to provide a *claim*, *evidence*, and *reasoning*.)

Figure 1   Data table of *Drosophila* (1)

▮ From the data presented, you can deduce that the F_1 cross was between individuals heterozygous for eye color: se^+ se X se^+ se (se^+ = red eyes, se = sepia) because this is the only cross that would yield offspring with a 3:1 distribution of red to sepia eyes. So your *CLAIM* is that the parents were all heterozygous for red eye color.

▮ You kept data showing both males and females with the trait because the unknown trait might be sex-linked. The data do not support a sex-linked trait but do support an autosomal trait; thus, you merge the data for males and females so you consider only the eye color in the cross. The *EVIDENCE* that supports your claim is the observed phenotypes and numbers seen in the chart. Both males and females show red and sepia eyes.

From this evidence, you could write the following working hypothesis concerning the relationship between the dominant red eye color to the recessive sepia eye color: *If the parents are heterozygous for eye color, there will be a 3:1 ratio of red eyes to sepia eyes in the offspring.* Do your results support this hypothesis? Yes! So your *REASONING* could be a Punnett square that shows the offspring predicted from a cross of two heterozygotes.

CALCULATING CHI-SQUARE

The formula for Chi-square is

$$\chi^2 = \Sigma \frac{(o - e)^2}{e}$$

where:
o = observed number of individuals
e = expected number of individuals

The actual results of an experiment are unlikely to match the expected results precisely. But how great a variance is significant? One way to decide is to use the Chi-square (χ^2) test. This analytical tool tests the validity of a **null hypothesis**, which states that there is no statistically significant difference between the observed results of your experiment and the expected results. When there is little difference between the observed results and the expected results, you obtain a very low Chi-square value; your hypothesis is supported.

Using the Chi-Square Critical Values Table

The Chi-square critical values table provides two values that you need to calculate Chi-square:

Degrees of freedom. This number is one less than the total number of classes of offspring in a cross. In a monohybrid cross, such as our Case 1, there are two classes of offspring (red eyes and sepia eyes). Therefore, there is just one degree of freedom. In a heterozygous dihybrid cross, there are four possible classes of offspring, so there are three degrees of freedom.

Probability. The probability value (p) is the probability that a deviation as great as or greater than each Chi-square value would occur simply by chance. Many biologists agree that deviations having a chance probability greater than 0.05 (5%) do not support the null hypothesis. Therefore, when you calculate Chi-square, you should consult the table for the p value in the 0.05 row.

Critical Values Table

Probability (p)	Degrees of Freedom (df)				
	1	2	3	4	5
0.05	3.84	5.99	7.82	9.49	11.1
0.01	6.64	9.21	11.3	13.2	15.1
0.001	10.8	13.8	16.3	18.5	20.5

1. **Set up a data chart as shown.** How do you figure out the expected phenotypes? Because your hypothesis predicted a 3:1 ratio in the offspring, you would expect 3/4 of the total offspring (44) to have red eyes = 33, and ¼ to have sepia eyes = 11.

Phenotypes	Observed (o)	Expected (e)	$(o - e)$	$(o - e)^2$	$\dfrac{(o - e)^2}{e}$
Red Eyes	31	33	2	4	4/33 = 0.12
Sepia Eyes	13	11	2	4	4/11 = 0.36
	44	44			Total = χ^2 = 0.48

2. **Determine the degrees of freedom.** This is the number of categories (red eyes or sepia eyes) minus one. For these data, the number of degrees of freedom is 1.

3. **Find the probability (p) value for 1 degree of freedom in the 0.05 row.** This is the **critical value**. For these data, the critical value = 3.84.

4. **Accept or fail to accept the null hypothesis.** The null hypothesis states that there is no statistically significant difference between the observed and expected data. Because the χ^2 value for this data is less than the critical value, you will accept the null hypothesis. This then supports your working hypothesis: *If the parents are heterozygous for eye color, there will be a 3:1 ratio of red eyes to sepia eyes in the offspring.*

▌ Don't forget this little nugget: **If the Chi-square value is greater than the critical value, you fail to accept the null hypothesis** and consider reasons for this variation, such as errors in sample size or data collection.

> ### TIP FROM THE READERS
> There was a Chi-square problem on the 2013 AP Biology Exam, and we found that a common error was that some students took the square root of the value they got for χ^2. Don't make this mistake! χ^2 is just the shorthand for the name of this mathematical technique: *Chi-square*.

Questions

1. You have a vial containing a red-eyed male with normal wings and a red-eyed female with normal wings. These are the F_1 generation. After two weeks, you collect the offspring from this pair and obtain the results shown in Figure 2. On the basis of the results shown in Figure 2, which statement is most likely true?

F₂ RESULTS	OBSERVED PHENOTYPE AND NUMBERS			
	Red eyes normal wings	Red eyes no wings	Sepia eyes normal wings	Sepia eyes no wings
♂ MALES	48	13	16	4
♀ FEMALES	50	9	10	10

Figure 2 Data table of *Drosophila* (2)

(A) The genes for red eyes and normal wings are linked.

(B) The gene for no wings is sex-linked.

(C) The F_1 mates were both homozygous for both eye color and wings.

(D) The gene for eye color is inherited independently from the gene for wings.

2. Based on the hypothesis that this is a dihybrid cross, with the two genes unlinked, calculate χ^2 using the data in the table of observed phenotypes.

(A) 6.043

(B) 7.815

(C) 4.977

(D) 24.038

3. Compare the Chi-square value obtained in question 2 with the Critical Values Table on page 355 for $p = 0.05$. Which of the following statements would be true?

(A) Because the calculated value for Chi-square is less than 7.82, the results support the hypothesis that the parents are heterozygous for two unlinked traits.

(B) Because the calculated value for Chi-square is less than 7.82, the results support the hypothesis that eye color and wings are linked.

(C) Because the calculated value for Chi-square is less than 7.82, the results are inconclusive. The experiment should be repeated.

(D) Because the Chi-square value is less than the critical value of 7.82, the null hypothesis is rejected for the hypothesis that the parents are heterozygous for two unlinked traits.

AP Biology Equations and Formulas

The following is the formula list that you will receive as part of your testing materials. *Source:* AP Biology—Course and Exam Description. © 2015. The College Board. www.collegeboard.org. Reproduced with permission.

Statistical Analysis and Probability

Standard Error

$$SE_{\bar{x}} = \frac{s}{\sqrt{n}}$$

Mean

$$\bar{x} = \frac{1}{n}\sum_{i=1}^{n} x_i$$

Standard Deviation

$$s = \sqrt{\frac{\sum(x_i - \bar{x})^2}{n-1}}$$

Chi-Square

$$\chi^2 = \sum \frac{(o-e)^2}{e}$$

s = sample standard deviation (i.e., the sample based estimate of the standard deviation of the population)

$\bar{x}$ = mean

n = size of the sample

o = observed individuals with observed genotype

e = expected individuals with observed genotype

Degrees of freedom equals the number of distinct possible outcomes minus one.

Chi-Square Table

p	\multicolumn{8}{c}{Degrees of Freedom}
	1	2	3	4	5	6	7	8
0.05	3.84	5.99	7.82	9.49	11.07	12.59	14.07	15.51
0.01	6.64	9.32	11.34	13.28	15.09	16.81	18.48	20.09

Laws of Probability

If A and B are mutually exclusive, then P (A or B) = P(A) + P(B)

If A and B are independent, then P (A and B) = P(A) x P(B)

Hardy-Weinberg Equations

$$p^2 + 2pq + q^2 = 1$$

$$p + q = 1$$

p = frequency of the dominant allele in a population

q = frequency of the recessive allele in a population

Metric Prefixes

Factor	Prefix	Symbol
10^9	giga	G
10^6	mega	M
10^3	kilo	k
10^{-2}	centi	c
10^{-3}	milli	m
10^{-6}	micro	μ
10^{-9}	nano	n
10^{-12}	pico	p

Mode = value that occurs most frequently in a <u>data set</u>

Median = middle value that separates the greater and lesser halves of a data set

Mean = sum of all data points divided by number of data points

Range = value obtained by subtracting the smallest observation (<u>sample minimum</u>) from the greatest (<u>sample maximum</u>)

Rate and Growth	dY= amount of change	**Water Potential (Ψ)**
Rate dY/dt	t = time	$\Psi = \Psi p + \Psi s$
Population Growth dN/dt=B-D	B = birth rate	Ψp = pressure potential
Exponential Growth $\dfrac{dN}{dt} = r_{max}N$	D = death rate N = population size	Ψs = solute potential The water potential will be equal to the solute potential of a solution in an
	K = carrying capacity	open container, since the pressure potential of the solution in an open
Logistic Growth $\dfrac{dN}{dt} = r_{max}N\left(\dfrac{K-N}{K}\right)$	r_{max} = maximum per capita growth rate of population	container is zero.
	t_2 = higher temperature	**The Solute Potential of the Solution**
Temperature Coefficient Q_{10} $Q_{10} = \left(\dfrac{k_2}{k_1}\right)^{\frac{10}{t_2-t_1}}$	t_1 = lower temperature	$\Psi_s = -\,iCRT$ i = ionization constant (For sucrose this is 1.0 because sucrose does not
	k_2 = metabolic rate at t_2	ionize in water)
Primary Productivity Calculation	k_1 = metabolic rate at t_1	C = molar concentration
mg O_2/L x 0.698 = mL O_2/L	Q_{10} = the *factor* by which the	R = pressure constant (R = 0.0831 liter bars/mole K)
mL O_2/L x 0.536 = mg carbon fixed/L	reaction rate increases when the temperature is raised by ten degrees	T = temperature in Kelvin (273 + °C)

Surface Area and Volume	r = radius	**Dilution - used to create a dilute solution from a concentrated stock solution**
Volume of Sphere V = 4/3 π r^3	l = length	$C_iV_i = C_fV_f$
Volume of a cube (or square column) V = l w h	h = height w = width	i = initial (starting) C = concentration of solute f = final (desired) V = volume of solution
Volume of a column V = π r^2 h	A = surface area	**Gibbs Free Energy**
Surface area of a sphere A = 4 π r^2	V = volume	$\Delta G = \Delta H - T\Delta S$ ΔG = change in Gibbs free energy
Surface area of a cube A = 6 a	Σ = Sum of all	ΔS = change in entropy ΔH = change in enthalpy
Surface area of a rectangular solid A = Σ (surface area of each side)	a = surface area of one side of the cube	T = absolute temperature (in Kelvin)
		$pH = -\log [H^+]$

Part IV

Sample Test

On the following pages is a sample examination that approximates the actual AP Biology Examination in format, types of questions, and content. Set aside 3 hours to take the test. To best prepare yourself for actual AP exam conditions, use only the allowed time for Section I and Section II.

You may want to review our test-taking hints on page 13! Before you begin, get a copy of the Equations and Formulas (page 346) and a four-function calculator. Remember, answer every question because there is no penalty for guessing! You have approximately 90 seconds for each question, so use your time wisely.

Sample Test

Biology
Section I

63 Multiple-Choice Questions
6 Grid-In Questions
Time—90 minutes

Part A Directions: Each of the questions or incomplete statements is followed by four suggested answers or completions. Select the one that is best in each case, and then fill in the corresponding circle on the answer sheet. When you have completed Part A, you should continue on to Part B.

Questions 1 and 2 refer to the climograph below.

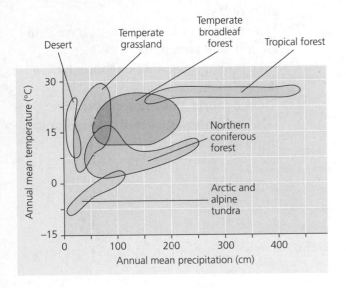

1. Based on the climograph of six specific biomes illustrated here, which of the following shifts in biomes and their related ecosystems would be most likely to result if global climate change continues to lead to a warmer Earth?
   (A) coniferous forest to temperate forest
   (B) coniferous forest to tundra
   (C) tropical forest to temperate forest
   (D) grassland to coniferous forest

2. If carbon dioxide levels continue to increase over the next century, which of the following would best predict the directional migration of the North American ecosystems from the biomes shown in this climograph?
   (A) The ecosystems will shift to the south due to decreasing transpiration rates.
   (B) The ecosystems will move to both the eastern and western coastlines because these areas will be more moderate.
   (C) The ecosystems will extend further down mountains in alpine regions as the temperatures warm.
   (D) The ecosystems will shift to the north as temperatures warm.

GO ON TO THE
NEXT PAGE

3. A diploid, sexually reproducing organism has the following genotype concerning three unlinked genes: *PpRrSs*. What is the probability of the alleles *P*, *R*, and *s* appearing in the same gamete?
   (A) 3/4
   (B) 1/2
   (C) 1/8
   (D) 1/4

4. The value for water potential in root tissue was found to be $\Psi = -0.15$ MPa. If the root tissue is placed in a 0.1 *M* solution of sucrose ($\Psi = -0.23$ MPa), which of these would describe the movement of water?
   (A) The net flow of water would be from the root tissue into the sucrose solution.
   (B) The net flow of water would be from the sucrose solution into the soil.
   (C) Water would flow in both directions with no net change.
   (D) Water would flow from the soil into the root tissue, where water potential is higher.

5. The segment of DNA shown in the next column has restriction sites I and II, which create restriction fragments a, b, and c. Which of the following gels produced by electrophoresis would represent the separation and identity of these fragments?

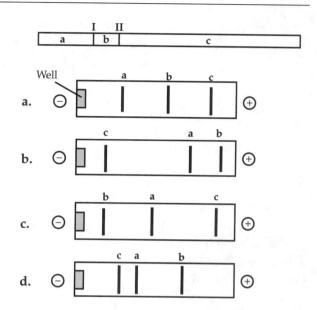

6. Which of the following statements best supports the idea that certain cell organelles are evolutionarily derived from symbiotic prokaryotes living in host cells?
   (A) The process of cellular respiration in certain prokaryotes is similar to that occurring in mitochondria and chloroplasts.
   (B) Mitochondria and eukaryotes have similar cell wall structures.
   (C) Like prokaryotes, mitochondria have a double membrane.
   (D) Mitochondria and chloroplasts have DNA and ribosomes that are similar to those of prokaryotes.

7. This phylogenetic tree illustrates the evolutionary relationships of tetrapods and was constructed using both anatomical and DNA sequence data. Using evidence from this tree, which statement most accurately reflects the relationship of mammals to amphibians and birds?

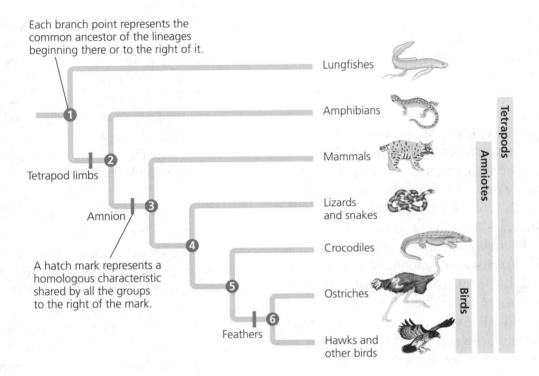

Each branch point represents the common ancestor of the lineages beginning there or to the right of it.

Tetrapod limbs

Amnion

A hatch mark represents a homologous characteristic shared by all the groups to the right of the mark.

Feathers

Lungfishes

Amphibians

Mammals

Lizards and snakes

Crocodiles

Ostriches

Hawks and other birds

Tetrapods

Amniotes

Birds

(A) Mammals are more closely related to amphibians and likely share more DNA sequences.

(B) Mammals are more closely related to amphibians because they share anatomical similarities.

(C) Mammals are more closely related to birds because they share a more recent common ancestor.

(D) Mammals, birds, and amphibians are all equally related because they share a common ancestor at the second branch point.

8. According to the figure above, which pair of organisms shares the most recent common ancestor?
(A) lungfishes and amphibians
(B) amphibians and lizards
(C) mammals and crocodiles
(D) lizards and ostriches

9. According to the figure, the group most closely related to lizards and snakes is
(A) lungfishes.
(B) amphibians.
(C) mammals.
(D) hawks and other birds.

GO ON TO THE NEXT PAGE

10. In dogs, the trait for long tail is dominant (*L*), and the trait for short tail is recessive (*l*). The trait for yellow coat is dominant (*Y*), and the trait for white coat is recessive (*y*). Mating many dogs gave multiple litters, totaling 305 long-tailed, yellow dogs and 95 long-tailed, white dogs. Which of the following is most likely to be the genotype of the parent dogs?
    (A) *LLYY* × *LLYY*
    (B) *LLyy* × *LLYy*
    (C) *LlYy* × *LlYy*
    (D) *LlYy* × *LLYy*

11. Muscle contractions occur when a motor neuron releases acetylcholine (ACh) into a synapse with a muscle cell. Receptors on the muscle cell membrane bind ACh, which triggers an action potential in the muscle cell. This leads to an interaction of actin and myosin filaments, and the muscle cell contracts. The enzyme acetylcholinesterase (AChE) breaks down ACh, which removes ACh from the synapse and ends the signal. This allows the muscle cell to relax, and contraction ends. The nerve gas sarin causes paralysis and death because it inhibits the action of AChE. Which of the following statements **best** explains the effect of sarin on muscle cells?
    (A) Paralysis occurs because ACh is quickly taken back into the motor neuron, which stops the signal, and the muscle cells are unable to contract.
    (B) Paralysis occurs because sarin blocks the receptors of the muscle cells, and actin and myosin cannot interact.
    (C) Paralysis occurs because the signaling molecule remains in the synapse bound to receptors, so actin and myosin continue to interact and contraction continues.
    (D) Paralysis occurs because the motor neuron cannot transmit a second signal to the muscle cell, so contraction ceases.

12. In *Escherichia coli* replication, the enzyme primase is used to attach a 5- to 10-base ribonucleotide strand complementary to the parental DNA strand. The RNA strand serves as a starting point for the DNA polymerase that replicates DNA. If a mutation occurred in the primase gene, which of the following would you expect?
    (A) Replication would only occur on the leading strand.
    (B) Replication would only occur on the lagging strand.
    (C) Replication would not occur on either the leading or lagging strand.
    (D) Replication would not be affected because the enzyme primase is involved with RNA synthesis.

13. Allolactose is a sugar that stimulates *Escherichia coli* to produce mRNAs that code for the enzyme β-galactosidase, which breaks down lactose into glucose and galactose. Which of the following is the best description of the role of allolactose?
    (A) It inhibits DNA replication when lactose levels are high.
    (B) It inhibits translation of the mRNAs for β-galactosidase.
    (C) It is an allosteric inhibitor of β-galactosidase.
    (D) It regulates expression of the gene for β-galactosidase.

Use the pedigree below to answer questions 14 and 15.

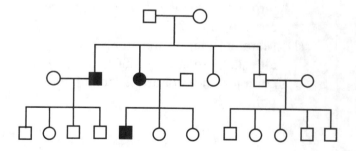

14. In the pedigree, squares represent males and circles represent females. Shaded figures represent individuals who possess a particular trait. Which of the following patterns of inheritance best explains how this trait is transmitted?
    (A) partially dominant
    (B) autosomal dominant
    (C) autosomal recessive
    (D) sex-linked recessive

15. What is the genotype of the shaded figure in the third generation if A is the dominant trait and a is the recessive trait?
    (A) aa
    (B) Aa
    (C) $X^a X^a$
    (D) $X^a y$

16. Which of the following provides evidence that glycolysis is one of the first metabolic pathways to have evolved?
    (A) It relies on fermentation, which is characteristic of archaea and bacteria.
    (B) It is found only in prokaryotes, whereas eukaryotes use mitochondria to produce ATP.
    (C) It produces ATP only by oxidative phosphorylation and does not involve redox reactions.
    (D) It is nearly universal, occurs in the cytosol, and does not involve O_2.

Questions 17 and 18 refer to the following reading.

Goldenrod is a common plant in old fields. It is parasitized by a gallfly, which causes a one-inch spherical gall chamber to form along the goldenrod stem. A single large gallfly larva develops in the chamber. The gallfly larvae may, in turn, be preyed upon by both a parasitic wasp that drills through the gall to lay its eggs on the gallfly larva or by birds that tear open the gall to eat the larvae. An ecologist wondered if gall size was linked to the success of the gallfly larvae. The chart shows the experimental data collected to answer this question.

Table 1   Fate of Goldenrod Galls from an Old Field

Gall Fate	Percentage of total galls	Mean diameter of gall (mm)	Number of galls in the category
Unsuccessful (larvae died)	23.5	17.5	110
Galls parasitized (larvae died)	21	19.9	98
Successful galls (larvae do not die)	32.55	20.9	152
Gall larvae eaten by birds	21.91	22.9	107

17. If the pattern of gall fates shown in Table 1 continued over many generations, what evolutionary pattern would you predict to emerge?
    (A) Stabilizing selection, which causes the average gall size to be pushed toward an intermediate value
    (B) Directional selection, which causes the average gall size to become larger over time
    (C) Diversifying selection, which causes the average gall size to become either larger *or* smaller over time with very few galls exhibiting the intermediate size
    (D) No selection because too many of the larvae die to change the evolutionary pattern

GO ON TO THE
NEXT PAGE

18. If the starting population showed a normal distribution of gall sizes as seen in Graph 1, what would the graph look like after natural selection pressures indicated in Table 1?

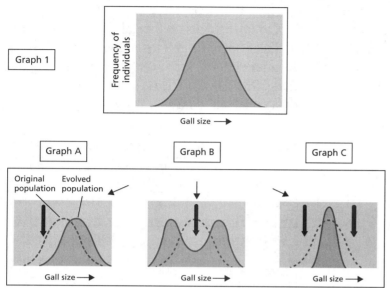

(A) Graph A
(B) Graph B
(C) Graph C
(D) no change (It would look like Graph 1)

19. What is the signal and its receptor in this pathway shown in the figure below?
   (A) Ca^{2+} is the signal; a membrane protein is the receptor.
   (B) Light is the signal; a cytoplasmic protein is the receptor.
   (C) cGMP is the signal; protein kinase is the receptor.
   (D) The protein kinases are the signal; transcription factors are the receptors.

20. Which of the following would occur if the Ca^2 channels were not functional?
   (A) Reception would be blocked, and phytochrome would not be activated.
   (B) cGMP molecules, the second messengers, would not be produced.
   (C) Transcription and translation of the de-etiolation proteins would not occur.
   (D) Transcription factor 2 would not be produced.

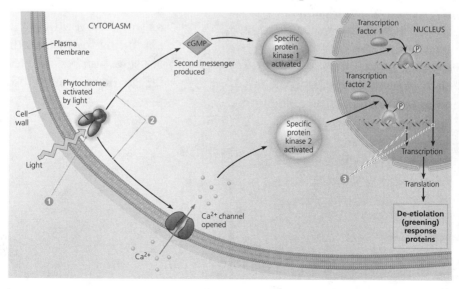

The figure shows the opening and closing of stoma. Study both figures before answering questions 21 and 22.

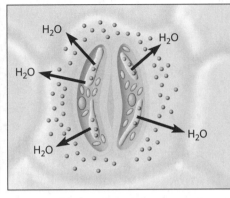

Stoma opening

Stoma closing

21. In the panel labeled "stoma opening," K^+ and water are both moving into the guard cells, and the use of ATP is high. Why?
   (A) Energy is required to move water molecules into the guard cells.
   (B) Water is being lost through the stoma by transpiration.
   (C) Energy is required to move oxygen into the leaf through the stoma.
   (D) Energy is required to move K^+ into the guard cells against the gradient.

22. What is true of the guard cells shown in the right-hand panel of this figure?
   (A) Their internal water pressure (turgor pressure) is increasing.
   (B) Their water potential is lower than the surrounding cells.

   (C) These cells are allowing gas exchange for photosynthesis.
   (D) These cells are hypotonic to their immediate surrounding.

23. Considering the possibilities of recombination during meiosis, which two genes on this chromosome are most likely to segregate together into a daughter cell?

   A   W   E   G
   | 5 | 3 | 12 |

   (A) A and W
   (B) W and E
   (C) A and G
   (D) A and E

GO ON TO THE
NEXT PAGE

Questions 24 and 25 refer to the following figure, which shows a food chain in a particular ecosystem. Each number represents a species in this ecosystem.

Solar Energy

Food Chain

24. Which of the following is a true statement about this food chain?
    (A) Energy flows one way through food chains, but nutrients are recycled.
    (B) Energy levels are highest in level 5.
    (C) Nutrient recycling only occurs from level 5, the top of the food chain.
    (D) The biomass of level 4 is greater than that of level 1.

25. DDT is an insecticide that accumulates in nature as a toxin. DDT accumulates in the bodies of organisms in this food chain. Which member of the food chain would you predict would have the highest level of DDT?
    (A) 1
    (B) 3
    (C) 4
    (D) 5

Question 26 refers to the following gel, which was produced from four samples of a radioactively labeled strand of DNA that were cut with a single restriction enzyme. The samples were separated by gel electrophoresis. Answer the questions based on the bands visualized below.

Samples

26. Which of the following statements is supported by the data from the gel?
    (A) All samples have the same number of restriction sites.
    (B) Samples 3 and 4 have the same number of restriction sites in the same locations on the DNA strand.
    (C) Samples 1, 3, and 4 have the same number of restriction sites but in different locations on the DNA strand.
    (D) Samples 1, 3, and 4 have the same number of restriction sites but were cut by different enzymes.

Questions 27 and 28 refer to an experiment in which there is an initial setup of a U-tube with its two sides separated by a membrane that permits the passage of water and NaCl but not molecules of glucose. Side A of the U-tube is filled with a solution of 0.4 M glucose and 0.5 M NaCl. Side B contains a solution of 0.8 M glucose and 0.4 M NaCl.

Side A   Initial setup   Side B

0.4 M glucose
0.5 M NaCl

0.8 M glucose
0.4 M NaCl

Membrane

27. After the experiment ran for 1 hour, the expected fluid levels in the U-tube would be
(A) higher on side A than side B.
(B) higher on side B than side A.
(C) equal.
(D) equal, but the solutes would be reversed.

28. At the conclusion of the experiment, the NaCl would
(A) show no movement.
(B) show some movement from side A to side B.
(C) show some movement from side B to side A.
(D) make the solute concentration higher on side A.

Questions 29 and 30 are based on the following reading.

Recent studies have shown that the onset of puberty in American girls has decreased from an average of 12 to 13 years of age to as young as 8 to 10 years of age. Scientists who study premature puberty suggest that steroids in our food and in the environment may be contributing factors because steroids are known to cross cell membranes and bind to receptors inside cells.

29. Which of the following is the best explanation for how steroid hormones are able to pass through the plasma membrane?
(A) Both steroid hormones and plasma membranes have receptor proteins.
(B) Steroid hormones are polar, and the cell membrane is polar on the inside of the lipid bilayer.
(C) Steroid hormones are nonpolar lipids, and the cell membrane is lipid based.
(D) Steroid hormones diffuse through open channel proteins in the membrane.

30. Based on the previous description, how do steroid hormones specifically alter the onset of puberty?
(A) Steroid hormones bind to intracellular receptors and serve as transcription factors, turning on genes.
(B) Steroid hormones bind to receptors on the cell membrane, turning on genes in the nucleus.
(C) Steroid hormones activate G-proteins to initiate an intracellular cascade that amplifies the amount of hormone within the target cell.
(D) Steroid hormones bind directly to DNA promoters, attract RNA polymerase, and initiate transcription.

31. A scientist wanted to determine if the metabolic rate of cancer cells is different from that of normal cells. Which of the following procedures would provide data to answer this question?
(A) Measure the CO_2 consumed by the cell.
(B) Measure the O_2 consumed by the cell.
(C) Measure the amount of water consumed by the cell.
(D) Measure the glucose produced by the cell.

Key ●— Sensory neuron ●— Motor neuron ● Interneuron

GO ON TO THE NEXT PAGE

32. The most basic nervous system response is a reflex arc, as shown in the previous figure. Predict how this response would be altered if structure 6 could not function.
   (A) Reception of the signal would not occur, but artificial stimulation of structure 6 would allow the response to occur.
   (B) The sensory neuron would be damaged, so the signal would not be transmitted to the interneuron.
   (C) Damage to structure 6 would prevent contraction of the hamstring muscle.
   (D) The signal would be rerouted to the brain, where another pathway would be initiated.

33. One hypothesis from climate scientists is that annual mean precipitation will increase if the planet continues to become warmer. With more precipitation, there is more evapotranspiration. Predict how this might affect the net primary productivity of ecosystems. (NPP = Gross PP − respiration).
   (A) Net Primary productivity would be unchanged because only temperature affects productivity.
   (B) Net primary productivity would decrease because increased precipitation would decrease solar energy into the system.
   (C) Net primary productivity would increase because an increase in precipitation would increase productivity within the ecosystems.
   (D) Net primary productivity would be unchanged, but gross primary productivity would decrease.

Questions 34 and 35 are based on the following figure.

Plant speciation can occur when the offspring receive extra sets of chromosomes, usually through a cell division error. The plant may then be referred to as a *polyploid*. In the diagram below, an upper-case letter represents not a gene but an entire haploid set of chromosomes.

34. Which species of wheat shown is polyploid?

   (A) *T. monococcum*
   (B) the AB sterile hybrid
   (C) *T. turgidum*
   (D) *T. tauschii*

35. At steps 1 and 3, sterile hybrids are formed. Which of the following best explains why the hybrids are sterile?
    (A) During meiosis, homologous pairs cannot form.
    (B) The sterile hybrids do not have enough genetic variability to be fertile.
    (C) The new hybrids are not suited for any open environmental niches.
    (D) Fertilization cannot occur when multiple sets of chromosomes are involved.

36. The figure shows a hypothetical embryo. Assume that for this embryo a high concentration of a morphogen, called *morpho*, is needed to activate gene *P*; gene *Q* is active at or above medium concentrations of morpho; and gene *R* is expressed so long as any quantity of morpho is present. A different morphogen, called *phogen*, activates gene *S* and inactivates gene *Q* when at medium to high concentrations. If morpho and phogen are diffusing from their sites of production at the opposite ends of the embryo, which genes will be expressed in region 2 of this embryo? (Assume a gradient of morphogen concentrations in the three regions, from high at the source, to medium in the middle, and to low at the opposite end.)

Morpho produced here   Phogen produced here

    (A) genes *P*, *Q*, *R*, and *S*
    (B) genes *P*, *Q*, and *R*
    (C) genes *Q* and *R*
    (D) genes *R* and *S*

37. If a mutation occurred that disabled the phogen gene, how would you predict this would affect gene expression in region 1 of the embryo?
    (A) Genes *P*, *Q*, *R*, and *S* would be expressed.
    (B) Genes *P*, *Q*, and *R* would be expressed.
    (C) Genes *Q* and *R* would be expressed.
    (D) Only gene *R* would be expressed.

38. In many prokaryotic cells, genes that are involved in the same pathway are clustered in operons under the control of a single promoter. How are the coordinated transcriptions of eukaryotic genes involved in the same pathways regulated?
    (A) Each gene has its own promoter, and the genes are all located on the same chromosome.
    (B) The genes are located in the same region of the chromosome, and enzymes methylate the entire region to activate transcription.
    (C) The genes respond to different transcription factors that are all activated simultaneously.
    (D) The genes may be on different chromosomes, but each responds to the same combination of control elements.

After reading the following paragraphs, answer questions 39 and 40.

Scientists believe that a shift from pollination by insects to pollination by birds occurred several times over the course of angiosperm evolution. Two researchers designed an experiment to investigate how these shifts might evolve using two species of monkey flower. *Mimulus lewisii* has violet-pink flowers and is pollinated by bumblebees. *Mimulus cardinalis* has orange-red flowers and is pollinated by hummingbirds.

The researchers switched flower-color genes between the two species. As a result of the gene transfer, they produced a variation of *M. cardinalis* with dark pink flowers (instead of the original orange-red). The new variety of *M. lewisii* had orange flowers (instead of the original violet-pink). Plants of both genetically altered varieties were placed in their original habitats and observed. The genetically altered variety of *M. cardinalis* was visited by bumblebees 74 times more often than plants with the original color flowers. The genetically altered variety of *M. lewisii* was visited by hummingbirds 68 times more often than plants with the original color flowers.

39. Which of the following represents a valid conclusion based on the data?
    (A) Petal color won't contribute to speciation because pollinators will select familiar plant species regardless of petal color.
    (B) Gene mutations that affect petal color will also affect nectar production and therefore pollinator choice.
    (C) Gene mutations affecting petal color can contribute to speciation by causing a shift in pollinator species.
    (D) The flowers of the two species must be so different in their shape that they can be pollinated by only bumblebees or only hummingbirds.

40. Which of the following is a scientific justification for the statement that the evolution of easily modified flower colors that make plants attractive to animals was an important factor in the diversification of flowering plants?
    (A) Flowering plants have no way to cross-pollinate without the intervention of animals.
    (B) Changes in flower color can result in a shift of animal pollinators, which can serve as an isolating mechanism.
    (C) Bright flowers are important to attract animals that can disperse the seeds of the plant.
    (D) Successful evolution requires interactions between plants and animals.

41. An allergic reaction occurs when the immune system overreacts to an allergen such as shellfish, wasp venom, or peanuts. When the immune system recognizes the foreign allergen, it releases histamines that cause localized swelling and other allergy symptoms such as red eyes or sneezing. These normally harmless allergens can cause life-threatening reactions in some individuals. Which of the following best explains this?
    (A) The initial exposure to the allergen causes the immune system to become overactive and release increasing amounts of histamine.
    (B) The innate immune response results in the formation of antibodies that continue to circulate in the blood and can trigger a more aggressive response upon subsequent exposures to the allergen.
    (C) Repeated exposures to the allergen lead to increases in the release of histamines through a positive feedback response.
    (D) Circulating memory B cells are activated by exposure to the allergen and produce large quantities of histamines in response to a second exposure to the allergen.

42. Wagtails are birds that feed primarily on insects such as the dung fly. Handling time is a measure of how much energy the wagtail must invest to capture a food item. Which of the following conclusions does this graph support?

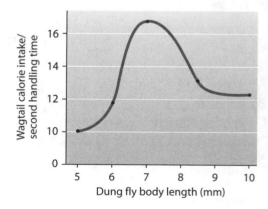

Graph from N. B. Davies. 1977. Prey selection and social behaviour in wagtails (Aves: Motacillidae). *Journal of Animal Ecology* 46: 37-57, fig. 9.

(A) Prey size does not affect the number of calories gained per second of handling time by wagtails.

(B) Wagtails get more calories per second of handling time with larger flies than with smaller ones.

(C) Wagtails get more calories per second of handling time with smaller flies than with larger ones.

(D) Wagtails get more calories per second of handling with a specific size of fly rather than taking flies at random.

43. Which of the following descriptions is not an accurate depiction of behavioral evolution?

(A) Most essential behaviors are the result of some type of learning.

(B) An individual's reproductive success depends in part on how the behavior is performed.

(C) Some component of the behavior is genetically inherited but may be modified by learning.

(D) An individual's genotype influences its behavioral phenotype.

Use the figure showing the formation of complementary DNA (cDNA) from a eukaryotic gene for questions 44 and 45.

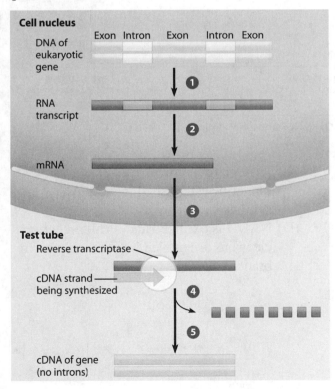

44. In the figure, how is the size of the original RNA transcript reduced in step 2?

(A) DNA polymerase removes some of the original DNA.

(B) RNA polymerase produces a second transcript.

(C) RNA acts as an enzyme in the removal of introns.

(D) Reverse transcriptase changes the larger transcript to a smaller one.

45. What complex is responsible for the step in the figure where the single strand of DNA, formed from RNA by reverse transcriptase, is used to produce the cDNA strand?

(A) ligase

(B) RNA polymerase

(C) DNA polymerase

(D) helicase

46. Two species, A and B, occupy adjoining environmental patches that differ in several abiotic factors. When species A is experimentally removed from a portion of its patch, species B colonizes the vacated area and thrives. When species B is experimentally removed from a portion of its patch, species A does not successfully colonize the area. Which of the following predictions do the data support?

(A) Both species A and species B are limited to their range by abiotic factors.

(B) Species A is limited to its range by competition and predation, and species B is limited by abiotic factors.

(C) Both species are limited to their range by competition, although species B has broader tolerance for different conditions.

(D) Species A is limited to its range by abiotic factors, and species B is limited to its range because it cannot successfully compete with species A.

GO ON TO THE NEXT PAGE

47. A child is brought to the hospital with a fever of 105°F. Doctors immediately order an ice bath to lower the child's temperature. Which of the following statements offers the most logical explanation for this action?
(A) An elevated body temperature will increase reaction rates in the child's cells and overload the limited number of enzymes found in the cells of a small child.
(B) An elevated body temperature may denature enzymes. This would interfere with cells' abilities to catalyze various reactions.
(C) An elevated body temperature will increase the energy of activation needed to start various chemical reactions in the body. This will interfere with the ability of enzymes to catalyze vital chemical reactions.
(D) An elevated body temperature will cause molecules to vibrate more quickly and prevent enzymes from easily attaching to reactants. This would slow vital body reactions.

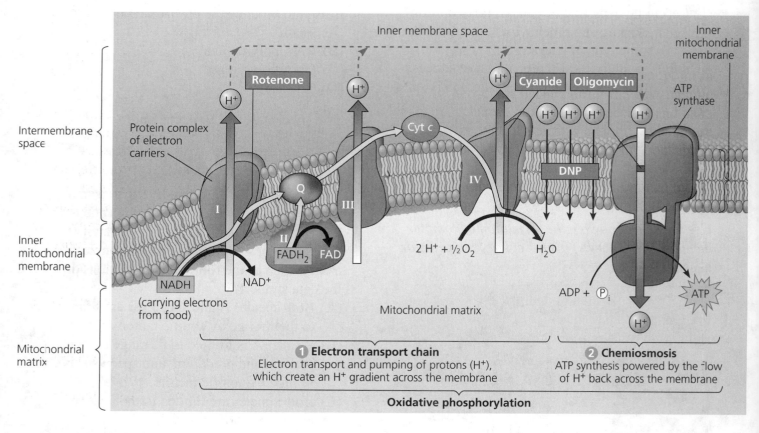

48. Rotenone binds tightly with one of the electron carrier molecules in the first protein complex of the electron transport chain. It is often used as an insecticide and to kill fish. Predict the specific change to normal cellular respiration that occurs with Rotenone.
(A) Exposed animals will no longer be able to perform anaerobic respiration.
(B) ATP synthases are denatured and can no longer generate ATP.
(C) An electrochemical gradient can no longer be established to drive ATP synthesis.
(D) NADH is oxidized and its high-energy electrons are moved into the inner membrane space.

49. In the figure, note that cyanide can bind to electron transport carrier IV. What is the immediate effect of cyanide binding?
    (A) The electron transport chain is no longer able to transfer electrons to oxygen, so its activity is halted.
    (B) An electron gradient cannot be established to drive the production of ATP by chemiosmosis.
    (C) Hydrogen ions bind to the electron transport molecules and interfere with their ability to generate an electron gradient.
    (D) Abnormally large quantities of water will be produced as a result of excess hydrogen ions in the matrix, leading to dehydration and death.

Question 50 refers to the following graph.

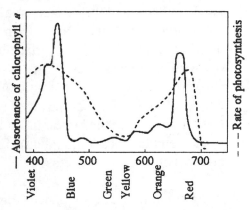

50. In the graph, the absorbance of light by chlorophyll *a* does not perfectly match the rate of photosynthesis. What is the best explanation for this?
    (A) The rate of photosynthesis is always fractionally slower than the rate of absorbance by chlorophyll *a*.
    (B) Chlorophyll *a* transmits light in the green and yellow parts of the spectrum, so the rate of photosynthesis is low at those wavelengths.
    (C) There are fewer chlorophyll *a* molecules in the cell than the other molecules involved in photosynthesis, so chlorophyll *a* is the rate-limiting reagent.
    (D) Chlorophyll *a* is not the only photosynthetically important pigment in chloroplasts.

Questions 51 and 52 refer to the following table, which compares the percentage of sequence homology of four different parts (two introns and two exons) of a gene that is found in five different eukaryotic species. Each part is numbered to indicate its distance from the promoter (for example, Intron I is the one closest to the promoter). The data reported for species A were obtained by comparing DNA from one member of species A to another member of species A.

Species	Intron I	Exon I	Intron VI	Exon V
A	100%	100%	100%	100%
B	96%	99%	82%	96%
C	88%	99%	89%	96%
D	92%	99%	92%	97%
E	86%	99%	86%	94%

51. Which of the following is the best explanation for the high degree of sequence homology observed in Exon I among these five species?
    (A) It is relatively close to the promoter, so fewer mutations have accumulated.
    (B) This exon may often be included as part of Intron I because of their proximity.
    (C) Exon I may be highly conserved because it codes for a critical portion of a polypeptide.
    (D) These species are very closely related, as indicated by the similarity of Exon I.

52. Based on the data shown in the chart, which of the following is most plausible?
    (A) Mutations are more likely to accumulate in introns compared to exons.
    (B) Species E is most closely related to species B.
    (C) A cladogram of these species would show species E as the common ancestor of the others.
    (D) With more time, the variation in Intron VI would decline due to natural selection forces.

Questions 53 through 56 are based on the following reading.

The unicellular yeast *Saccharomyces cerevisiae* divides by budding off a small new cell that then grows to full size. During its growth, the new cell synthesizes new cytoplasm, which increases its volume, and new plasma membrane, which increases its surface area.

Budding cell — Mature parent cell

1 μm

The shape of a yeast cell can be approximated by a sphere, so you can calculate the volume of each cell using the formula for the volume of a sphere:

$$V = 4/3\pi r^3$$

Note that π (the Greek letter *pi*) is a constant with an approximate value of 3.14, and *r* stands for radius, which is half the diameter.

53. Rounding the diameter to the nearest micron, what is the approximate volume of the mature parent cell and the small new cell?
    (A) 17 μm³; 9 μm³
    (B) 33 μm³; 14 μm³
    (C) 268 μm³; 113 μm³
    (D) 2144 μm³; 904 μm³

54. Approximately how much additional cytoplasm will the budding cell have to synthesize as it grows to the size of the parent cell?
    (A) 19 μm³
    (B) 42 μm³
    (C) 47 μm³
    (D) 462 μm³

55. Using the formula A = $4\pi r^2$ for surface area, a value of 50 μm² for the surface area of the parent cell and 28 μm² for the surface area of the budding cell were calculated. What is the surface-area-to-volume ratio of both the parent and budding cell, and what does this reveal about nutrient acquisition?
    (A) The surface-area-to-volume ratio of the parent cell is 33, and the surface-area-to-volume ratio of the budding cell is 14. As the cell becomes larger, the surface-area-to-volume ratio increases.
    (B) The surface-area-to-volume ratio of the parent cell is 17, and the surface-area-to-volume ratio of the budding cell is 9. As the cell becomes larger, the surface-area-to-volume ratio decreases.
    (C) The surface-area-to-volume ratio of the parent cell is 3, and the surface-area-to-volume ratio of the budding cell is 6. As the cell becomes larger, the surface-area-to-volume ratio increases.
    (D) The surface-area-to-volume ratio of the parent cell is 1.5, and the surface-area-to-volume ratio of the budding cell is 2. As the cell becomes larger, the surface-area-to-volume ratio decreases.

56. Following are amino acid sequences for six species for critical parts of the *FOXP2* gene. Each letter represents a single amino acid. It is possible to use the data to determine the relatedness of the six species. Assuming that mutation rates are equal for all species over time and based only on these data, which number represents the species *least* related to the other species?
    1. ATETI...PKSSD...TSSTT...NARRD
    2. ATETI...PKSSE...TSSTT...NARRD
    3. ATETI...PKSSD...TSSTT...NARRD
    4. ATETI...PKSSD...TSSNT...SARRD
    5. ATETI...PKSSD...TSSTT...NARRD
    6. VTETI...PKSSD...TSSTT...NARRD
    (A) Species 2
    (B) Species 3
    (C) Species 4
    (D) Species 6

After reading the paragraphs, answer question 57.

You're conducting an experiment to determine the effect of different wavelengths of light on the absorption of carbon dioxide as an indicator of the rate of photosynthesis in aquatic ecosystems. If the rate of photosynthesis increases, the amount of carbon dioxide in the environment will decrease and vice versa. You've added an indicator to each solution. When the carbon dioxide concentration decreases, the color of the indicator solution will change.

You've placed small aquatic plants in three containers of water, which is mixed with carbon dioxide and the indicator solution. You've placed container A under normal sunlight, B under green light, and C under red light. You observe the containers for 24 hours.

57. Based on your knowledge of the process of photosynthesis, the plant in the container placed under red light would probably
    (A) absorb more CO_2 than the plant in normal sunlight.
    (B) absorb the same amount of CO_2 as the plants under both the green light and normal sunlight.
    (C) show the greatest color change in the indicator solution compared to plants in sunlight.
    (D) absorb more CO_2 than the plants under the green light.

58. Which of the following mutations would be *most* likely to have a harmful effect on an organism?
    (A) a deletion of three nucleotides near the middle of a gene
    (B) a single nucleotide deletion in the middle of an intron
    (C) a single nucleotide deletion near the end of the coding sequence
    (D) a single nucleotide insertion at the start of the coding sequence

59. The following diagram shows a fertilized human egg dividing to form a two-celled embryo. After the initial cleavage division, chemical analysis will reveal that the cells of the embryo are not identical. These two cells will have different fates in the embryo due to differential gene expression. Which of the following statements gives the most scientifically plausible explanation?

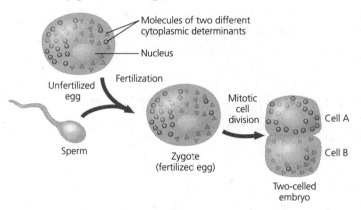

(A) Each of the daughter cells receives slightly different cytoplasmic determinants because these are not evenly distributed in the fertilized egg.
(B) As a result of cleavage, each cell has different receptor proteins expressed on the cell surface, which respond differently to hormones produced by the embryo.
(C) When the zygote divides, one cell receives cytoplasmic determinants from the sperm, whereas the other receives cytoplasmic determinants from the egg.
(D) The first mitotic cell division of the embryo results in independent assortment of the homologous chromosomes and therefore slightly different genes in each cell.

60. The pancreas produces insulin in response to high blood glucose levels, and insulin lowers blood glucose by stimulating its uptake into body cells. In type 2 diabetes, the pancreas produces normal insulin, but body cells are unable to efficiently absorb glucose. This disease possibly has a genetic component, but increased age and weight gain also increase the likelihood of it occurring. Which of the following genetic mutations would be most likely to make a person more susceptible to type 2 diabetes?

(A) a mutation in a gene responsible for the production of the precursor of normal insulin
(B) a mutation in a gene that allows detection of blood glucose levels and so provides feedback regulation
(C) a mutation in a gene for a receptor protein for insulin in target cells
(D) a mutation in liver cells that prevents the breakdown of glycogen to glucose

Questions 61 through 63 are based on the following graph.

Effects of an Auxin on Cell Elongation

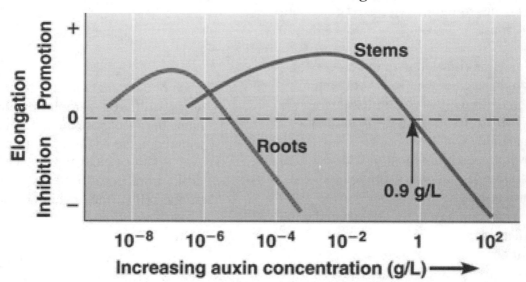

© Pearson Education, Inc.

An auxin is a type of plant hormone that affects cell elongation in roots and stems. The concentration of auxins is critical in obtaining specific plant responses.

61. What does the distance between two white vertical lines on this graph represent?
    (A) an increase in elongation
    (B) a change in auxin concentration of 1 g/L
    (C) a 100-fold change in auxin concentration
    (D) a doubling of auxin concentration

62. As labeled on the graph, the stems line crosses the dashed zero line at an auxin concentration of 0.9 g/L. What does this indicate?
    (A) At this auxin concentration, elongation of roots is neither promoted nor inhibited.
    (B) At this auxin concentration, elongation of stems is promoted, but elongation of roots is inhibited.
    (C) At this point on the graph, the auxin concentration is 0 g/L.
    (D) At this auxin concentration, elongation of stems is neither promoted nor inhibited.

63. Which of the following statements is supported by the graph?
    (A) Any given concentration of auxin either promotes stem elongation or promotes root elongation, but never both.
    (B) Very low concentrations of auxin inhibit elongation of the roots.
    (C) There are concentrations of auxin that promote stem elongation while simultaneously inhibiting root elongation.
    (D) Auxin concentrations below 0.9 g/L always promote elongation.

Grid-In Questions

Part B Directions: The next six questions require numeric answers. Determine the correct answer for each question and enter it in the grids provided at the end of this section.

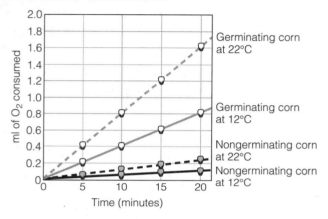

1. A scientist is interested in how temperature affects the rate of respiration (and therefore growth) in germinating corn. Use the graph to calculate the difference between the rate of germination at 22°C and the rate of germination at 12°C. Calculate the rates at 5 to 20 minutes, and determine the difference between the two rates to the nearest hundredth.

2.

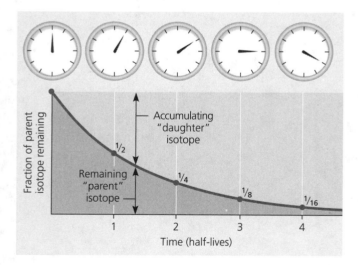

The figure provides information about radiometric dating. Note that the radioactive "parent" isotope decays to a "daughter" isotope at a characteristic rate. It is possible to accurately date the age of artifacts containing wood to about 75,000 years ago using carbon dating. The half-life of radioactive decay of carbon-14 to carbon-12 is about 5,730 years. In a sample to be analyzed, the carbon-14 to carbon-12 ratio is 1/8. What is your estimate of the age of the artifact to the nearest year?

3. Potato cores in solutions of varying concentrations neither gained nor lost mass in a sucrose solution of 0.32M. Use this information to calculate the solute potential of the potato cores. The temperature of the solution is 22°C. (Refer to Appendix A, AP Biology Equations and Formulas.)

4. Glutamine is an amino acid not commonly found in human diets. Glutamine is synthesized from glutamic acid by adding an ammonium molecule to glutamine. The overall reaction is endergonic, requiring 3.4 kcal/mole. The energy for the reaction comes from the exergonic splitting of a phosphate from ATP to form ADP, which releases 7.3 kcal/mole. What is the free energy change for this coupled reaction?

5. In a population of trogons (a type of bird), tail banding (*B*) is dominant to no tail banding (*b*). If 68% of the population shows tail banding, what percentage of the population, to the nearest tenth, is heterozygous for tail banding?

6. Ecologists often cannot count all the individuals in a population. In such cases, they may use the mark-recapture method to estimate population size. An ecologist wished to estimate the population of snapping turtles in an isolated farm pond. On the first trapping, the ecologist caught and marked 19 turtles with a harmless mark on the top of the shell. Two weeks later, the ecologist conducted a second trapping and caught 22 turtles, of which 9 were marked. Using the formula

$$N = sn/x$$

where N = population size estimate, s = number of turtles marked in the first trapping, n = number of turtles caught in the second trapping, and x = the number of turtles that were marked in the second trapping, what is the population estimate of snapping turtles to the nearest *hundredth*?

GO ON TO THE NEXT PAGE

Biology
Section II

8 Questions
Planning Time—10 minutes
Writing Time—80 minutes

Directions: Questions 1 and 2 are long free-response questions that require about 22 minutes each to answer and are worth 10 points each. Questions 3–8 are short free-response questions that require about 6 minutes each to answer. Questions 3 through 5 are worth 4 points each, and questions 6 through 8 are worth 3 points each.

1. The plasma membrane allows the selective passage of materials into and out of the cell.

   (a) Several macromolecules are involved in the formation of the plasma membrane. **Identify three** macromolecules of a typical animal plasma membrane that are involved in the transport of materials across the plasma membrane, and **describe** the role each of these components plays in regulating the cell's internal environment.

   (b) **Describe** how *each* of the following can enter an animal cell
   - viral RNA
   - steroid hormones
   - water molecules
   - O_2

2. Human activities are having a significant impact on biodiversity. The following diagram represents different forest communities.

Community 1   Community 2

(a) **Describe** the factors involved in species diversity.
(b) **Calculate** the percentage of *each* community represented by species A.
(c) Which of the two communities in the figure is more diverse? **Explain** how two communities that contain the same number of species can differ in species diversity.
(d) **Predict** and **justify** the impact on community stability in each forest community of a disease that affects species A.

Data from J. N. Walters et al., Regulation of human microsomal prostaglandin E synthase-1 by IL-1β requires a distal enhancer element with a unique role for C/E BPβ, *Biochemical Journal* (2012). doi: 10.1042/BJ20111801

3. The promoter of a gene includes the DNA immediately upstream of the transcription start site, but the gene's expression can also be affected by control elements. These control elements can be thousands of base pairs upstream of the promoter, grouped in an enhancer. Because the distance and spacing of these control elements make them difficult to identify, scientists begin by deleting sections of DNA that contain possible control elements and measuring the effect on gene expression. The figure shows data obtained from DNA deletion experiments that tested possible control elements for the human gene *mPGES-1*. This gene codes for an enzyme that synthesizes a type of prostaglandin, a chemical made during inflammation. Control elements regulate whatever gene is in the appropriate downstream location. To test the activity of the possible elements, researchers synthesized four types of DNA molecules ("constructs").

GO ON TO THE
NEXT PAGE

In all constructs, the enhancer region was located upstream of a "reporter gene," a gene whose mRNA product could be easily measured experimentally. The researchers then introduced each DNA construct into a separate human cell culture, where the cells took up the artificial DNA molecules. After 48 hours, the researchers measured the amount of reporter gene mRNA the cells made. Comparing these amounts allowed the researchers to determine if any of the deletions had an effect on the expression of the reporter gene.

(a) **Provide evidence** that all three possible control elements are actual control elements.
(b) **Describe** the role of control element *b*, and **cite data** to support your response.
(c) If similar results were obtained in a study of control elements of a type of tumor cell, **explain** which element, if deleted, would have the greatest effect in promoting tumor growth.

4. Glucose 6-phosphatase, which is found in mammalian liver cells, is a key enzyme in control of blood glucose levels. The enzyme catalyzes the breakdown of glucose 6-phosphate into glucose and inorganic phosphate (P_i). These products are transported out of liver cells into the blood, increasing blood glucose levels.

A researcher placed isolated rat liver cells in a dish with buffer at physiological conditions (pH 7.4, 37°C). He added glucose 6-phosphate (the substrate) to the dish, where it was taken up by the cells. The researcher then removed a sample of the buffer every 5 minutes and measured the concentration. The following graph shows the data collected over 40 minutes.

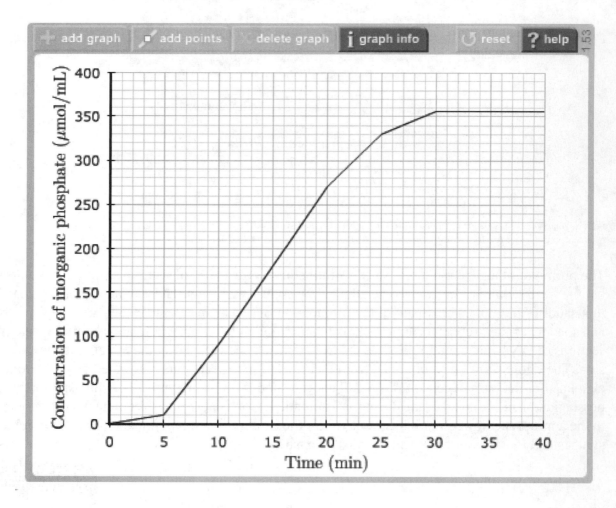

(a) **Describe** the pattern you see in the graph.

(b) **Calculate** the rate of the reaction to the nearest whole number in the time interval between 5 and 20 minutes.

(c) When the substrate (glucose 6-phosphate) is first added to the liver cells, it is transported into the cells and processed by the enzyme (glucose 6-phosphatase). Then the product is released from the cells into the buffer. **Propose a hypothesis** to explain the slope of the line between 25 and 40 minutes.

(d) If your blood sugar level is low from skipping lunch, the following reaction will occur in your liver cells:

$$\text{Glucose 6-phosphate} \xrightarrow{\text{Glucose 6-phosphatase}} \text{Glucose} + \textcircled{P}_i$$

Predict how this reaction will affect your blood sugar level. What type of feedback is this?

Use the mRNA codon chart to do the following tasks.

5. The DNA template strand of a gene contains the sequence

3'-TACTTCAAACCGATT-5'

(a) **Draw** the mRNA sequence from this strand, indicating 5' and 3' ends.

(b) **Predict** the amino acid sequence from this gene.

(c) **Describe** the most likely effect of a mutation that substitutes a thymine for the second cytosine.

(d) **Describe** the most likely effect of a mutation that deletes the second cytosine.

6. A tray of germinating oat seedlings is placed in a window that has light shining through most of the day, and it is given adequate water and soil nutrients. After 3 days, the tray is rotated 180°.
   (a) **Predict** and **explain** the effect this will have on the growing seedlings.
   (b) **Propose** an evolutionary reason for this response to light.

7. It is theorized that glycolysis was the first metabolic pathway for the production of ATP. Glycolysis begins the process of making ATP by breaking glucose into two molecules of pyruvate. **Justify** this claim with *three* pieces of evidence that support this point.

8. Sickle-cell anemia is caused by a single base-pair substitution in the amino acid sequence for the β-globin gene. Under conditions of low oxygen, the mutant form of hemoglobin can result in a change in shape (sickling) of red blood cells and lead to serious health complications and even premature death. Red blood cells with abnormal hemoglobin are less likely to be destroyed by malaria, a potentially fatal disease transmitted by mosquitoes. Individuals who are heterozygous for the mutation produce both normal and abnormal hemoglobin, while individuals homozygous for the mutation produce only abnormal hemoglobin.

   (a) **Predict** how the sickle-cell mutation might alter the overall structure of the protein.
   (b) **Explain** why this mutation is common in Sub-Saharan Africa.
   (c) If the frequency of the allele is 0.07 in Sub-Saharan Africa, **predict** a biologically plausible frequency for the allele in a population of Native Americans in Alaska.

Part V

Answers and Explanations

Topic 1: The Chemistry of Life

ANSWERS AND EXPLANATIONS

Level 1: Knowledge/Comprehension Questions

1. (B) is correct. RNA is made up of a phosphate group, a ribose sugar, and one of the following four nitrogenous bases: cytosine, guanine, uracil, and adenine. DNA is similar to RNA in many ways but different in two important ways: DNA contains deoxyribose instead of ribose as its sugar and it contains the base thymine instead of uracil.

2. (C) is correct. The answer is water, H_2O. Polar covalent bonds are those in which valence electrons are shared between atoms, but they are shared unequally. (The more electronegative atom will attract the electrons more strongly, and that end of the molecule will have a slightly negative charge, whereas the less electronegative atom will attract the electron less strongly and be slightly positive.) The two atoms involved in the bond must differ significantly in electronegativity to form a polar covalent bond.

3. (A) is correct. Use this question to review the unique properties of carbon. The electronegativities of carbon and hydrogen are not different enough to form polar covalent bonds.

4. (D) is correct. The three terms you should keep in mind as you think of water traveling up through the xylem of a plant are transpiration (in which water evaporates from the plant's leaves); cohesion, in which the water molecules stick together because of the hydrogen bonds; and adhesion, whereby the water molecules stick to plant cell walls by hydrogen bonding and resist the downward pull of gravity. Translocation is the movement of solutes in the phloem.

5. (A) is correct. Lipids are the only one of the four major classes of biological molecules that is not a polymer. The diverse group of molecules known as lipids are grouped together because they are hydrophobic. Nucleic acids are polymers of nucleotide monomers, proteins are polymers of amino acid monomers, and carbohydrates are polymers of monosaccharide monomers.

6. (B) is correct. The linkages between the amino acids of proteins are peptide bonds. Peptide bonds are covalent bonds formed in dehydration reactions. The carboxyl group of one amino acid is joined to the amino group of an adjacent amino acid, resulting in the loss of one molecule of water.

7. (C) is correct. One common secondary structure of proteins is the alpha (α) helix; another is the beta (β) pleated sheet. The secondary structure of a protein refers to hydrogen bonding along the backbone (not the side chains) of the amino acid chain.

8. (D) is correct. Cellulose is the polysaccharide that forms the strong cell walls of plant cells. It is a polymer of glucose.

9. (D) is correct. Recall that hydrolysis means to use water to split a molecule, so look for a large molecule reduced to its monomers. Answers A and C are examples of dehydration synthesis.

10. (C) is correct. Denaturation is the process by which proteins lose their overall structure, or conformation, as a result of changes in pH, temperature, or salt concentration. Denatured proteins have reduced biological activity.

11. (B) is correct. The ratio of carbon, hydrogen, and oxygen atoms in carbohydrates approximates 1:2:1. For example, glucose is $C_6H_{12}O_6$ and sucrose is $C_{12}H_{22}O_{11}$. Notice that a water molecule is removed in dehydration synthesis to form sucrose.

12. (B) is correct. Proteins have many functions, which encompass most of a cell's metabolic activity.

13. (B) is correct. Phospholipids are unique macromolecules. Their hydrophilic heads and hydrophobic tails contribute to the semipermeability of cell membranes, and they make up most of the membrane. Proteins function as surface receptors and channels, and cholesterol stabilizes the fluid membrane.

14. (D) is correct. The partial negative charge of the electronegative oxygen of one water molecule is attracted to the partial positive charge of hydrogen of another water molecule.

15. (C) is correct. The monomers in macromolecules are joined when a molecule of water is removed during a dehydration reaction.

16. (B) is correct. Because the pH scale is logarithmic, each unit change is by a factor of 10. A drop in pH means the solution is more acidic and has 10 times more H^+ ions. The H^+ concentration has gone from 10^{-7} to 10^{-6}. Note the negative exponents!

17. (C) is correct. An amino acid is composed of a central carbon that forms four bonds. One bond is with a carboxyl group (the acid part of the name); one bond is with an amino group (the amino part of the name); one bond is with a variable (R) chain; the fourth bond is with a hydrogen.

Level 2: Application/Analysis/Synthesis Questions

1. (D) is correct. Hydrogen bonds occur when a slightly positive hydrogen atom of a polar covalent bond in one molecule is attracted to a slightly negative atom of a polar covalent bond in another molecule. In living systems, hydrogens are often attracted to the highly electronegative elements oxygen (as in this question with water) or nitrogen.

2. (A) is correct. Proteins fold into precise shapes because of interactions between R groups. The 20 different amino acids are different due to differences in their R chains.

3. (D) is correct. Hydrolysis is a chemical process that splits molecules by the addition of water. Digestive enzymes work by hydrolysis. Water is removed to join the molecules; water is added to separate the molecules.

4. (D) is correct. Use the figure to see the pattern of water removal. To join two amino acids, one water is removed. How many waters would be needed to join three amino acids? Four?

5. (D) is correct. Recall that enzymes are proteins and proteins are made of amino acids. With all molecules, *change the shape, change the function.*

6. (A) is correct. Two common environmental factors that affect the three-dimensional structure of enzymes are temperature and pH. As the structure of the enzyme is altered, the enzyme will become less effective.

■ **7. (C) is correct.** Ten glucose molecules would have a combined molecular formula of $C_{60}H_{120}O_{60}$. To form a polymer, a molecule of water would have to be removed as each glucose is added to the chain. Because 10 glucose molecules are bonded together, 9 H_2O molecules must be removed (18 hydrogen atoms and 9 oxygen atoms). This leaves a formula of $C_{60}H_{102}O_{51}$.

■ **8. (D) is correct.** This conceptual question is based on your knowledge of the structure of DNA. Recall that the molecule is antiparallel, meaning one strand runs 5′ to 3′, whereas the opposite strand of the double helix runs 3′ to 5′. Choices B, C, and D are given with both strands running 5′ to 3′. To get the proper answer, convert the second strand given in the answer to 3′ to 5′ and see which one has the proper, matching base-pair sequence. Choice A shows correct complementary base pairing for RNA but not DNA.

■ **9. (A) is correct.** B is a false statement, and although C and D are true statements, they do not justify how water acts as a solvent. Only choice A gives a true property with correct justification.

■ **10. (C) is correct.** To get this correct, you should first add up all the C, H, and O molecules in three fatty acid chains plus one glycerol. This would be 51 C, 74 H, and 9 O. Then, recall that to join two molecules by dehydration synthesis, one molecule of water must be removed. Because three fatty acid chains will be attached to one glycerol, three water molecules will be removed. Subtract 6 H and 3 O to arrive at the answer.

■ **11. (C) is correct.** Although tedious, a careful scanning along the sequence shows 8 amino acid differences. In large databases, computers are used to tally differences in sequence.

■ **12. (B) is correct.** The data shows 8 of 146 amino acids are different or 5.5% (8/146 × 100). This means that 94.5% of the amino acids are identical.

■ **13. (D) is correct.** With only two amino acid differences, the percentage is 1.4% (2/146 × 100). This means that an amazing 98.6% of the amino acids are identical!

■ **14. (A) is correct.** The first line of the reading below the data chart provides the key information: DNA and polypeptide sequences from closely related species are more similar to each other than sequences from more distantly related species. With only two amino acid differences and a percentage identity of 98.6, the gibbon is most closely related to humans.

■ **15. (A) is correct.** The more proteins that were compared, the clearer the relatedness there was between species. No firm conclusions can be reached by comparing only one protein. The other three choices do not give insight into the genetic relatedness between monkeys, gibbons, and humans.

Grid-In Questions

1. 92 hydrogen atoms. To get this result, remember that you must remove 8 molecules of H_2O as you join together 9 molecules by dehydration synthesis. Multiply 12 hydrogen atoms × 9 = 108, but you must remove 8 molecules of H_2O, so subtract 16 H.

2. 10,000. To obtain this answer, remember that the pH scale is logarithmic, so every number of difference results in a 10X difference of H^+. The change from pH 2 to pH 6 is a change of 4 units, 10 × 10 × 10 × 10 = 10,000. Because

there are *more* hydrogen ions in pH 2, the sign is positive and does not need to be recorded in your response. If you had been asked to compare pH 6 to pH 2, you would need to remember that there are 10,000 fewer H^+ ions in a solution with pH 6, requiring a negative sign in the answer.

Free-Response Questions

(a) A phospholipid molecule contains a hydrophilic "head" (containing a glycerol molecule and a phosphate group) and two hydrophobic fatty acid tails. In cell membrane surfaces, phospholipids are arranged in a bilayer in which the hydrophilic heads are in contact with the cell's watery interior and exterior, whereas the tails are pointed away from water and toward each other in the interior of the membrane. The fatty acid chains of phospholipids can contain double bonds, which makes them unsaturated. Because of the kinks in the tails, phospholipids aren't packed together tightly, which contributes to the fluidity of the membrane. The fluidity of the cell membrane is very important in its function; the less fluid the membrane is, the more impermeable it is. There is an optimum permeability for the cell membrane at which all the substances necessary for metabolism can pass into and out of the cell.

The fluidity of cell membranes enables hydrophobic molecules such as hydrocarbons, carbon dioxide, and oxygen to dissolve in the bilayer and easily cross the membrane. However, ions and polar molecules (including water, glucose, and other sugars) cannot readily pass through because of the hydrophobic interior. Protein channels and transport proteins allow these required substances to cross membranes.

(b) If all the fatty acid chains of phospholipids were saturated, no "kinks" would occur in the phospholipids, resulting in membranes that would be less fluid. At very low temperatures, this would lead to plant membranes with drastically reduced fluidity. The loss of fluidity would make the movement of essential nutrients across the membrane much less efficient, which could lead to the death of the plant.

(c) There are numerous functions of proteins in the membrane. One important function is that some proteins protrude on the extracellular side of the membrane and serve as receptors for signaling molecules. A second function is seen with proteins that extend through the interior of the bilayer and serve as channels for the passage of molecules or ions that cannot pass through the phospholipids.

(d) Receptor proteins have regions or domains that are made up of unique amino acids to bind only specific ligands. The specificity of amino acid sequences makes this possible.

Transport proteins may act as channels for molecules and ions that cannot pass through the phospholipid bilayer. Ligands that bind to transport proteins can help alter their conformation to permit the passage of molecules through them and into the cell interior.

This response should show thorough knowledge of the processes of the structure of phospholipids, cell membrane structure and components, and movement across membranes. A satisfactory answer would show that in part (d) you followed the direction to explain the role of a protein selected in part (c). Be sure you underline important instructions like this, and follow them!

A strong response to this item requires an understanding of topics from Units 1 and 2 of the textbook. Your response could contain information about other protein functions, including specific examples of cell-cell signaling or enzymatic function.

Topic 2: The Cell

ANSWERS AND EXPLANATIONS

Level 1: Knowledge/Comprehension Questions

▌ **1. (B) is correct.** This question is centered around proteins for export, which would require large numbers of ribosomes, rough ER, and many Golgi bodies.

▌ **2. (C) is correct.** Linear chromosomes are the only cell structure on this list not found in both prokaryotes and eukaryotes. Eukaryotic cells have a true nucleus, which is surrounded by a double membrane called a nuclear envelope, and contain linear chromosomes, with their DNA wrapped around histone proteins. The genetic material of prokaryotes is localized in a clump in one particular region of the cell called the nucleoid region, and the main chromosome is a single molecule of circular DNA without associated histone proteins.

▌ **3. (D) is correct.** The smooth ER proliferates in cells that detoxify poisons.

▌ **4. (B) is correct.** The Golgi apparatus is the organelle that has a *cis* and *trans* face, and it acts as the packaging and secreting center of the cell. It consists of a series of flattened sacs of membranes called *cisternae.*

▌ **5. (A) is correct.** Cellular respiration takes place in the mitochondria, forming ATP, the cell's energy currency. Mitochondria are bound by double membranes, and the proteins involved in ATP production are embedded in the inner membranes of the mitochondria. Red blood cells lack mitochondria as well as nuclei, making them well adapted to their function of oxygen transport.

▌ **6. (C) is correct.** Lysosomes are characteristic of animal cells but not most plant cells. They are large membrane-bound structures that contain hydrolytic enzymes, and they are responsible for the breakdown of proteins, polysaccharides, fats, and nucleic acids. They function best at a low pH (around 5), so they pump hydrogen ions from the cytosol into their lumen to achieve this acidic pH.

▌ **7. (D) is correct.** The radioactive tracking starts with the formation of the protein, which occurs on the ER. The protein then moves to the Golgi and out of the cell via vesicles that will fuse with the membrane. Choice C is the proper pathway, but the radioactive amino acids will not be used in the nucleus and would therefore not be tracked with this system.

8. (A) is correct. Surface proteins bind to signaling molecules (ligands), and this binding activates a signal transduction pathway, resulting in intracellular responses.

9. (D) is correct. The only substance listed that can passively diffuse through the cell membrane unaided by proteins is carbon dioxide. Remember that passive diffusion occurs without the cell doing any work. The other choices all need the processes of facilitated diffusion and transport proteins to cross the membrane. This is a question a student could answer at the end of the course (we hope), but not if you are covering cell biology at the beginning of your course.

10. (B) is correct. Large molecules are moved out of the cell by exocytosis. In exocytosis, vesicles that are to be exported from the cell (often coming from the Golgi apparatus) fuse with the plasma membrane, and their contents are expelled into the extracellular matrix. Vesicles are involved in exocytosis, but vesicles are a structure—not a process, as the question requires.

11. (A) is correct. When a signal molecule binds to the receptor protein, the gate of the ion channel opens or closes, allowing or blocking the flow of specific ions.

12. (A) is correct. Because the substance is being moved against the concentration gradient, energy is required. Requiring energy to move a substance against its concentration gradient is a characteristic of active transport. All the other choices are modes of passive transport and require no energy, but they can move a substance down its concentration gradient only.

13. (B) is correct. Choice A is a reference to a G-protein-coupled receptor, not the G protein. Choice A can be a quick but incorrect pick if the question is not read carefully. The G protein is activated by the G-protein-coupled receptor, which is a protein and eliminates D as a possible answer.

14. (D) is correct. Kinase enzymes are involved with ATP. Protein kinase enzymes are used to amplify the signal during the transduction phase of cell signaling by activating cell proteins with a phosphate from ATP. Protein phosphatases remove phosphates from proteins and in the process turn off the signal transduction pathway.

15. (C) is correct. Many signaling pathways involve small, nonprotein water-soluble molecules or ions called *second messengers*. Calcium ions and cyclic AMP are two common second messengers. Once activated, the second messengers can initiate a phosphorylation cascade, resulting in a cellular response.

16. (D) is correct. Intracellular receptors work with signal molecules that are hydrophobic compounds and are therefore able to cross the plasma membrane. Testosterone, as indicated in the question, is a steroid hormone and thus is hydrophobic. Once activated, intracellular receptors often act as transcription factors.

17. (C) is correct. Cytokinesis is the division of the cytoplasm to form two separate daughter cells.

18. (A) is correct. In eukaryotic cells, DNA is replicated during S phase, a subphase of interphase. The important thing is to recognize that before identical cells can be produced by mitosis, the amount of DNA must be doubled by replication.

19. (B) is correct. Interphase is a busy time in the cell as growth and cell functions are occurring. Interphase is divided into Gap 1, S phase, and G2. In G1 the cell has just completed mitosis and is growing and performing its specific cell functions. Because the cell has not passed the G1 checkpoint, no energy is being used for preparations for cell division.

20. (A) is correct. During S phase, the DNA is replicated. If S phase were attempted and failed, mitosis would be halted and apoptosis would occur.

21. (D) is correct. The fluid mosaic model is a reference to a membrane with a mosaic of various proteins embedded or attached to a double layer of phospholipids.

22. (A) is correct. Because membranes are hydrophobic, hydrophobic molecules easily pass across the membrane. Remember: Hydrophilic dissolves hydrophilic; hydrophobic dissolves hydrophobic.

23. (D) is correct. The important parts of this question are the three correct statements in choices A, B, and C. Think about how these big picture ideas are incorporated into the cell signalling sequence of reception, transduction, and cellular response.

Level 2: Application/Analysis/Synthesis Questions

1. (A) is correct. Water moves in a hypotonic-to-hypertonic direction. Cells A, B, and C are all animal cells (red blood cells) and lack a cell wall. Cell D is a plant cell with a cell wall. Cell A is in a hypotonic solution, cell B is in an isotonic solution, and cell C is in a hypertonic solution. When answering this type of question, pay close attention to whether the solution or the cell is referenced as being hypertonic or hypotonic. In A, the solution is hypotonic but the cell is hypertonic.

2. (C) is correct. In plant cells, the relatively inelastic cell wall exerts a back pressure on the cells, called turgor pressure. In cell D, the plant cell is immersed in a hypotonic solution, causing the cell to uptake water, thus creating the highest levels of turgor pressure. Animal cell A lyses ("pops") because it has only a thin, flexible membrane.

3. (C) is correct. The solution in Tank A started with more solutes; then, as the water is purified, its concentration of solutes increases through the process of reverse osmosis. Tank A becomes increasingly hypertonic over the course of the purification treatment.

4. (B) is correct. Tank A, with the tap water, is hypertonic to the purified water. Because water flows from hypotonic to hypertonic, water would move from Tank B into Tank A.

5. (C) is correct. Epinephrine is the ligand that activates the G protein-coupled receptor responsible for glycogen breakdown. Epinephrine does not enter the cell, suggesting a second messenger. Only in intact cells could the first messenger (epinephrine) be translated to a cellular response–glycogen breakdown.

6. (D) is correct. Substances will move down their concentration gradient until their concentration is equal on both sides of the membrane. The concentration of glucose on side B is 2.0 M, whereas the concentration of glucose on side A is 1.0 M; therefore, glucose will move from side B to side A. Solutes move down their own concentration gradients, not the combined gradients as answer A would indicate.

7. (B) is correct. First, you must note that glucose is the smaller molecule and focus only on where it is in higher concentration. Because its highest concentration is on side B, it will move to side A.

8. (A) is correct. As glucose moves into side A, the total amount of solute on that side increases, becoming hypertonic, causing water to follow.

9. (A) is correct. Notice that the H^+ ions in the diagram are moving against their concentration gradient. Movement of solutes against their concentration gradient requires energy and, therefore, active transport.

10. (B) is correct. Recall that decreasing the extracellular pH (for example, going from pH 7 to pH 6) would increase the H^+ ion concentration, providing more H^+ ions for cotransport as well as a steeper gradient into the cell.

11. (C) is correct. Cell A in the figure for question 1 demonstrates what happens when red blood cells are placed in a hypotonic solution. With the RBCs destroyed, the WBCs will be easier to observe.

12. (C) is correct. The clue is given in the stem of the question, where melanin is identified as a protein for export. With that information, you would expect an increase in ribosomes, rough ER, Golgi bodies, and vesicles.

13. (B) is correct. When the DNA is damaged beyond the ability of the cell to repair it, apoptosis pathways are initiated. Damaged cells may become cancerous, so it is better for the organism to destroy the cell than to take a chance on a cancerous cell.

14. (B) is correct. Because both prokaryotes and eukaryotes use ATP, choice B does not provide evidence for the endosymbiotic hypothesis. Notice that the other three choices do provide evidence and would be the key points in developing an answer to essay questions about the evidence for endosymbiosis.

15. (A) is correct. The hypothesis being tested is tied directly to the ΔFus3 gene. Option B is a testable hypothesis, but it is not involved with the ΔFus3 gene. When determining the proper hypothesis, do not stray to the big picture of the experiment; be precise about the specific experiment being conducted.

16. (D) is correct. Wild-type yeast cells act as a control for observation of shmoo formation because wild-type cells have both Fus3 and formin present under the experimental conditions.

17. (C) is correct. If Fus3 kinase is critical to shmoo formation, cells that don't produce Fus3 kinase should not be able to form shmoos. Don't be intimidated by long, complicated-looking questions. This question may look hard, but the underlying concept is straightforward: If the Fus3 gene does not function, shmoos do not form.

18. (A) is correct. Because the mating factor is diffusing from the direction of the other mating-type yeast, it is the G protein-coupled receptors on that side of the cell that bind the mating factor, become activated, and start the phosphorylation cascade that activates Fus3, which activates formin, which leads to localized shmoo formation.

19. (C) is correct. If the G protein could not bind GTP, it would not become activated, and so it would not start the phosphorylation cascade. Be aware that the questions do not necessarily get harder as you progress through the set. All the multiple-choice questions count the same, and there is no penalty for guessing. If you try a hard question, do not just assume that all of the remaining questions will be hard. Try each question and be aware that sometimes the last question is the easiest.

Grid-In Questions

▌ **1. The correct answer is 8,000 (μm^3).**

▌ **2. The correct answer is 8.**

▌ **3. The correct answer is −10.40 (bars).** The formula of solute potential is −iCRT. In this case the values are −(1.0) (0.42) (0.0831) (298) = −10.40. Sucrose does not ionize, which makes the value of i in the formula 1. If you find these problems difficult, go to the lab section of this book to Investigation 4, Diffusion and Osmosis, where you can find an explanation of water potential and how to work water potential problems.

Free-Response Questions

(a) Eukaryotic cells might have evolved by taking in free-living prokaryotes. One piece of evidence is that prokaryotic cells are much smaller than eukaryotic cells. Mitochondria and chloroplasts are comparable in size to prokaryotic cells.

A second piece of evidence is that mitochondria and chloroplasts both consist of a double membrane exterior, which would be a possible result of a prokaryotic cell being engulfed by another cell.

Mitochondria and chloroplasts also contain their own DNA and are capable of dividing on their own. The presence of DNA could be evidence that they were independent organisms at some time.

(b) To trace the path of proteins in the cell from their creation to their expulsion, we must start in the nucleus. In the nucleus, mRNA is transcribed from DNA. The mRNA travels out of the nucleus through a nuclear pore to the cytoplasm, ending up at ribosomes, which are associated with the endoplasmic reticulum (called rough endoplasmic reticulum because of this association). As the mRNA is translated into protein, the amino acid chain is threaded into the lumen of the ER, where it undergoes folding to assume its final shape, or conformation.

Secretory proteins travel in vesicles from the endoplasmic reticulum to the series of flattened membranous sacs known as the Golgi apparatus. They enter at the *cis* face and eventually bud from the *trans* face after undergoing a series of modifications to prepare them for secretion. The vesicles may then fuse with the cell membrane, and the contents are released from the cell in a process called exocytosis.

The student response in (a) might have used the presence of ribosomes in mitochondria and chloroplasts that translate genes unique to the organelles as one of the arguments for endosymbiosis. However, the question asked for three explanations, so this would be substituted for one of the others. Specific sizes of cells and organelles are not expected. Additional points would probably be awarded in (b) if the student included a discussion of signal peptides and signal recognition particles. (This is covered in Chapter 17.)

Topic 3: The Energy of Life

ANSWERS AND EXPLANATIONS

Level 1: Knowledge/Comprehension Questions

1. (D) is correct. The shape of the curve in the figure most closely depicts an exergonic reaction. The free energy of the products is lower than that of the reactants—meaning that in the course of the reaction, energy is given off. This is characteristic of exergonic reactions.

2. (D) is correct. Enzymes speed up chemical reactions by lowering energy barriers. Notice in the graph that the energy of activation is lower with an enzyme than without an enzyme. The lower energy of activation allows reactant molecules to absorb enough energy to reach the transition state even at moderate temperatures.

3. (A) is correct. In allosteric regulation, the enzyme is usually composed of more than one polypeptide chain, with an allosteric site remote from the active site. When an allosteric activator binds to the allosteric site, the enzyme assumes a stable conformation with a functional active site, and the reaction can proceed. When an allosteric inhibitor binds to the allosteric site, the enzyme is stabilized in an inactive form.

4. (C) is correct. Competitive inhibitors compete for the active site of the enzyme. They are able to occupy the active site because they closely resemble the normal substrate. One way to overcome the effects of competitive inhibitors is to increase the amount of substrate so that chances are greater that a substrate molecule (rather than the competitive inhibitor) will bind to the enzyme's active site.

5. (B) is correct. In feedback inhibition, the product of a metabolic pathway switches off the pathway by binding to and inhibiting an enzyme involved somewhere along the pathway.

6. (D) is correct. In noncompetitive inhibition, the inhibitor binds to a site other than the active site of the enzyme, and this causes the enzyme to change shape. The change in conformation makes the substrate unable to bind to the active site of the enzyme, and this prevents the action from taking place.

7. (C) is correct. The purpose of cellular respiration in eukaryotes is to produce energy for cellular work in the form of ATP. Respiration is an aerobic process, meaning that it requires oxygen. Answer choices A and B are incorrect because respiration involves the breakdown (not the synthesis) of carbohydrates, fats, and proteins. Choice D is wrong because oxygen is required, not produced, for cellular respiration.

8. (B) is correct. Note that this question is framed per glucose, not per single turn of the citric acid cycle. In the breakdown of glucose in the citric acid cycle, two ATPs are produced. The citric acid cycle takes in a molecule called acetyl CoA (pyruvate is converted into acetyl CoA before it enters the citric acid cycle), and this is joined to a four-carbon molecule of oxaloacetate to form a six-carbon compound citrate that is then broken down again to produce oxaloacetate; the oxaloacetate reenters the cycle. In the course of the citric acid cycle, the following are produced by two trips through the citric acid cycle *per glucose*: 4 CO_2, 2 ATP, 6 NADH, and 2 $FADH_2$.

9. (A) is correct. Groups of photosynthetic pigment molecules in the thylakoid membrane are called photosystems. The two photosystems involved in photosynthesis are photosystem I and photosystem II. Both contain chlorophyll molecules and many proteins and other organic molecules, and both have a light-harvesting complex that harnesses incoming light. Each of these photosystems contains a reaction center, where chlorophyll *a* and the primary electron acceptor are located.

10. (B) is correct. The main products of the light reactions of photosynthesis are NADPH and ATP. NADPH and ATP are used to convert CO_2 to sugar in the Calvin cycle. The enzyme rubisco combines CO_2 with ribulose bisphosphate (RuBP) and electrons from NADPH and energy from ATP to synthesize a three-carbon molecule called glyceraldehyde 3-phosphate. You should recognize that $FADH_2$ is a product of the citric acid cycle (aerobic respiration), so choices A and C could not be correct.

11. (D) is correct. The organic product of the Calvin cycle, which may be used later to build both glucose and large carbohydrates, is glyceraldehyde 3-phosphate, or G3P. This molecule is created as a result of the fixation of three molecules of CO_2, which costs the cell ATP and NADPH that were created in the light reactions of photosynthesis.

12. (B) is correct. During the Calvin cycle, chemical energy produced during the light reactions (ATP and NADPH) is used to reduce CO_2 and produce G3P (sugars). D is wrong because the electron transport chains pump protons across membranes from regions of *low* H^+ concentrations to regions of *high* H^+ concentrations. Choice C describes the light reaction—not the Calvin cycle—so is incorrect. Choice A is partially correct; the light reactions yield ATP but not glucose. The second product of the light reactions is NADPH.

13. (D) is correct. ATP synthase is located in the inner thylakoid membrane, not the double membrane that surrounds the chloroplast. Notice the direction of flow of protons through ATP synthase in photosynthesis: The protons flow from the thylakoid space to the stroma. ATP is produced in the stroma, where it will be used by the Calvin cycle.

14. (C) is correct. When water is split, three products are formed: two protons, an oxygen atom that immediately bonds with another oxygen to form O_2, and two electrons. The electrons immediately feed into the P680 chlorophyll *a* in the reaction center of photosystem II. The ultimate electron donor in photosynthesis is water.

15. (D) is correct. Each turn of the Calvin cycle involves the enzyme rubisco fixing one atom of carbon. It follows that it would take six turns to produce the six-carbon sugar glucose. Students sometimes miss this question by confusing the Calvin cycle with the citric acid cycle of cellular respiration. Read these questions carefully, and be sure to identify what the question is asking.

   16. (C) is correct. The light reactions of photosynthesis move electrons from their low-energy state in water to a higher energy level when the electrons are donated to NADP$^+$ to make NADPH. In cellular respiration, electrons pass down the electron transport chain from high to low potential energy, ultimately combining with O_2 and hydrogen ions to form water.

Level 2: Application/Analysis/Synthesis Questions

   1. (D) is correct. Plant leaves are green because they reflect and refract green light, which is not utilized in photosynthesis. Red light is used in photosynthesis; the plant absorbs CO_2 for photosynthesis, but not at the rate of normal sunshine, which has all the wavelengths of visible light. Check the action and absorption spectra for photosynthesis in your text and be prepared to explain the peaks and valleys shown in the graphs.

   2. (A) is correct. The light reactions convert solar energy to the chemical energy of ATP and NADPH, which are utilized in the Calvin cycle to reduce CO_2 to sugar.

   3. (A) is correct. By making the mitochondrial membrane permeable to H$^+$, the inner membrane no longer has a sufficient electrochemical gradient to utilize ATP synthase to generate ATP.

   4. (C) is correct. In energy coupling an exergonic process (catabolic reactions) is used to drive an endergonic process (anabolic reactions).

   5. (B) is correct. The breakdown of glucose requires many chemical reactions involving energy transfers. The second law of thermodynamics states that with each energy transfer some of the energy is lost to the system, primarily as heat. When you exercise heavily, sweat cools your body from the gain of heat that results from cellular respiration.

   6. (D) is correct. Molecular shape is directly related to molecular function (change the shape—change the function). As the pH dropped to 6, the enzyme was a more active shape. Choice A is not correct because we do not know the enzyme is at its optimum at pH 6. For example, the enzyme might work even better at pH 5.

   7. (D) is correct. Noncompetitive inhibitors bind to the enzyme away from the active site, thereby changing the shape of the enzyme and reducing the effectiveness of the active site. Because more substrate did not increase product formation as it would have if substance A were a competitive inhibitor, choice C is eliminated.

   8. (B) is correct. The process in photosynthesis that bears the closest resemblance to chemiosmosis and oxidative phosphorylation in cellular respiration is linear electron flow. In this process, energy from the transfer of electrons down the electron transport chain is used to create a hydrogen ion gradient for the making of ATP. Later, the energy stored in this ATP is used during the formation of carbohydrates in the Calvin cycle.

   9. (D) is correct. Many of the proteins embedded in the inner mitochondrial membrane are proton pumps powered by the flow of electrons through the system. Cyanide stops the flow of electrons, which shuts down the pumps and stops the H^+ gradient, causing ATP synthesis to cease.

▌ **10. (B) is correct.** ATP and NADH are obvious products of glycolysis, but most of the energy of glucose at the end of glycolysis is held in the pyruvate molecules.

▌ **11. (D) is correct.** This question would make a good short essay question; your response should center on the three reasons cited in choice D. All three reasons given reflect a pathway that evolved early in the evolution of life on earth.

▌ **12. (C) is correct.** In feedback inhibition, a metabolic pathway is switched off by the binding of its end product to an enzyme that functions early in the pathway, causing the pathway to be inhibited. Tryptophan is the end product of the pathway and serves as the molecule that binds to an enzyme early in the pathway, causing a change in the shape of the enzyme and inhibiting the pathway.

▌ **13. (C) is correct.** Making the inner membrane leaky to H^+ ions means the mitochondria are much less efficient and must burn much more fuel to produce the ATP necessary for life. The burning of the extra fuel creates extra heat, which is used to maintain body temperature. Can you think of how surface area-to-volume ratios are also part of this answer?

▌ **14. (A) is correct.** B is not correct because glycolysis does not perform oxidative phosphorylation. C is not correct because the electron transport system does not occur in the cytoplasm. D is not correct because no CO_2 is produced in the mitochondrial membrane from NADH or ATP. Everything in A is correct, even if most of the ATP formed in the citric acid cycle will occur when the electrons from NADH and $FADH_2$ are fed into the electron transport chain. A is the best answer, even if you might feel it isn't the perfect answer.

▌ **15. (B) is correct.** For Engelmann to be able to draw meaningful conclusions from his experiment, he had to assume that the number of bacteria at any location on the slide was proportional to the amount of oxygen produced by the alga at that location. If this were not the case, the distribution of the bacteria around the alga would be of no use in determining the level of photosynthesis occurring at each wavelength.

▌ **16. (D) is correct.** The information in the question indicates that the sun emits the most photons in the yellow part of the spectrum and emits relatively fewer photons in the red and violet-blue parts of the spectrum. Thus, the red and violet-blue regions of Engelmann's action spectrum were measured with fewer photons than in the yellow part of the spectrum. To correct for this, you have to consider how increasing the number of photons in the red and violet-blue parts of the spectrum—to match the emission level in the yellow part—would change the amount of oxygen produced, and thus the number of bacteria that accumulated, in the red and violet-blue spectral regions. The corrected action spectrum would show higher peaks in the red and violet-blue parts of the spectrum, but the plot in the yellow part of the spectrum would be approximately the same as Engelmann's.

▌ **17. (A) is correct.** Although the scenario for this question is probably new to you, the answer is actually straightforward. Using Figure 3.8 as a guide, note that the two components necessary for ATP synthesis are the electron transport proteins and ATP synthase. Don't let new scenarios fool you into thinking the question is too hard to answer. Look carefully at what the question is asking, and often you will find that the answer is simpler than it first seemed.

▌ **18. (A) is correct.** Again, use Figure 3.8 as a guide to visualize the structure of the inside-out vesicle. Note that instead of ATP synthase discharging its protons into the matrix of the mitochondria, it would be discharging the protons into the interior of the vesicle. The increase in hydrogen ions would cause the inside of the vesicle to become more acidic.

▌ **19. (D) is correct.** The radioactive carbon that enters the Calvin cycle serves as the source of carbon for all the molecules shown in the figure. Therefore, all of the molecules in answer D could be radioactive. It may help to visualize this by noting that G3P is used both as the output product *and* to regenerate ribulose bisphosphate, thus both D and E are included in the answer.

▌ **20. (C) is correct.** Using the figure as a guide, note that ribulose bisphosphate (E) is the CO_2 acceptor molecule (Phase 3 shaded information). The acceptor molecule will increase in concentration if no CO_2 is available (A in the figure) to continue the cycle. RuBP is not used and accumulates. Conversely, if the light is cut off, RuBP is no longer produced because of the lack of energy products made in the light stage of photosynthesis. The lack of light means no G3P and therefore no RuBP. Use the figure to help visualize the answer options.

Grid-In Questions

1. **The answer is 90 molecules of ATP.** Each molecule of glucose that goes through fermentation will produce 2 ATP and 2 NADH. The NADH will not enter the electron transport system (there is no oxygen available) and will generate no ATP. The total for three glucose molecules is 6 ATP.

    Each molecule of glucose that goes through aerobic respiration will yield 2 ATP and 2 NADH from glycolysis; 2 NADH from pyruvate oxidation (2 molecules of pyruvate); the citric acid cycle will yield 2 ATP, 6 NADH, and 2 $FADH_2$ (two pyruvates). Using the conversions to ATP given, each molecule of glucose will yield 32 ATP. Therefore, 3 molecules of glucose yields 96 total ATP. The difference between the two scenarios is 90 molecules.

    The point of this exercise, in part, is to drive home the huge difference the evolution of aerobic respiration made in making energy available to the processes of evolution. With this energy base, the evolution of the complex web of life was possible. A second point is that this calculation required quite a bit of time. When this occurs on your AP exam, wise students move on to the easier problems and return to ones like this once they have gathered all the easier points.

2. **The answer is −3.9 kcal/mole. Note that you must grid in the negative sign to get credit for this one.** The coupled reaction requires +3.4 kcal/mole but obtains −7.3 kcal/mole from ATP, which leaves −3.9 kcal/mole. Be sure you recognize that endergonic reactions have a positive delta G and that exergonic reactions have a negative delta G. This reaction is detailed in the 11th edition of *Campbell Biology*, Figure 8.10, or the second edition of *Focus*, Figure 6.9.

3. **The answer is 18 μmol/mL/min.** This is determined by 270 μmol/mL − 180 μmol/mL/5 minutes = 18 μmol/mL/min.

Free-Response Questions

(a) Although plants have two photosystems, they both work in the same way. Both photosystems have two components: the light-harvesting complexes and the reaction center. The light-harvesting complex is made up of many chlorophyll and accessory pigment molecules. When one of the pigment molecules absorbs light energy in the form of photons, one of the molecule's electrons is raised to an orbital of higher potential energy. The pigment molecule is then said to be in an "excited" state. The increase in potential energy is transferred to the reaction center of the photosystem. The reaction center consists of two chlorophyll *a* molecules, which use the increased potential energy passed to them by the photosynthetic pigments to donate electrons to the primary electron acceptor. The solar-powered transfer of an electron from the reaction-center chlorophyll *a* pair to the primary electron acceptor is the first step of the light reactions. This is the conversion of light energy to chemical energy. Water provides a constant flow of electrons to the chlorophyll *a* molecules in the reaction center.

(b) Glycolysis is the first stage of cellular respiration and occurs in the cytoplasm. Glycolysis involves the breakdown of glucose to two pyruvate molecules. To accomplish this, 2 ATP molecules are invested, which helps to destabilize glucose, making it more reactive and allowing glucose to break into two three-carbon molecules. By the time the pathway has produced pyruvate, 4 ATP molecules have been produced along with 2 NADH molecules. This gives a net energy gain of 2 ATP and 2 NADH. Thus, one important role of glucose is to produce energy molecules for the cell to use in its life processes. The second role is to produce pyruvate, which can feed into the citric acid cycle in the mitochondria and ultimately into the electron transport chain, where most of the ATP in cellular respiration is produced.

(c) In cellular respiration, water is a product of the reaction, whereas in photosynthesis water is a reactant. In cellular respiration, water is formed when the electrons at the end of the electron transport chain in the inner membrane of the mitochondria combine with hydrogen ions and an atom of oxygen to form water. Oxygen is the ultimate electron acceptor in cellular respiration and, when combined with protons, water is formed. In photosynthesis, an enzyme splits a water molecule into two electrons, two hydrogen ions, and an oxygen atom. The electrons are supplied as needed directly to the chlorophyll molecules in the reaction center of photosystem II. In photosynthesis, water is the ultimate electron donor. In addition, the oxygen atom released immediately joins with another oxygen atom to form O_2. The oxygen on Earth comes almost entirely from the splitting of water in photosynthesis.

This student has written a particularly clear essay. Notice how carefully sequenced the responses are. Also note the clarity of each sentence and the absence of third-person pronouns. Avoiding pronouns may require a little more time and patience, but it pays off in added clarity and higher scores.

PRACTICE THE PRACTICE: *Making Predictions and Interpreting Data*

1. Your graph should show a diagonal line going up from the point of the arrow. This is because hydrogen ions would continue to be pumped across the membrane into the intermembrane space but could not flow back through ATP synthase, since the enzyme is inhibited by the poison. The accumulation of hydrogen ions in the intermembrane space would cause the pH difference to increase across the inner mitochondrial membrane.

2. Phosphofructokinase is more active under low ATP concentrations. Under both conditions, the PFK enzyme increases in activity as the concentration of the substrate increases—up until a point at which the rate levels off. Under conditions of low ATP concentration, however, PFK enzyme activity increases faster and reaches its maximum rate sooner.

3. PFK must be an allosteric enzyme that is inhibited by ATP. When levels of ATP are low, its active site conformation is changed, and this results in greater catalytic activity.

4. At higher concentrations of ATP, PFK is less active. At low ATP concentrations in the cell, the concentrations of AMP and ADP are higher, and AMP stimulates the activity of PFK. This conserves the cell's resources so that ATP production does not occur when it is not needed.

Topic 4: Mendelian Genetics

ANSWERS AND EXPLANATIONS

Level 2: Application/Analysis/Synthesis Questions

1. **(D) is correct.** The probability that the woman will have a seventh child who is a daughter is ½. Because the probability that a sperm carrying an X chromosome and the probability that a sperm carrying a Y chromosome will fertilize an egg is equal—both 50%—fertilization is considered an independent event. The outcome of independent events is unaffected by what events occurred before or will occur after. Therefore, the probability that this woman's next child will be a girl is ½. Likewise, the probability that she will have a child that is a boy is also ½.

2. **(A) is correct.** If the probability of allele *R* segregating into a gamete is ¼ and that of *S* segregating is ½, calculate the probability of two independent events occurring in a specific combination, order, or sequence by multiplying their probabilities; in this case, multiply ¼ by ½.

3. (B) is correct. Note that this cross involves incomplete dominance because there are three possible phenotypes in the offspring in this monohybrid cross. Let's say that the yellow-coat parent is $C^Y C^Y$ and the homozygous brown coat parent is $C^B C^B$. Because the yellow-coat parent can produce only gametes C^Y and the brown-coat parent can produce only gametes C^B, the F_1 generation will all have genotype $C^Y C^B$. Crossing two members of this generation would give a ratio of one yellow coat: two gray coats: one brown coat. This means that 25% of the offspring would have brown coats, 25% would have yellow coats, and 50% would have gray coats.

4. (A) is correct. All of the statements about meiosis are true except A. During the first division, homologous pairs separate.

5. (D) is correct. Immediately rule out choices A and B because A would give you only offspring that exhibited the recessive traits—long hair and blue eyes—and B would give you all offspring that had the dominant traits—short hair and green eyes. Choice C yields a 9:3:3:1 ratio and also would give long hair, which is not seen in our results. Choice D fits the data because it can produce only short hair and yields both green and blue eyes in a ratio of 3:1.

6. (A) is correct. If the boy has hemophilia, he must have inherited the recessive hemophilia gene from his mother. Sex-linked genes are usually located on the X chromosome. For the child to be a boy, he must have inherited a Y chromosome from his father. Because the gene causing hemophilia is located on the X chromosome, you can rule out choices B and C because males cannot pass on their X chromosomes to their sons. Therefore, you need to look for an answer choice that shows that the source of his X chromosome was a carrier of the allele—afflicted or not. This is choice A.

7. (A) is correct. Although genes that are on the same chromosome tend to be inherited together, the process of crossing over enables "linked" genes to sort independently. Those that are linked but located farther apart on the chromosome will undergo crossing over more frequently than those located very close together on a chromosome simply because there are more sites between the two genes at which crossing over can take place.

8. (D) is correct. Autosomal dominant traits appear with equal frequency in both sexes, and they do not normally skip generations. Also note that each afflicted person has a copy of the dominant allele, and homozygous recessive individuals do not have the disorder.

9. (A) is correct. The father has type A, B, or O blood. The mother, who has the phenotype for type A blood, has the genotype $I^A i$. To produce a son with genotype ii (the genotype of people with type O blood), she would need to reproduce with a man who had genotype $I^A i$, genotype $I^B I$, or genotype ii. Try writing out the Punnett square if you aren't confident of this.

10. (B) is correct. If the individual with type O blood were to mate with an individual who has type AB blood, since I^A and I^B are both dominant over i, the genotypic ratio would be $1\ I^A i : 1\ I^B i$, and the phenotypes would be in a ratio of 1 type A blood:1 type B blood.

11. (B) is correct. The most likely reason for this 2:1 ratio in the offspring is that Y is lethal in homozygous form, and this caused the death of all of the YY

individuals in the litter. The expected ratio of this cross would be 1 *YY*:2 *Yy*:1 *yy*. If you remove the *YY*, you get a ratio of 2 *Yy* (yellow mice, since the gene for yellow, *Y*, is dominant) to 1 *yy* (nonyellow mouse).

12. (D) is correct. The only process listed that does not lead directly to genetic recombination, or the recombining (scrambling) of genes in the offspring, is gene linkage. If genes are linked, they are located on the same chromosome and are more likely to segregate together into the same cell, reducing genetic recombination.

13. (C) is correct. Recall that a dihybrid cross between two heterozygotes produces a 9 double dominants:3 dominant, recessives:3 recessive dominants:1 double recessive offspring ratio. The question is asking for one of the heterozygotes (which would be one of the 3s in the above ratio). To come up with the answer, multiply $\frac{3}{16}$ by 144 to get 27; the closest answer choice to 27 is 28.

14. (B) is correct. Fertilization restores the diploid number in a sexually reproducing organism. The two major events in the life cycle of sexually reproducing organisms are meiosis and fertilization.

15. (D) is correct. Homologous chromosomes are a key conceptual point in Mendelian genetics. Choices A, B, and C all occur during the first meiotic division, in which homologous pairs synapse, crossing over occurs, and pairs separate. Also note that the cells at the end of the first meiotic division are haploid! If you missed this question, review more thoroughly the concept of homologous chromosomes.

16. (B) is correct. The number of possible gametes can be determined by using the formula 2^n, where *n* equals the haploid number. With a diploid number of 6, and therefore a haploid number of 3, the answer is $2 \times 2 \times 2 = 8$.

17. (A) is correct. Recall that in G_1 the chromosomes have not replicated. After S phase of interphase, the chromosomes have replicated, which doubles the amount of DNA. When the homologs separate in meiosis I, the amount of DNA is reduced by one-half and back to the original amount.

18. (A) is correct. In meiosis II, the most important event is the separation of sister chromatids. Mitosis involves only the separation of sister chromatids; homologs do not form in mitosis.

19. (D) is correct. Begin by drawing a straight line to represent a chromosome, and then place genes A and B 8 units apart. Note that A and C are 28 units apart, with B and C 20 units apart. This means the genes are found in order: A, B, C. Next, consider the map distances between A and D and B and D. Because map distance represents the frequency of crossing over, it will only work if D precedes A on the chromosome. The correct gene sequence must be D-A-B-C.

20. (B) is correct. Because males have only one X chromosome, they have only a single allele for genes found on this sex chromosome. A single defective allele can therefore be the source of the X-linked condition.

21. (D) is correct. Given that the diploid (2*n*) number is 4 and some of the cells in the diagram have an (*n*) or haploid number with two chromosomes, this could be meiosis. However, the improper separating of a chromosome in meiosis, termed *nondisjunction*, would yield cells with differing chromosome numbers. Specifically, the diagram shows sister chromatids not separating, thus leaving one cell $n + 1$ and the other cell $n - 1$. This is not normal meiosis but an example of a nondisjunction event.

▎ **22. (B) is correct.** Type O blood is recessive. This means that the woman could be heterozygous for blood type A ($I^A i$) and the father heterozygous for type B blood ($I^B i$). If each parent donates his or her recessive allele, the baby would be ii, type O blood.

▎ **23. (C) is correct.** It appears that the mother has inherited the color-blind gene from her father and passed it to her son. This is a typical inheritance pattern seen in sex-linked genes.

▎ **24. (C) is correct.** The question and correct answer describe independent assortment as it occurs in meiosis. Independent assortment increases variability or, as phrased in the question, increases the possible combinations of characteristics.

Additional Sample Problems

▎ **1.** Albino (b) is a recessive trait; black (B) is dominant. First cross: parents $BB \times bb$; gametes B and b; offspring all Bb (black coat). Second cross: parents $Bb \times bb$; gametes ½ B and ½ b (heterozygous parent) and b; offspring ½ Bb and ½ bb.

▎ **2.** Recognize that this is a heterozygous, dihybrid cross (GgIi × GgIi) and all heterozygous dihybrid crosses yield the same results: 9 double dominants: 3 dominant, recessives: 3 recessive dominants: 1 double recessive. For this specific cross, 9 green, inflated: 3 green, constricted: 3 yellow, inflated: 1 yellow, constricted. You could do this problem with a Punnett square, but it would take a lot of time. Know the common monohybrid and dihybrid crosses and the expected ratios.

▎ **3.** Parental cross is $AAC^R C^R \times aaC^W C^W$. F_1 genotype is $AaC^R C^W$, phenotype is all axial-pink. F_2 phenotypes are 3 axial-red:6 axial-pink:3 axial-white:1 terminal-red:2 terminal-pink:1 terminal-white.

Grid-In Questions

1. **The answer is 12 (fg).** As with mitotic cell division, the DNA content in meiosis is replicated during the synthesis portion of interphase, bringing the DNA total to 48 fg, which is equally distributed to the four haploid cells.

2. **The answer is ⅜.** This question is most quickly answered by calculating probabilities. To do this, consider the two traits of the dihybrid cross individually. For example, both plants are heterozygous for tall, so ¾ of the offspring will be tall to ¼ dwarf (Tt × Tt = 1TT:2Tt:1tt, or three tall to one dwarf). The second trait crosses Rr × rr, resulting in a ratio of ½ round to ½ wrinkled. Multiplying the two independent events together, ¾ Tall × ½ wrinkled = ⅜ Tall *and* wrinkled. The problem could be solved with a Punnett square, but that would be quite time consuming on a test, when every minute is important.

3. **The answer is 17 (%).** All the information to solve the problem is given, but you must recognize that the phenotypes gray body/vestigial wings and black body/normal wings are recombinants (phenotypes that differ from the true

breeding parents), whereas gray body/normal wings and black body/vestigial wings are parental types. The data indicate 195 total recombinants divided by 1,149 total flies times 100 equals 17%. The genes are 17 map units apart.

Answer from page 102: The karyotype in Figure 4.1 is that of a male. Note the unpaired X and Y in the bottom right corner.

Topic 5: Molecular Genetics

ANSWERS AND EXPLANATIONS

Level 1: Knowledge/Comprehension Questions

1. (B) is correct. Viruses have *either* a DNA genome or an RNA genome surrounded by a protein coat. The answer is not A because retroviruses have an RNA genome. HIV is a retrovirus.

2. (D) is correct. Restriction enzymes can be used to cut DNA at specific locations and this enables researchers to perform recombinant DNA techniques. When specific restriction enzymes are added to the DNA, they produce cuts in the sugar-phosphate backbone and create "sticky ends," which can bind to DNA fragments from a different source to produce recombinant DNA. DNA ligase is then added to seal the strands together permanently.

3. (C) is correct. Transposons are also called transposable genetic elements, and they are pieces of DNA that can move from location to location in a chromosome—or a genome. Transposons are also called "jumping genes," and most of them are capable of moving to many different target sites in the genome. They are important in generating genetic diversity.

4. (D) is correct. One of the two important ways that the cell has of controlling gene expression is through DNA methylation. In DNA methylation, methyl groups are attached to certain DNA bases after DNA is synthesized. This appears to be responsible for the long-term inactivation of genes.

5. (B) is correct. *Be sure you don't confuse the vocabulary! Many students reverse the terms* transcription *and* translation. The process by which genetic information flows from mRNA to protein is called translation. Translation occurs in the cytoplasm of the cell at the ribosomes. A molecule of mRNA is moved through the ribosome, and codons are translated into amino acids one at a time. Transfer RNAs add their associated amino acids onto a growing polypeptide as its anticodon pairs with a codon on the mRNA and then departs from the ribosome to bind more free amino acids.

6. (A) is correct. In transcription, RNA is synthesized using the genetic information encoded by DNA. Transcription occurs in the nucleus of eukaryotic cells. The double-stranded DNA helix unwinds, allowing enzymes and proteins to synthesize a new complementary single-stranded RNA molecule from the template strand of DNA.

7. (B) is correct. In histone acetylation, acetyl groups are attached to certain amino acids of histones. Acetylation makes the histones change shape so they are less tightly bound to DNA, and this allows the proteins involved in transcription to move in and begin the process. Therefore, acetylation is one way for the cell to initiate transcription and to control the expression of its genes.

■ **8. (B) is correct.** In the lysogenic cycle, the phage genome becomes incorporated into the host cell's DNA without destroying the host cell. There, it lurks much like a Trojan horse, waiting to receive the chemical signals that would trigger it to enter the lytic cycle. In the lytic cycle, the phage hydrolyzes the host cell's DNA and uses the cell's machinery to produce phage proteins and to replicate its genome. The phage proteins are then assembled in the cell until the host cell lyses (breaks open), and the new phages are released to infect other cells.

■ **9. (C) is correct.** In genetic engineering (the manipulation of genes for practical purposes), DNA ligase is an enzyme that is used to seal the strands of newly recombinant DNA (DNA that is spliced together from two different sources) by catalyzing the formation of phosphodiester bonds.

■ **10. (C) is correct.** The addition of a poly-A tail after transcription is one example of post-transcriptional modifications that the mRNA undergoes. This poly-A tail inhibits the degradation of the newly synthesized mRNA strand and is thought also to help ribosomes attach to it. Another important modification that mRNA undergoes is the addition of a 5' cap. The 5' cap helps protect mRNA from degradation and also acts as the point of attachment for the ribosomes, just prior to translation.

■ **11. (D) is correct.** RNA polymerase is the most prominent enzyme involved in the transcription of DNA to make mRNA. It is responsible for binding to the promoter sequence on the template DNA, prying the two DNA strands apart and hooking the RNA nucleotides together as they base pair along the DNA template. RNA polymerases add nucleotides to the 3' end of the growing chain until a terminator sequence is reached.

■ **12. (A) is correct.** tRNA, or transfer RNA, interprets the genetic message coded in mRNA. It transfers amino acids taken from the cytoplasmic pool to a ribosome, which adds the specific amino acid brought to it by tRNA to the end of a growing polypeptide chain. Each type of tRNA binds to a specific amino acid at one end; its other end contains an anticodon, which base pairs with a complementary codon on the mRNA strand.

■ **13. (B) is correct.** mRNA, also known as messenger RNA, is a type of RNA that is synthesized from DNA and attaches to ribosomes in the cytoplasm to specify the primary structure of a protein. Because mRNA is the product of transcription, which occurs in the nucleus of eukaryotic cells, it must travel out of the nucleus and into the cytoplasm to participate in translation.

■ **14. (B) is correct.** In the modification of mRNA that occurs after transcription, a process called RNA splicing occurs. In this process, noncoding regions of nucleic acid that are situated between coding regions are cut out. These noncoding regions are called introns. The remaining regions are called exons, and these are spliced together to form the final mRNA product. When you think of exons, think expressed—because they are actually translated into proteins, whereas introns are not.

Level 2: Application/Analysis/Synthesis Questions

❚ **1. (D) is correct.** The process of genetic engineering is, in part, possible because of the universal nature of DNA and RNA as carriers of genetic information. Once the spider gene or genes that were responsible for coding for the silk proteins were isolated and then inserted into a bacterial plasmid (which would serve as the vector), the cloning vector would be taken up by the goat's cells, and the goat's cells' transcription/translation machinery would begin the process of producing the spider protein, following the universal codon chart.

❚ **2. (B) is correct.** DNA ligase is the enzyme that joins DNA fragments; it is used by cells to join Okazaki fragments as well as in biotechnology to generate engineered plasmids. You are expected to know the following four enzymes involved in replication: DNA polymerase, ligase, helicase, and topoisomerase.

❚ **3. (D) is correct.** PCR, the polymerase chain reaction, is a technique by which any piece of DNA can be copied many times without the use of cells. With each turn of the cycle, the amount of DNA is multiplied by 2. After only 30 cycles, which can occur in just a few hours, over 1 billion molecules match the target sequence.

❚ **4. (C) is correct.** The fragments of DNA separated out from one another along the gel once the electric field was applied because they differ in size. For DNA in gel electrophoresis, how far a molecule travels through a gel (while the current is applied) is inversely proportional to its size. The larger a fragment is, the shorter the distance it will migrate.

❚ **5. (C) is correct.** The restriction enzyme used to cut the DNA that was placed into the first well of the gel must have cut the DNA at eight sites because it produced nine DNA fragments. In linear DNA, the number of fragments produced is always one more than the number of restriction sites cut. (How would this answer be different if the DNA was a circular plasmid?)

❚ **6. (C) is correct.** You should recall that a T4 phage injects its DNA, which is used to assemble new protein coats and viral DNA. The protein coat of the infecting phages is left outside the bacterium and is not involved in forming new viruses.

❚ **7. (B) is correct.** Reverse transcriptase is an enzyme that is required to produce DNA from the RNA of a retrovirus. Reverse transcriptase is not normally produced in host cells.

❚ **8. (C) is correct.** The introduction of a "stop" codon will result in an abbreviated polypeptide chain and is therefore likely to do more harm to the final protein than choice B, a frameshift mutation occurring near the terminal end of the gene.

❚ **9. (B) is correct.** The amount of adenine in DNA will equal the amount of thymine; guanine will equal cytosine, which leads to the mathematical equality $A + G = C + T$. Try this: If a certain species has 15% adenine in its DNA, what would be the percentage of guanine? (It would be 35%. $A + T = 30\%$, so $G + C = 70\%$, and $G = 35\%$.)

❚ **10. (A) is correct.** Choice A is correct because the signals that control gene expressions and promoter regions are different between prokaryotes and eukaryotes. Several of the other possible answers have errors that would be instructive to note. Choice B is false because the genetic code is nearly universal; choice C is false because the genetic code includes start and stop codons and is universal; choice D is false because ribosomes are not governed by the length of the gene.

11. (A) is correct. Genes that are active are producing mRNAs. The mRNAs of the active genes are used to make cDNA, which will bind to the single-stranded DNA on the microarray. The DNA on the chip serves as a probe and will bind to a complementary sequence of DNA, so cDNA must be made from the mRNA of the tissue. In the light, the chlorophyll genes are on, producing mRNAs, which are used to produce cDNA and washed across the chip.

12. (B) is correct. The number of genes in the human genome has been revised sharply downward since the Human Genome Project. Less than a decade ago, the number of human genes was at 100,000; now it is about 20,000! How can only 20,000 genes be enough for a human? The answer is alternative gene splicing yielding multiple proteins per gene.

13. (D) is correct. This is an example of a multigene family. The alpha-globin gene family is on chromosome 16, whereas the beta-globin gene family is on chromosome 11. The genes arose by duplication and translocation.

14. (D) is correct. In HIV (the virus that causes AIDS), the envelope glyco-protein enables the virus to bind to specific receptors on certain white blood cells. After binding, the virus fuses with the cell's plasma membrane, entering the cell. The mutated gene *CCR5* prevents binding and subsequent entering of the cell by HIV.

15. (D) is correct. In HIV infections, recall that the infectious agent is a retrovirus with RNA as the genetic material. In the cytoplasm of the host cell the viral RNA is converted to DNA, then incorporated as a provirus into the host cell's DNA. The provirus can direct the production of new viral particles.

16. (C) is correct. Bacteria do not perform mitosis, meiosis, or sexual reproduction. However, the processes of transformation, transduction, and conjugation are processes that bacteria use to increase their genetic diversity. Be sure to review all three processes.

17. (B) is correct. These profiles were done using short tandem repeats as genetic markers. All 13 sites must match because this shows the highest degree of certainty between the pilot's DNA and the DNA from the three families. In addition, because the DNA for comparison comes from a probable twin of the pilot, it is expected that the bands would be identical for the twins of the same family.

18. (D) is correct. Family 3 matches in all 13 sites. This is a good time to review the principles of gel electrophoresis, making sure you understand which poles on the gel are positive and negative, how the bands are arranged by size on the gel, and the role of restriction enzymes in preparing the DNA.

19. (A) is correct. Introns, not exons, are removed before mRNA leaves the nucleus. The rest of the choices in this question are true and worthy of your perusal and understanding. RNA editing is a fundamental concept in molecular genetics.

20. (C) is correct. The polymerase enzymes, both DNA and RNA, can only add nucleotides to the 3′ end of a growing strand. This is the underlying reason for the leading strand, where DNA polymerase is adding a continuous, unbroken new strand of nucleotides, and the lagging strand, where DNA polymerase is moving away from the unwinding replication fork, forming new nucleotides in Okazaki fragments. Knowing all the enzymes of replication is not required for the exam, but understanding how DNA polymerase works and the formation of leading and lagging strands is fundamental and worth your time investment.

21. **(C) is correct.** Species 5 has the fewest amino acid differences (one) when compared to Species 1. Note the assumptions made in the question. Mutation rates for all genes are not equal over time, and answering questions about relatedness between species would require much more data. The assumptions simplified the question so it is answerable within the confines of the exam.

22. **(D) is correct.** The control treatment was the construct that had no DNA deleted from the enhancer. The top bar on the graph represents this construct. All the other treatment groups were compared to that control group (note the label on the *x*-axis).

23. **(C) is correct.** All three elements appear to be control elements because when they were deleted, the levels of reporter mRNA differed from the level produced by the intact enhancer construct (which is the control). The control (the top bar on the graph) established the 100% mark for the experiment. The three elements (the next three bars on the graph) are all different from the 100% expression of the control; therefore, all three must function as control elements.

24. **(D) is correct.** This question refers to the bottom bar on the graph, showing a reduction in reporter mRNA of over 50%. If the absence of the control element causes a reduction, its presence must activate gene expression by producing activators that normally increase the level of gene expression.

25. **(D) is correct.** The question could refer to either the second or third bar on the graph because they are both over 100% of the control. The control element in both cases represses gene expression by producing a repressor protein as its normal function. It is important to note that control elements do not turn the volume of a gene up as high as possible but turn the volume to the proper level for the cell. Too much gene product can cause just as many problems as too little gene product.

Grid-In Questions

1. **The answer is 6.** On questions like this, check to see if the DNA being cut is circular or linear. Draw a linear strip of DNA, then mark the cut sites, and count the fragments.

2. **The answer is 26%.** If guanine is 24%, then thymine is also 24%, totaling 48% of the DNA. That leaves 52% of the DNA to be split evenly between guanine and cytosine. These calculations are based on Chargaff's rules and are the same rules that Franklin, Watson, and Crick used in solving the structure of DNA.

Free-Response Questions

(a) Nondisjunction occurs when the chromosomes fail to separate properly in meiosis and one cell ends up with two copies of a chromosome, whereas the other cell gets no copies. This results in a condition called aneuploidy. If a gamete received an extra copy of chromosome #21 and was successfully fertilized, the child would exhibit Trisomy 21, which is characterized by mental retardation and reduced stature.

A base-pair deletion can occur when a DNA copying error results in the loss of a single nucleotide, and a frameshift means that the triplets being read will all be different. If this occurs within an intron, there will be no phenotypic effect because introns are removed prior to translation.

A base-pair substitution results when one nucleotide, such as thymine, is substituted for another, such as guanine. This type of error causes sickle-cell disease. When a different amino acid is placed into the polypeptide, it can affect the secondary or tertiary structure of the protein so that it does not fold into the correct conformation. Change the shape, change the function. If it is an enzyme or other protein, it may no longer function as it did.

(b) Colorblindness is more common in males than females because males are hemizygous for these traits. The trait is found on the X chromosome, and because males have only one copy of the X chromosome, they will show the phenotype for whatever allele they receive. Females, on the other hand, have two copies of the X chromosome and, if one X chromosome has an allele for colorblindness and the other X chromosome carries an allele for normal vision, the female will have normal vision. She is a "carrier" for colorblindness because she can pass it on to her sons.

(c) When fertilization occurs and a sperm carrying a Y chromosome penetrates the egg first, a male zygote with one X and one Y chromosome is produced. If a sperm carrying an X chromosome penetrates the egg first, a female zygote with XX is produced. Although it seems as though the female zygote would have twice the cell product as the male, due to its double dose of genes located on the two X chromosomes, this is not the case. The reason for this is that in every cell of the female human body one of the X chromosomes is inactivated. The mechanisms for this are not fully understood, but the X chromosome that is inactivated condenses into a structure called a Barr body, which then associates with the nuclear envelope. This is called X-inactivation, and the condensed DNA is heterochromatin. As a Barr body, most of the X chromosome's genes are not expressed. As a result of this, females are a mosaic consisting of cells with the X chromosome from their mother activated and other cells with the X chromosome from their father activated in about a 50:50 ratio. This is also the reason sex-linked disorders are usually not expressed in females. Although one of the X chromosomes may be incapable of producing a crucial gene product, this mosaic effect ensures that the other half of the somatic cells produces sufficient amounts of the protein in question.

Note that the response for part (c) covers more than the question asks. The graded response does not actually begin until the fourth sentence. Also, the last two sentences go beyond the question. Because your time is limited, always focus on JUST the question.

Topic 6: Mechanisms of Evolution

ANSWERS AND EXPLANATIONS

Level 1: Knowledge/Comprehension Questions

1. (B) is correct. When two populations of the same species are prevented from breeding by a geographic barrier such as a mountain range or other physical obstruction, the two populations are said to be geographically isolated.

2. (C) is correct. The concept of punctuated equilibrium was put forth recently by Niles Eldredge and Stephen Jay Gould. It explains periods of apparently little change (stasis) "punctuated" by sudden changes observed in the fossil record. Punctuated equilibrium is about the pace of evolution, not about differences in how evolution occurs.

3. (B) is correct. Because selection favors the average-sized wings and reduces the frequency of two extremes, this is an example of stabilizing selection. This would be a good time to also review directional and disruptive selection, shown in Figure 6.1 of this guide.

4. (D) is correct. The founder effect occurs when a few individuals from a population colonize a new, isolated habitat. The smaller the number of individuals who start this new population, the more limited the starting gene pool for the population and the less the new gene pool will resemble that of the parent population.

5. (B) is correct. Homology is the result of descent from a common ancestor. It can be described as the underlying structural or molecular similarities (even in structures that are no longer used for the same function) that exist in organisms as a result of common ancestry. An example would be the wing of a bat, which is homologous to the flipper of a whale.

6. (A) is correct. Bottleneck effects are often the result of a natural disaster such as a flood, drought, fire, or anything that destroys most members of a population. The gene pool of the surviving members of the population may not resemble the gene pool of that of the parent population—some genes will be overrepresented, and some will be underrepresented. Bottlenecking reduces the genetic variability in a population because of the random loss of alleles.

7. (C) is correct. An example of analogous structures would be a bat wing and a butterfly wing—both are useful for flight, but they do not share evolutionary relatedness.

8. (A) is correct. Prezygotic barriers are those that prevent or hinder the mating of two species, or they prevent fertilization even if two species mate. All the answers are examples of prezygotic barriers except hybrid breakdown. It is an example of a postzygotic barrier (postzygotic barriers are those that prevent hybrid zygotes from developing into viable, fertile adults) in which the second generation of offspring from two species is either weak or sterile.

9. (C) is correct. In convergent evolution, species from different evolutionary branches appear alike as a result of undergoing evolution in very similar ecological roles and environments. Similarity between species that have undergone convergent evolution is known as analogy, and structures they share are analogous (not homologous) structures. (Remember, similar problem, similar solution. However, convergence does *not* indicate a common ancestor.) Homologous structures are those that are shared in two species as a result of those species' having a common ancestor.

▌ **10. (C) is correct.** It is important to recall that the early atmosphere did not have oxygen and that the evolution of linear electron flow in photosynthesis by cyanobacteria resulted in the accumulation of oxygen in the atmosphere.

▌ **11. (C) is correct.** The smallest unit capable of evolution is the population. Individuals cannot undergo evolution because they cannot change their genetic make-up. Evolution is the changing and refinement of a population's gene pool over many generations to best fit the environment.

▌ **12. (A) is correct.** Darwin's observations can be summarized as follows: Organisms produce more offspring than the environment can support. Further, the offspring vary in their heritable characteristics. Those individuals well suited to their environment leave more offspring than other individuals (differential reproductive success). Over time, favorable traits accumulate in the population.

Level 2: Application/Analysis/Synthesis Questions

▌ **1. (D) is correct.** If the frequency of the recessive allele is 0.09, then we know that the frequency of the other allele is $1.0 - 0.09$, which is equal to 0.91. If your answer was B, you assigned 0.09 as q^2 rather than q. Remember, the allelic frequency is q; the genotypic frequency is q^2. If the genotypic frequency were 0.09, B would have been the correct answer. In every H-W problem, note whether the information given is about allelic frequency (q) or genotypic frequency (q^2).

▌ **2. (C) is correct.** Did you select A? You were too hasty and forgot a very important concept: The 64% of the population that show the dominant trait includes heterozygotes, so you cannot simply take the square root of 0.64. You must subtract 0.64 from 1.00 to obtain $0.36 = q^2$. Taking the square root of q^2 yields $q = 0.6$, so $p = 0.4$. On the AP exam do not expect p and q to always be perfect squares.

▌ **3. (C) is correct.** This scenario mirrors the human disorder of sickle-cell disease and is an example of heterozygote advantage. In sickle-cell disease, two dominant alleles for normal hemoglobin leave the individual susceptible to malaria, but two recessive alleles cause sickle-cell disease. The heterozygote does not have sickle-cell disease and tends to have milder cases of malaria. Hence, the heterozygote is the advantageous genotype. The mouse population appears to be undergoing a similar situation. For an explanation of sickle-cell (commonly used on the AP exam) see Making Connections, in *Biology*, 11e (pp. 500–501), or *Focus*, 2e (pp. 428–429). The frequency of the recessive allele is 0.22.

▌ **4. (B) is correct.** This question describes the two major categories of speciation, and you must analyze the data to select the most plausible mechanism. Although choice A could account for 30 different species, it would not explain why the species seem to occur in related pairs. Only choice B does this.

5. (D) is correct. One mechanism that can lead to sympatric speciation is the formation of autopolyploids through nondisjunction in meiosis. This mechanism is common in plants but not common in animals. These plants, for example, have $4n$ chromosomes instead of the normal $2n$ number. They are unable to breed and produce fertile offspring with members of the diploid parent population, although they are able to breed with other tetraploids.

6. (A) is correct. For this question, recall that the endosymbiotic hypothesis proposes that mitochondria and plastids were engulfed by other cells and have their own genomes. It is most likely that over time some of their genes were incorporated into the host cell's genome. (*Hint:* Review the endosymbiotic hypothesis.)

7. (C) is correct. The key to this selection is the phrase "natural selection can only edit existing variations." The other answers deal mostly with misconceptions. Evolution does not produce perfect organisms, and it does not operate by a preconceived plan. Read and note the misconceptions in the wrong answers in this question.

8. (B) is correct. Directional selection is a form of natural selection in which individuals at one end of the phenotypic range (darker fur in this question) survive or reproduce more successfully than do other individuals. Use this question to review directional, stabilizing, and disruptive selection.

9. (B) is correct. Allopatric speciation is the formation of new species in populations that are geographically isolated. The stem of the question gives us information indicating that *H. erectus* became isolated on an island, out of genetic contact with the rest of its species.

10. (D) is correct. Reproductive barriers impede members of two closely related species from interbreeding and producing viable, fertile offspring. Barriers are divided into prezygotic and postzygotic barriers and have been used as the basis for essay questions in the past.

11. (B) is correct. Each individual has two alleles, so the total number of alleles at day 7 is 216 seedlings times two alleles per seedling for a total of 432 alleles. Each of the 49 individuals of genotype $C^G C^G$ has two C^G alleles (98 alleles), and each of the 111 individuals of genotype $C^G C^Y$ has one C^G allele (111 alleles). Thus, the frequency of the C^G allele (p) is $98 + 111/432 = 0.484$.

12. (C) is correct. You can use the same procedure that you used to calculate p (let p equal C^G) to calculate q (where q equals C^Y). However, an easier way to calculate q is to remember that $p + q = 1$. Because you know that $p = 0.484$, you can calculate that $q = 1 - p = 0.516$.

13. (D) is correct. The first step is to recognize that the green-yellow phenotype is expressed in the Hardy-Weinberg equation as $2pq$. Thus, the expected frequency of genotype $C^G C^Y$ is $2pq = 2 \times 0.484 \times 0.516 = 0.499$. To move from frequency to percentage multiply by 100 to yield 49.9 or 50%.

14. (C) is correct. The genotype frequency for $C^Y C^Y$ is significantly lower than expected at day 21, suggesting that there is selection against $C^Y C^Y$ individuals. The yellow plant production of chlorophyll is so low that the plants are dying, which explains why the observed genotypic ratio is below the expected genotypic ratio. Hint: In questions dealing with the Hardy-Weinberg equilibrium, it is important to notice whether the question is centered on alleles or genotypes. In each question, consciously note alleles or genotypes.

■ **15. (A) is correct.** C^YC^Y plants cannot produce chlorophyll and are likely to continue to die. This suggests that the frequency of the C^Y allele should decrease, and the frequency of the C^G allele should increase.

■ **16. (D) is correct.** The critical relationship with DNA comparison data is if two samples have a low difference between nucleotides, they are likely to be the same or closely related species. A high difference between nucleotides implies that they are likely to be from different species. Only a 1% difference in DNA data separates the test sample from *S. salar*, whereas comparisons to the other species are over 14%.

■ **17. (A) is correct.** Using the same logic as for question 16, *O. kisutch* is only 4% different from *O. tshawytscha*.

■ **18. (B) is correct.** According to the chart, there are three pairs that are closely related to each other: The test sample is closely related to *S. salar;* *O. keta* is closely related to *O. gorbuscha;* and *O. tshawytscha* is closely related to *O. kisutch*. Each of these pairs is therefore clustered together in the tree. Because *O. nerka* is not as closely related to any of the other samples, it branches off farther back in the tree (i.e., closer to the root). The five Pacific salmon form a single clade, and the test sample is separated from these into a different clade containing the Atlantic salmon.

Grid-In Questions

1. **The answer is 2.6 (billion years).** The rock layer shows one-fourth the current ratio, which indicates that two half-lives have passed ($\frac{1}{2} \times \frac{1}{2}$). 1.3 billion $\times$ 2 = 2.6 billion years ago.

2. **The answer is 45.2%.** The 12% that show no banding represent q^2 because no banding is the recessive genotype. This means q equals the square root of 0.12 or 0.346; therefore, p equals 0.654. The heterozygote is represented as $2pq$, so 2(0.654)(0.346) = 0.452. Change to a percentage by multiplying by 100 to yield 45.2%. The exam allows for different rounding of figures, so a range of answers around this one would be acceptable.

3. **The answer is 7.8.** Note that the dominant allele (p) is given, meaning the frequency of the recessive allele (q) can be found by 1.0 − 0.72 = 0.28. The genotype for the recessive phenotype is q^2 or $(0.28)^2$, which equals 0.078. This number times 100 yields the percentage that will have red shells.

Free-Response Questions

(a) Miller demonstrated the formation of organic molecules by using an apparatus that mimicked the conditions thought to have existed on the early Earth. Using electricity sparks to mimic the energy from lightning and an atmosphere containing a mixture of hydrogen gas, methane, ammonia, and water vapor, Miller generated a variety of organic molecules that are common in organisms. This was a demonstration that abiotic synthesis of organic molecules was possible.

(b) RNA has two important features that make it likely to have been the earliest genetic material. RNA can function as an enzyme, known as a ribozyme.

Some ribozymes can make complementary copies of short pieces of RNA, so RNA can be self-replicating. This combination of catalytic and self-replicating ability makes it likely that RNA was the earliest genetic material.

(c) Because the earliest prokaryotes evolved in an atmosphere without oxygen, it is likely that most species were anaerobic and the development of oxygen in the atmosphere may have resulted in a mass extinction of species that were not able to tolerate some level of oxygen. This would have opened many niches and made it a time of adaptive radiation for organisms capable of dealing with oxygen in the atmosphere.

Note that this question has three parts, and these are clearly labeled on the response. The student chose to describe the Miller experiment but might also have discussed reactions on solid reactive surfaces. The formation of vesicles would also have been appropriate in this discussion. Essay questions on evolution are common occurrences on the AP Biology exam. When answering essay questions on evolution, avoid clichés such as "survival of the fittest" because the phrase does not convey any specific information about evolution. Be descriptive in your discussions of evolution, and remember to define key terms as they are used.

Topic 7: The Evolutionary History of Life

ANSWERS AND EXPLANATIONS

Level 1: Knowledge/Comprehension Questions

▌ **1. (B) is correct.** Animals are heterotrophic—they are not capable of fixing carbon and must obtain it from other organisms. They belong to the domain Eukarya and are multicellular. The fungi are also eukaryotic, multicellular heterotrophs but have a cell wall made of chitin.

▌ **2. (B) is correct.** The three domains into which all the living organisms are placed by systematists are Bacteria, Archaea, and Eukarya. Domains are one taxonomic level above kingdoms. Prokaryotes make up Archaea and Bacteria, whereas eukaryotes make up Eukarya.

▌ **3. (C) is correct.** In mutualism both organisms benefit from the association; in commensalism one organism benefits while the other is neither helped nor harmed; and in parasitism one organism benefits while the other is harmed.

▌ **4. (A) is correct.** The amniotic egg is composed of extraembryonic membranes that function in gas exchange, waste storage, and the delivery of nutrients to the embryo. The amniotic egg was a key evolutionary adaptation for terrestrial life, allowing the embryo to have its own "pond" in which to develop.

5. (D) is correct. Mitosis and meiosis do *not* occur in bacteria. In plants and animals, however, meiosis *will* introduce variation through independent assortment and crossing over. You should be able to explain the three ways in which bacteria receive new genes (transduction, transformation, and conjugation) as well as know that mutation is the ultimate source of genetic variation.

6. (A) is correct. This is the definition of a shared derived character. An example that may help you to remember is that hair is a shared derived characteristic for all mammals. All mammals have hair, and no organism that is not a mammal has hair.

Level 2: Application/Analysis/Synthesis Questions

1. (A) is correct. This question hinges on knowing the difference between shared ancestral characters and shared derived characters. Shared derived characters are evolutionary novelties unique to a specific clade, whereas shared ancestral characters originate in the ancestor of the taxon. Having four limbs is not unique to birds and mammals but is an ancestral trait shared by other clades.

2. (C) is correct. A, B, and D are all cats. Outgroups are used as points of comparison to help determine shared ancestral and shared derived characters.

3. (C) is correct. Transformation is the uptake of external DNA by a cell. Transformation is one of the ways in which bacteria are able to increase genetic diversity. When bacteria take up DNA from a different species, transformation results in horizontal gene transfer.

4. (C) is correct. Scientists can use mtDNA sequences for faster-evolving gene sequences and rRNA sequences for distantly related groups. The concept of assessing relationships is the same in both instances. The closer the DNA sequences match, the closer the evolutionary relationship.

5. (C) is correct. *Archaeopteryx* had teeth, a flat sternum, and claws—all reptile characteristics that the fossil displayed.

6. (C) is correct. This question is concerned with the ecological roles of fungi. Fungi play an important role as decomposers and are involved in many symbiotic relationships with plants, such as mutualistic mycorrhizal associations.

7. (A) is correct. Moving onto land was an evolutionary challenge for both plants and animals. The scales of reptiles are waterproof and protect the organism from desiccation, whereas the amniotic egg protects the embryo from drying while on land. In plants, the cuticle protects the plant body from desiccation, whereas the seed protects the embryo from drying while on land. Note the parallels.

8. (D) is correct. In both cases, homologous genes are exchanged. Many evolutionary biologists think that the enzymes used in bacteria are the evolutionary forerunners of the recombination enzymes used in eukaryotic crossing over.

9. (D) is correct. Remember that a clade includes all the descendants. All of the other choices include only a part of the descendants.

10. (C) is correct. In many phylogenetic trees, the *x*-axis is given in relative time rather than the specific millions of years ago as in this figure. In this case, specific data can be derived concerning time from the *x*-axis.

11. (D) is correct. Each node or branch point represents a common ancestor of the two branches that come from the node. Lizards share a more recent common ancestor with humans than do salamanders and are therefore more closely related to humans. The "not supported" part of the question should be a red flag to be very careful with the question. Read carefully!

12. (B) is correct. The question specifies vertebrate linage, which eliminates choice A. As described in the stem of the question, lancelets are chordates but not vertebrates. The next key phrase is that branch lengths are proportional to the amount of genetic change in each lineage. Of the three remaining vertebrates, zebrafish clearly have the longest branch length and therefore the greatest amount of genetic change.

13. (C) is correct. Find 30 on the y-axis (number of mutations). Then read across until you intersect the plotted graph line. Read down to the x-axis to read the divergence time, which is approximately 45 million years.

14. (C) is correct. Even without actually counting the number of amino acids shared, it is clear that the fungus *Ustilago* shares the most amino acids with the aphid. How can such distantly related organisms share so many amino acids? If needed, review horizontal gene transfer for the explanation.

15. (D) is correct. The aphid's sequence is similar with organisms that are distantly related. Without any obvious evolutionary ties, how can this be? Horizontal gene transfer is the transfer of genes from one genome to another by factors such as plasmid transfer or viral activity. In this way, organisms not closely related may share very similar DNA and amino acid sequences.

16. (B) is correct. Sequence data from the remainder of this polypeptide and others involved in carotenoid biosynthesis could support the close similarity between aphid and fungal genes for this group of proteins.

Grid-In Questions

1. **The answer is 10%** of the time. The tree shows humans present for 6 million years out of the 60 million years charted. This gives $6/60 \times 100 = 10\%$.
2. **The answer is 1.6** mutations per 1 million years. The y-axis reveals a total of 75 mutations over the 120 million years charted. This gives 120 million years divided by 75 mutations or 1.6 mutations/1 million years.

Free-Response Question

(a) Mutation: A mutation is a change in the nucleotide sequence of an organism's DNA. Mutations occur in basically the same way in both prokaryotes and eukaryotes, but because prokaryotes have such short generation times and extremely large population sizes, their populations accumulate mutations at a much faster rate than do eukaryotes.

(b) Transformation: In transformation, naked, foreign DNA from the environment is taken up by the prokaryotic cell. Once the DNA is brought into the cell, it can be incorporated into the host cell genome, adding new nucleotides and even new genes to the host genome.

(c) Transduction: In transduction bacteriophages carry bacterial genes from one bacterial cell to another. In the chaos of bacteriophage reproduction, sometimes DNA from the infected bacteria cell is incorporated into the viral shell. When the virus next infects a bacterium, it delivers the original host DNA into its newly infected host. The new host can now incorporate the new DNA into its genome by a process similar to crossing over.

(d) Conjugation: In conjugation, a bacteria cell directly transfers plasmid or host DNA to another cell by way of a temporary mating bridge. The receiving cell can then make copies of the plasmid, as in R plasmids and antibiotic resistance, or it can incorporate DNA into its chromosome, changing its nucleotide sequence and adding genetic diversity. *This student clearly and succinctly addressed the question. Notice that the question asked for two specific tasks within each part of the answer. For each part the student is to describe the biological process and explain how it increases genetic diversity. The response follows the instructions for each part of the question, leading to a clear, precise answer. We would not be surprised to see a question much like this one on the AP exam.*

Topic 8: Plant Form and Function

ANSWERS AND EXPLANATIONS

Level 1: Knowledge/Comprehension Questions

1. **(D) is correct.** When the light source on a plant is uneven, the plant will grow toward the light source. This is the result of auxin moving from the tip of the stem down to the cells that are less exposed to light and causing them to elongate faster than the cells on the side that is illuminated. This uneven growth bends the plant toward the light source.

2. **(C) is correct.** Transpiration is the evaporative loss of water from a plant. The driving force behind the movement of sap in xylem (in the direction from the roots to the leaves) is the transpiration of water through the stomata on the leaves.

3. **(D) is correct.** In the transpiration-cohesion-tension mechanism, water is lost through transpiration from the leaves of the plant as a result of the lower water potential of the air. The cohesion of water because of hydrogen bonding plus the adhesion of water to the plant cell walls by hydrogen bonding enables the water to form a water column. Water is drawn up through the xylem as water evaporates from the leaves, each evaporating water molecule pulling on the one beneath it through the attraction of hydrogen bonds.

4. **(A) is correct.** The production of ATP in plant cells occurs in the mitochondria, as it does in the cells of animals, but it also occurs in the chloroplasts during photosynthesis. The light reactions of photosynthesis convert solar energy into the chemical energy of ATP and NADPH, and these light reactions take place in the chloroplasts in the mesophyll cells of the plant leaf.

5. (D) is correct. All of the factors listed aid in the uptake of water and minerals by the roots of a plant except the last choice, gravity. The large surface area of leaves plays an important role in transpiration.

6. (A) is correct. This question requires you to know that the sperm of angiosperms do not swim! This is the adaptive value of pollen: It allows fertilization without water. Sperm nuclei enter a pollen tube that grows down the style, discharging the two sperm nuclei for double fertilization.

7. (C) is correct. The ovule contains the egg and, when fertilized, will become the seed. The ovule is found within the ovary. The ovary may contain one ovule and, therefore, one seed, or many ovules, like a watermelon. The ovary wall becomes the fruit. A watermelon is a single swollen ovary!

Level 2: Application/Analysis/Synthesis Questions

1. (B) is correct. Short-day plants require a period of continuous darkness longer than a critical period in order to flower. These plants flower in early spring or fall. Short-day plants are actually long-night plants; that is, what the plant measures is the length of the night.

2. (B) is correct. Long-day plants require a night period that is shorter than a critical period. The critical length for flowering is 9 hours, but the question asks which choice prevents flowering. Only answer B has a 24-hour period with more than 9 consecutive hours of darkness, thus preventing flowering.

3. (A) is correct. Understanding signal transduction pathways is an important concept for this unit and in biology. Keep its role in allowing plants (and other organisms) to adapt to their environment in your mind as you study. A ligand such as a hormone or an environmental stimulus such as light activates the receptor protein in a signal transduction pathway, not a relay molecule.

4. (C) is correct. This experiment by Went centered on phototropism—the growth of a shoot in response to light. Light causes auxins to move to the dark side of the stem, where the increase in auxins results in cell elongation. Cell elongation causes the dark side of the stem to expand more rapidly, causing the plant to grow toward the light. Consider this question in the context of the environment, causing changes in the behavior of an organism.

5. (B) is correct. Because Went applied only the plant tip to the agar, he must have used knowledge from prior experiments (by Darwin) that demonstrated that only the tip influenced movement of the plant toward light. This question tests your ability to design an experiment.

6. (C) is correct. This is the type of question you can expect to see on the exam. Choice A is wrong because it is not a conclusion about the treatment. Choice B in incorrect because you see that plant A does not bend. When you compare what happens with plants A, B, and C, you will see that elongation has occurred in each case (note the dotted line in the figure). Therefore, the chemical must be necessary for cell elongation.

7. (A) is correct. Charles Darwin and his son Francis demonstrated in 1880 that seedlings covered with a darkened cap would not grow toward the light. We now know that without the stimulus of light, auxins do not move to the side of the plant opposite the light stimulus. Without the auxins, cell elongation does not occur, so no bending of the plant toward the light occurs.

■ **8. (A) is correct.** In plants, phloem is responsible for carrying sugar from a source (leaves for example) to sinks (other locations that are consuming energy). This process is called *translocation*. As sugar is added to the phloem, water follows and the solutes are moved by bulk flow (pressure flow) toward the sink, where sugar is unloaded and water is lost. A sugar sink is any tissue that is a net consumer or depository of sugar.

■ **9. (B) is correct.** This is the beginning of the transduction step, which enables the plant to amplify the signal received in reception.

■ **10. (C) is correct.** In most of the signal transduction pathways you have seen, reception is initiated by a ligand (a hormone, for example) interacting with a cell membrane protein. However, other environmental stimuli, light for instance, can also initiate a signal transduction pathway. In the figure, the phytochrome is located in the cytoplasm and stimulated by light, whereas the calcium channel is located in the cell membrane and activated by a molecular stimulus.

Grid-In Questions

1. The correct answer is –8.67 (bars). The formula of solute potential = –iCRT. In this case the formula is $-(1.0)(0.35)(0.0831)(298) = -8.67$. The exam answer will take into account the variability of reading the solute concentration of the potato cores; thus, a reasonable range of answers around the one given would be acceptable. If you find these problems difficult, go to the lab section of this book to Investigation 4, Diffusion and Osmosis, where you can find an explanation of water potential and how to work water potential problems.

Free-Response Question

(a) It was originally thought that plant flowering depended on the length of the daylight, but then scientists concluded that it is actually night length that determines when a plant will flower. Plants monitor the length of the night by the molecular switching of two forms of the phytochrome pigment. Phytochromes respond to a shift in red (**r**) light to far-red (fr) light. This is a photoreversible response, and the threshold to trigger flowering is called the critical dark period. The accumulation of specific phytochrome isomers combined with the biological clock of plants allows for the specific monitoring of the length of the night. Long-day plants and short-day plants actually monitor the length of the night, not the day. Short-day plants must have a period of darkness longer than a specific critical period to flower, so you get chrysanthemums to flower by keeping them in a greenhouse where shades are pulled to block light to simulate a long night. The total amount of light must not exceed the critical period to induce flowering.

(b) The response described is phototropism. Early experiments determined that only the tip of the coleoptiles responds to light by producing a chemical, now known to be auxin, whose concentration increases on the dark side of the stem. Auxin causes elongation (not cell division) of the cells on the dark side, and this will bend the seedling towards the light source.

(c) Because in many plants, flowering is related to day length, photoperiodism increases fitness by ensuring that flowering resources are not committed until growing conditions are most favorable for survival of flowers, fruits, and seeds. For example, short-day plants will not set flower buds unless they receive a critical period of darkness, and any interruption in this will keep them from flowering. These plants will, therefore, in nature, flower in the earliest days of spring, whereas long-day plants will not flower until the longer days of summer. In each case, the time of flowering will enhance reproductive success.

Phototropism increases fitness because it ensures that plants will maximize their exposure to light, which increases their ability to do photosynthesis. A higher rate of photosynthesis results in more energy storage by the plant, which is then available for reproduction (larger flowers, greater seed set).

This response clearly delineates the three parts of the question, making it easier for the reader to locate points in each section. In part 3, the student correctly draws the connection between the response and how it increases reproductive success (fitness).

Topic 9: Animal Form and Function

ANSWERS AND EXPLANATIONS

Level 1: Knowledge/Comprehension Questions

1. (D) is correct. You will want to review events at the synapse that trigger the release of neurotransmitter from the presynaptic cell. Vesicles filled with neurotransmitter migrate to the plasma membrane and fuse with it. At this point the neurotransmitter is released by exocytosis into the synapse, where it will bind receptors on the next neuron or cell in the pathway and generate a response.

2. (D) is correct. When the threshold level of depolarization occurs, Na^+ channels open, beginning a positive feedback loop that results in a rush of Na^+ entering the cell, creating an action potential.

3. (B) is correct. All of the answers listed—except phagocytes—are examples of barrier defenses. Phagocytosis is the process by which invading organisms are ingested and destroyed by white blood cells.

4. (B) is correct. When a lymphocyte is activated by an antigen, it is stimulated to divide and differentiate, and it forms two clones. One clone is of effector plasma cells that combat the antigen. The second clone is of memory cells that stay in circulation, recognize the antigen if it infects the body in the future, and launch an attack against it.

5. (C) is correct. Neurotransmitters are secreted by the synaptic vesicles and act as signaling molecules. When they bind with receptors on the postsynaptic plasma membrane, the nerve impulse is transmitted from one neuron to the next neuron or another cell. A single postsynaptic neuron can receive signals from many neurons that secrete different neurotransmitters.

6. (D) is correct. You will want to review the role of each of these important cell types. Helper T cells are targeted by HIV infections, which is why AIDS patients have compromised immune systems. When helper T cells are compromised, both arms of the adaptive immune system (B cells and T cells) malfunction.

7. (C) is correct. Four stages of animal development are briefly listed in the proper order in answer C. You do not need to know the terms that indicate the stages, but be familiar with the proper sequence of development.

8. (C) is correct. The autonomic nervous system is also referred to as the involuntary nervous system and has two components, the sympathetic branch and the parasympathetic branch. Nerves of the sympathetic nervous system activate organ systems to deal with stress, as in a "fight or flight" situation. The parasympathetic nervous system generally causes opposite responses, maintaining a steady, relaxed situation, as in "rest and digest."

9. (C) is correct. This figure depicts clonal selection, a central idea in immunology. The active plasma cell is the plasma cell producing antibodies. Use this figure to review clonal selection. This would be a good time to label plasma cells, memory cells, and antibodies on the figure.

10. (C) is correct. Homeostasis is the ability of many animals to regulate their internal environment. In case C, the body fails to maintain body temperature within narrow limits. All the other choices describe events that are triggered when the body is outside normal homeostatic bounds with regard to a specific factor.

Level 2: Application/Analysis/Synthesis Questions

1. (B) is correct. Maintenance of glucose homeostasis by insulin and glucagon is the classic system for explaining negative feedback. The two hormones are antagonistic, with insulin triggering the uptake of glucose by the cells, thus lowering blood glucose levels, and glucagon promoting the release of glucose into the blood from liver glycogen, raising blood glucose levels. Sensors monitor glucose levels, whereas the two antagonistic hormones are used to maintain steady glucose levels in the blood. *It is important to be able to explain both negative and positive feedback systems.*

2. (B) is correct. Glucagon raises blood glucose levels, as noted in the previous explanation for question 1.

3. (C) is correct. How the environment affects energy budgets and behavior and how free energy flows through organisms are the key points. In this case, if the organism is increasing in mass, the inflow of energy must be greater than the outflow.

4. (C) is correct. B cells are part of the humoral immune response, which occurs in the blood and lymph. In the humoral response, antibodies help neutralize or eliminate toxins and pathogens in the blood and lymph. Cytotoxic T cells are part of the cell-mediated immune response, which destroys infected host cells. Always pick the *best* answer; choice B is close, but C is better.

5. (D) is correct. Lymphocytes (B cells and T cells) have receptors for a single antigen. Antigens are *anti*body *gen*erating and generally stimulate more than one lymphocyte, but each lymphocyte is specific for the one antigen it is genetically equipped to recognize. Also note the true statements in this question to help review basic information about antibodies, antigens, and epitopes.

6. (C) is correct. This question is at the center of understanding active immunity, vaccinations, and how B cells protect the body by producing antibodies and memory cells.

7. (B) is correct. The secondary immune response is a heightened response to the same antigen that generated a primary immune response. Figure 9.3 on page 244 clearly shows primary and secondary immune responses and has been on numerous AP exams.

8. (B) is correct. Membranes are hydrophobic, so only hydrophobic molecules can pass directly through them. Hydrophilic molecules remain on the outside, unless transported across the membrane. The signal molecule (ligand) in Figure A does not enter the cell; therefore, it is hydrophilic and not lipid soluble.

9. (B) is correct. When a receptor protein is embedded in the plasma membrane, it is positioned to bond with a hydrophilic ligand (signal molecule).

10. (D) is correct. This diagram uses a steroid hormone (testosterone and estradiol are examples) that is lipid soluble. The hormone functions in cell-to-cell communication by causing the production of transcription factors that activate genes.

11. (A) is correct. Structure C is the myelin sheath that functions as insulation that surrounds the axon, increasing the rate of impulse transmission by creating the nodes of Ranvier, which enable saltatory conduction.

12. (D) is correct. Altruism is thought to occur in populations because helping other close relatives increases the chances that they will survive to pass on genes that are shared between them and the altruistic member.

13. (C) is correct. The insecticide blocks the enzyme acetylcholinesterase, which normally removes acetylcholine from the synapse after the signal is received. Without this removal, the neurotransmitter acetylcholine remains in the synapse, causing constant muscle contraction. Knowing the names of specific neurotransmitters is not required, but understanding how neurotransmitters work is required.

14. (B) is correct. Because the neurotransmitter acetylcholine stimulates muscle contraction in both roaches and people, it is logical to conclude that the mechanism of stimulating skeletal muscle contraction must be similar in humans and roaches.

15. (C) is correct. If depolarization shifts the membrane potential enough, the result is a change in membrane potential called an action potential. Action potentials occur fully or not at all; they represent an all-or-none response to stimuli.

16. (A) is correct. The action potential depolarizes the presynaptic membrane, which opens voltage-gated calcium channels. The key to this question is the emphasis on the word *next*.

17. (B) is correct. Immediately behind depolarization caused by Na^+ inflow is a zone of repolarization caused by K^+ outflow. In the repolarized zone, the sodium channels remain inactivated. This prevents an action potential from moving backward. The interval between the onset on an action potential and end of the refractory period is only 1–2 milliseconds.

18. (B) is correct. Learned behavior occurs when behavior is modified based on specific experiences. If the salmon returned to Cold Bay, then they learned the new magnetic bearings during the experiment.

19. (A) is correct. Imprinting occurs at a specific stage in life and results in a long-lasting behavioral response. Imprinting has a sensitive or critical period when the learning must occur. The pictures of young geese following Konrad Lorenz or whooping cranes following an ultralight plane are both examples of imprinting in action during young animals' sensitive period. In the case of salmon, it is believed they imprint on chemical cues in the water of their home stream.

20. (D) is correct. The traditional example of a negative feedback system is the thermostat example. In the body, one very prominent example of negative feedback is the regulation of our body temperature at about 37°C. A section of the brain is responsible for keeping track of the temperature of the blood, and if the blood is too warm, for example, it tells the sweat glands to increase production. Remember, in negative feedback situations more gets you less! In positive feedback, as described in choice B, more gets you more!

21. (B) is correct. A difference between two individual population lines could arise by a process such as genetic drift, which occurs randomly rather than in response to selection. Since the study found that all three populations in one set behaved consistently and in a distinct manner from the populations in the other set, it is unlikely that the difference arose randomly three separate times. Therefore, these results strongly suggest that the differences in foraging behavior between the R and K lines arose by natural selection. Proper experimental design would eliminate the other possible alternative hypotheses.

22. (B) is correct. The graph indicates that at high population density the for^R ("Rover") allele is selected for. Both answers B and D meet this criteria, but B reflects evolutionary change while D is clearly Lamarckian. The environment does not signal genetic change to populations. Answer C is eliminated as the graph shows that the population is changing allelic frequencies for foraging, a clear violation of the no natural selection condition of Hardy-Weinberg equilibrium.

23. (B) is correct. Three things are at play in this question. You have to keep track of primary and secondary immune responses, different antibodies are formed from exposures to different antigens, and the difference between a T cell and B cell response. Carefully reading the information on the graph makes this question much easier than it might be otherwise. The graph with this set of questions has been featured on numerous AP exams.

24. (C) is correct. The solid line on the graph shows a sharp increase in antibody concentration on the second exposure to antigen X. Notice that the response is not only stronger but also quicker.

25. (C) is correct. The graph only shows exposures one and two, but does not provide any data for a third exposure. Therefore, the correctness of the statement cannot be determined from the graph.

Grid-In Questions

1. **The answer is 302.4 L.** One way to solve this is to multiply the number of beats per minute by 60 minutes per hour (72 × 60 = 4,320 heartbeats per hour), then multiply that by 70 mL per beat (4,320 × 70 = 302,400) and convert to liters by dividing by 1,000 to give 302.4 L/hour!

2. **The answer is 52.5 mm Hg.** The peak has a partial pressure of oxygen (510 × 0.21 = 107.1 mm Hg) of 107.1 mm Hg. Subtracting that from the sea level value of 159.6 mm Hg, the final answer is 52.5 mm Hg, or about one-third the amount of oxygen at sea level. Did you remember to find the *difference?* Be sure to read questions carefully.

3. **The answer is 435 action potentials per second.** The action potential lasts from the beginning of the rising phase to the point of maximal undershoot, about 2.3 msec in the graph shown. Therefore, an action potential can be produced every 2.3 msec. The fastest rate at which a neuron could produce action potentials would be 1,000 msec divided by 2.3 msec, or 435 events/sec. When our students miss this question, it is usually because they do not divide into 1,000. They do not pay enough attention to the *milli-* prefix on the *x*-axis!

Free-Response Question

(a) Innate behaviors are behaviors that are not learned but are genetically programmed. An example of an innate behavior would be when birds begin migration based on day length cues. This behavior enhances survival because the changes in day length correlate to seasonal changes in food supplies and place the birds in habitats with more food for survival and reproduction.

(b) An example of a learned behavior would be the species-specific song of a bird. It is learned during a critical period by imprinting. If a bird is fostered by another species, it may learn the song of the foster species. Because the song is important to attract mates, failure to learn the species-specific song limits reproductive success.

(c) Cooperative behavior occurs when group actions enhance survival and reproduction of all members of the group. An example is seen in colonial insects such as bees. A reproductive female produces all the eggs, nonreproductive females tend the larvae and obtain food for the group, and the males mate with the queen. The needs of the entire population are met through this cooperative behavior. In another example, the worker bees will fan their wings to cool the hive, and this cooperative behavior ensures survival of the entire group.

(d) Pheromones are chemical signals produced by members of a population that affect other members of the species. Termites will deposit a pheromone trail that other blind members of the colony will follow to locate a food supply. This behavior is adaptive because it enables the entire colony to access a resource. One worker may stumble upon the resource and be able to deposit this chemical trail that leads others to the source.

This question could have been answered with many different examples; what is important to note is that the student not only provided a description of the behavior in a particular species but also carefully explained how the behavior increased survival. Be careful to always follow directions! Many students would answer such a question with great examples but then forget to relate this behavior to natural selection. Note that in part C, the student gives two good examples—the reader will always grade the first example, so this was wasted time.

Topic 10: Ecology

ANSWERS AND EXPLANATIONS

Level 1: Knowledge/Comprehension Questions

▮ **1. (C) is correct.** The ozone layer is located in the stratosphere and surrounds Earth. It is composed of O_3, and it absorbs UV radiation, reducing the level of UV radiation reaching the organisms in the biosphere. Researchers have been observing the thinning of the ozone layer since about 1975. One reason for the destruction of the ozone layer has been attributed to the widespread use of chlorofluorocarbons.

▮ **2. (B) is correct.** The carrying capacity of a population is defined as the maximum population size a particular environment can support at a particular time with no degradation of the habitat. It is fixed at certain times, but it varies over the course of time with the amount of resources that exist in an environment.

▮ **3. (C) is correct.** Tundra is characterized by having permafrost (which is a permanently frozen layer of soil), very cold temperatures, and high winds. These factors prevent tall plants from growing. Tundra generally does not receive much rainfall throughout the year, and when rain does fall it cannot soak into the soil because of the permafrost.

▮ **4. (B) is correct.** Tropical forests generally have thick canopies that prevent much sun from filtering through. This means that in breaks in the canopy other plants grow quickly to compete for sunlight. Tropical forests are home to epiphytes, and rainfall is frequent.

▮ **5. (A) is correct.** Temperate grasslands are characterized by having thick grass, seasonal drought, occasional fires, and large grazing animals. Their soil is generally rich with nutrients, making them good areas for agriculture. Most of the temperate grassland in the United States is used today for agriculture.

▮ **6. (D) is correct.** Deserts experience very little rainfall, so they are home to many plants and animals that have adaptations for storing and saving water. Deserts are marked by drastic temperature fluctuation; they can be very hot in the day but freezing at night. Many desert plants rely on CAM photosynthesis.

▮ **7. (D) is correct.** A bacterial colony growing where it has limitless nutrients, and other ideal conditions, will experience what is called exponential growth. In exponential growth, all members are free to reproduce at their physiological capacity.

8. (C) is correct. All the others are $+/-$ interactions. This notation indicates that one species benefits ($+$) and the other species is harmed ($-$). Choice C does not fit this notation because both the honeybee and the flower benefit—an example of mutualism ($+/+$).

9. (D) is correct. Figure 10.5 shows the effect of the removal of a keystone species from a tide pool. In this case, the removal of *Pisaster* allowed for the unrestrained growth of a specific mussel, which eventually took over the rock faces of the tide pool and eliminated most other invertebrates.

10. (D) is correct. An early fall frost is a *density-independent factor*; it occurs without regard to the density of the population. *Density-dependent factors* increasingly slow population growth as density increases.

11. (A) is correct. An increase in the carrying capacity does not directly relate to an increase in human population size; it could allow better nutrition and health for humans. All of the other answers directly contribute to increased human population growth. Death rates have fallen, but birth rates are much slower to change.

12. (B) is correct. The type I survivorship curve is the pattern described in the question and is typical of large mammals. Type II curves show an equal chance of death throughout the life span, whereas Type III shows heavy mortality in early stages of the life cycle.

13. (C) is correct. The greenhouse effect is the process by which carbon dioxide and water vapor in the atmosphere intercept reflected infrared radiation from the sun and rereflect it to Earth. Global warming is the process by which the amount of carbon dioxide in the atmosphere is increasing because of humans' combustion of fossil fuels, leading to higher temperatures on Earth.

14. (C) is correct. A species' ecological niche is defined as the sum of its use of the abiotic and biotic factors in an environment. For instance, a particular bird's niche refers to many things, including the food it consumes, where it builds its nest, the time of day it is active, and what climate it lives in.

15. (C) is correct. The dominant species in a community has the greatest biomass, or sum weight, of all of the members of a population. Dominant species are also hypothesized to be the most competitive in exploiting the resources in its ecosystem.

16. (B) is correct. Secondary succession refers to a situation in which a community has been cleared by a disturbance of some kind, but the soil is left intact. The area will begin to return to its original state through the process of plants invading the area and recolonizing.

Level 2: Application/Analysis/Synthesis Questions

1. (C) is correct. The answer gives the sequence of events leading to the environmental degradation of the ecosystem. Had the stem of this question been the basis for an essay question, you might have been asked to explain how the alteration of an abiotic factor impacted the ecosystem. Choice C would have been the backbone of your response.

2. (C) is correct. Nitrogen and phosphorus are often limiting factors in both aquatic and terrestrial ecosystems because they are often in short supply for producers. This is why our lawn fertilizers are rich in nitrogen and phosphorus.

This is a good example of the impact of an abiotic factor on populations in an ecosystem.

3. **(C) is correct.** The carrying capacity is the number of individuals that the environment can sustain. This is indicated by a decrease in the growth rate and a leveling of the graph. When the graph line becomes horizontal, the rate of growth is zero. The population growth reaches that point in this graph very close to 1940.

4. **(A) is correct.** When $K = N$, the population estimate (N) and the carrying capacity (K) are equal. This causes the right side of the equation to equal zero, as indicated by the flat line in 1945.

5. **(B) is correct.** This is an example of a biotic factor impacting an ecosystem. Introduced species may reduce species diversity by increasing competition for resources and sometimes replacing native species that cannot compete as well. This is a good time for you to review the components of species diversity and the reasons introduced species are often invasive.

6. **(B) is correct.** Option B is the best of the answers suggested. In practical terms, finding a native predator that only eats nonnative snakeheads is problematic at best.

7. **(C) is correct.** As with any population, if the number of individuals entering the reproductive years is much greater than the number of postreproductive individuals, the population will expand. The large increase in the number of individuals entering the childbearing years in Nigeria foretells rapid population growth.

8. **(B) is correct.** The expanding population will place increased demands on resources. Although this question and question 7 deal with human populations, the underlying concepts of population ecology apply. The demands of a population that is above carrying capacity can result in the degradation of the ecosystem.

9. **(C) is correct.** Almost all organisms use solar energy stored in organic molecules produced by green plants to power life processes. Autotrophs convert solar energy to a form useful to both autotrophs and heterotrophs. At each successive trophic level, less energy is available because so much is converted to a form not useful to the organisms. Energy cannot be recycled.

10. **(B) is correct.** The graph shows an increase in mortality as the density of kelp perch increases. Thus, an increase in density leads to a decrease in population size—more gets you less—an example of negative feedback. The key step in answering the question is found in the first part of sentence two.

11. **(B) is correct.** The graph clearly shows a dramatic decrease in the percentage of young sheep producing lambs (y-axis) as the population size increases (x-axis). As competition for limited resources increases with increases in population density, available energy for reproduction decreases.

12. **(B) is correct.** The answer is the gross grass production divided by the solar radiation or $34{,}580 / 600{,}000 = 0.0576$ times 100 to convert to percentage equals 5.8%.

13. **(C) is correct.** The answer is the net grass production divided by the solar radiation $= 6{,}585 \div 600{,}000 = 0.011$ or 1.1%.

14. **(D) is correct.** The energy lost by primary producers as respiration is the gross grass production minus the net grass production $= 34{,}580$ kcal/(m$^2 \cdot$ yr) $- 6{,}585$ kcal/(m$^2 \cdot$ yr) $= 27{,}995$ kcal/(m$^2 \cdot$ yr).

■ **15. (D) is correct.** The answer is the amount of energy in detritus leaving the marsh divided by the net grass production = 3,671 ÷ 6,585 = 0.56 or 56%.

■ **16. (A) is correct.** Energy does not move efficiently through food webs, nor does it ever recycle! Your calculations show the amount of energy lost to respiration at several trophic levels. The loss of energy means that after 4 or 5 trophic levels there is simply not enough energy to finance another trophic level. Remember, nutrients cycle, but energy flows one way through an ecosystem.

Grid-In Questions

1. **The answer is 32.** Using a starting population of 20 bobcats, multiply that number by the birth rate of 0.48 to yield the increase (9.6); then get the number of deaths (20 × 0.21 = 4.2). The overall gain is 9.6 − 4.2 or + 5.4 bobcats. Add this to the beginning population of 20 to get the estimate for year one, 25.4 bobcats. Follow the same procedure for the second year using 25.4 bobcats as the starting population. The question specifies to the nearest whole number, so round to the nearest tenth with all numbers until the final answer; only then should you round to the nearest whole number. Rounding every number may put your answer outside the acceptable range.

2. **The answer is 461.** $N = (142)(133)/41 = 460.6$, rounded to 461.

Free-Response Questions

(a) The hawk, mouse, and plant in this particular ecosystem are related by the passage of energy. Together they make up a food chain: The mouse is a primary consumer, and it consumes the plant, which is a primary producer (the plant is an autotroph—capable of trapping the energy of the sun and converting it into chemical energy in the form of carbohydrates). The hawk then is a predator of the mouse—and a secondary consumer. Secondary consumers eat herbivores. Energy is lost at each trophic level. The loss of energy as it flows through ecosystems is what limits the number of trophic levels in a food chain.

(b) One example in which the biotic factors of the biosphere impact the abiotic factors is seen in the case of global warming. We rely on the greenhouse effect (in which atmospheric carbon dioxide acts as an insulator, trapping infrared radiation from the sun and rereflecting it) to help maintain the hospitable temperature of Earth. Yet, as a result of burning fossil fuels—beginning during the Industrial Revolution—the concentration of carbon dioxide in the atmosphere has increased significantly, and this has led to an increase in global temperatures.

　　The thinning of the ozone layer is another way in which humans (a biotic factor of the biosphere) impact abiotic processes. Organisms are protected from ultraviolet radiation from the sun by a layer of ozone that surrounds Earth. Decreased ozone levels are expected to increase human skin cancer rates as well as increase DNA damage in a wide variety of organisms. The ozone layer has been degraded by humans' use of chlorofluorocarbons (CFCs), which are chemicals used in refrigeration and other industrial processes. Many countries have stopped using these chemicals, but chlorine molecules already in the atmosphere continue to have an effect on ozone.

This student clearly marks part (a) and (b), which is a good technique to be sure the reader follows your answer. In part (b), the student limits the response to only two examples, as directed, and gives a clear explanation of each. If the student had added a third example, it would not have been graded. Pick your best examples and use them in the response, but do not waste time adding additional examples in the hope that the reader will choose the best ones for you.

BIG IDEA 1: Investigation 1, Artificial Selection

1. **The correct answer is 8.1.** The mean is determined by adding the height of all the plants (80.7) and dividing by the number of plants (10) = 8.07, then rounding to the nearest tenth.
2. **The correct answer is 8.8.** The mode is the most common value in the data set.
3. **The correct answer is 5.8(%).** This is determined by taking the change in height from Generation 1 to Generation 2 and dividing it by the mean height for Generation 1 (0.47/8.47). This gives 0.0582; convert to a percentage by multiplying by 100, and note that your answer is to be given to the nearest tenth. If you used the rounded figures (8.1 and 8.5) your answer would be 4.9%. Any answer between these two figures (4.9% and 5.8%) would be considered correct on the exam.
4. **The correct answer is (C).** This is the only choice that selects for height.

PRACTICE THE PRACTICE: Graphical Analysis of Data

1. The correct graph is a bar graph. Sample I should have an error bar that extends from 5.9 to 7.1 cm. Sample II should have an error bar that extends from 8.4 to 9.3 cm, and Sample III should have an error bar that extends from 8.4 to 9.6 cm.
2. **Claim:** Sample I falls outside the expected height variation for the population. **Evidence:** For Sample I, the mean +/−2 SEM falls below the means +/−2 SEM for Samples II and III. The error bars for Sample I do not overlap those for the other two samples.
   Reasoning: Because the error bar of Sample I does not overlap either of the other two samples, this indicates that its height variation is outside what might have been expected. Perhaps Sample I is actually a different population, or some other factor is at play to cause its plants to be so short.

BIG IDEA 1: Investigation 2, Mathematical Modeling: Hardy-Weinberg

1. **(C) is correct.** The question tells you that $p = 0.9$ and $q = 0.1$. From this, you can calculate the heterozygotes: $2pq = 2\,(0.9)\,(0.1) = 0.18$.
2. **(B) is correct.** The conditions described all contribute to genetic equilibrium, where it would be expected for initial gene frequencies to remain constant generation after generation.
3. **(D) is correct.**
$$q^2 = 0.09, \text{ so } q = 0.3$$
$$p = 1 - q, \text{ so } p = 1 - 0.3 = 0.7$$
$$AA = q^2 = 0.49$$

BIG IDEA 1: Investigation 3, Comparing DNA Sequences to Understand Evolutionary Relationships with BLAST

▌ **1. (C) is correct.** This is a good time to recall convergent evolution, the independent evolution of similar features (similar problem – similar solution), as seen in comparing a shark to a dolphin. They look similar but are distantly related. Organisms with similar gene sequences demonstrate a recent shared ancestry. Genetic similarity rather than appearance is a better evidence for relatedness.

▌ **2. (D) is correct.** The nodes on a phylogenetic tree can rotate like a mobile and not change the relationship between species. Choices a, b, and c all do this, but not choice d. In choice d the taxons C and D have changed positions, making their relationships to each other and taxa E and F different.

▌ **3. (B) is correct.** This answer provides maximum parsimony, the simplest explanation that is consistent with the facts.

▌ **4. (B) is correct.** Understanding this answer involves the idea of a molecular clock: the number of nucleotide substitutions in related genes is proportional to the time that has elapsed since the genes branched from their common ancestor. The greater the number of changes, the greater the time that has passed since the two species shared a common ancestor.

PRACTICE THE PRACTICE: Using Traits to Construct a Cladogram

1. (The cladogram) There are other ways to correctly represent the relationships shown in the chart. You also could have drawn a cladogram similar to that shown in Question 2, choice A.
2. Vascular tissue
3. Seeds
4. Note the location of A and B on the cladogram.

BIG IDEA 2: Investigation 4, Diffusion and Osmosis

▌ **1. (B) is correct.** The water potential of distilled water in a container open to the environment is 0. The water potential of the beet core is -0.2. (Since water potential = solute potential (-0.4) + pressure potential (0.2), water potential of the beet core = -0.2.)

▌ **2. (B) is correct.** The water potential for both the distilled water and the beet core in beaker a is 0. In choice C the beet core in (b) has a pressure of 0.2 whereas the beet core in (a) is 0.4, so the beet in (b) would be less turgid.

▌ **3. The solute potential is -8.55 bars.** $\psi_S = -iCRT.$ $\psi_S = -(1)(0.35M)$ $(0.0831$ liter bar/mole K$)(273 + 21)$. Check your gridded response—did you remember to use the minus sign?

BIG IDEA 2: Investigation 5, Photosynthesis

▌ **1. (C) is correct.** DPIP is reduced in this experiment because it receives high-energy electrons from chlorophyll. With the disruption of the thylakoid membranes (remember the blender) $NADP^+$ is no longer positioned to capture electrons. DPIP replaces $NADP^+$ as the electron acceptor, turning from blue to colorless as it does so.

▌ **2. (B) is correct.** When DPIP becomes colorless very rapidly either there are too many chloroplasts or the concentration of DPIP is so dilute that the quantity can be reduced rapidly.

▌ **3. (C) is correct.** A flat line indicates that no DPIP is being reduced. This must mean the chloroplasts are not functioning. In the DPIP lab boiled chloroplasts are used as a comparison to normal chloroplasts. The boiled chloroplasts give a flat line when graphed.

▌ **4. (B) is correct.** You should recall the equation for photosynthesis. Without a source of CO_2, photosynthesis cannot proceed.

BIG IDEA 2: Investigation 6, Cellular Respiration

▌ **1. (B) is correct.** To calculate this, it is easiest to find the change in y at 10 minutes (0.4 mL − 0 mL = 0.4 mL) and divide by the change in x (10 minutes − 0 minutes = 10 minutes). 0.4 mL/10 minutes = 0.04 mL/min. (As the data form a straight line, you get the same answer if you use 20 minutes.)

▌ **2. (A) is correct.** Study Figure 6.2 carefully to see that at 10 minutes the 22°C germinating corn consumed 0.8 mL of oxygen, whereas the 12°C germinating corn consumed 0.04 mL of oxygen.

▌ **3. (D) is correct.** This is the only statement that is supported by information provided on the graph in Figure 6.2.

▌ **4. (D) is correct.** As carbon dioxide is released, it is removed from the air in the vial. Because oxygen is being consumed during cellular respiration, the total gas volume in the vial decreases. This causes pressure to decrease inside the vial, and water begins to enter the pipette.

BIG IDEA 3: Investigation 7, Cell Division: Mitosis and Meiosis

<u>Null Hypothesis:</u> There is no significant difference between the observed number of cells in interphase and mitosis in the control group compared to the experimental group.

	Observed (o)	Expected (e)	$(o-e)^2/e$
Interphase cells	186	220	5.25
Mitosis cells	64	30	5.25
Total	250	250	10.50

$$X^2 = 10.50$$

Degrees of Freedom = 1 p **value** = 0.05   **critical value** = 3.84

Accept or reject the null hypothesis? Reject the null hypothesis.

Explanation: The chi square value of 10.50 is greater than the critical value of 3.84. This means there was a significant difference in the number of cells in mitosis between the control group and the experimental group.

▌ **1. (D) is correct.** There are two nuclear divisions in meiosis, and only one in mitosis. Crossing over occurs only in meiosis; it does not occur at all in mitosis. Replication occurs only once in preparation for both mitosis and meiosis. The daughter cells of mitosis are identical to the parent cell, but in meiosis the daughter cells have only one of each homologous chromosome pair. Synapsis occurs only in prophase I of meiosis.

2. (D) is correct. Remember that if crossing over does not occur, the arrangement of spores will be 4 light and 4 dark. All other combinations are the result of crossing over.

3. (B) is correct. Map distance = number of crossovers divided by total number of asci × 100 divided by 2.

BIG IDEA 3: Investigation 8, Biotechnology: Bacterial Transformation

1. (B) is correct. Because not every cell takes up the plasmid with resistance to kanamycin, the result will be scattered colonies of bacteria.

2. (D) is correct. Plate IV has kanamycin but the bacteria cells were not exposed to the kanamycin plasmid, and so there was no transformation. The antibiotic killed all the *E. coli* cells.

3. (D) is correct. Plate II has colonies of transformed cells, so these should be used to verify transformation. If these cells are spread on agar with kanamycin, all cells will be able to grow and a lawn will result.

4. (C) is correct. Because not every cell takes up the plasmid with resistance to kanamycin, the result will be scattered colonies of bacteria when the cells are spread on LB agar with kanamycin.

BIG IDEA 3: Investigation 9, Biotechnology: Restriction Enzyme Analysis of DNA

1. (D) is correct. There are approximately 3,500 base pairs in the circled fragment. To determine this, measure the migration distance of the circled fragment. It is 22 mm. Locate 22 mm on the graph, and take a straightedge up to the point of intersection with the curve. Read the number of bp from the *y* axis (left side of graph).

2. (B) is correct. Small fragments migrate farther than large fragments. All DNA is negatively charged and so moves toward the positive electrode.

3. (C) is correct. Because *Bam*HI has three restriction sites on the plasmid, there will be three fragments measuring 6 kb, 12 kb, and 2 kb. Does lane III have the expected banding pattern?

4. (C) is correct. There are four restriction sites for both enzymes, so there will be four fragments. Does the banding pattern match the fragment sizes?

BIG IDEA 4: Investigation 10, Energy Dynamics

▌ **1. (C) is correct.** This is the point where the line crosses the x axis and where respiration therefore exceeds photosynthesis. Imagine a dark, rainy day where algae in a pond are not able to carry out photosynthesis but are still performing cellular respiration. On these days cellular respiration may exceed photosynthesis.

▌ **2. (A) is correct.** Net primary productivity is determined by subtracting the energy lost by cellular respiration from gross primary productivity, or NPP = GPP − Cellular respiration.

▌ **3. (C) is correct.** Primary productivity is directly correlated with photosynthesis, so having more sunny days as well as more frost-free days will allow greater productivity. Although Ecosystem B gets more rain, light and growing days are most significant.

BIG IDEA 4: Investigation 11, Transpiration

▌ **1. (D) is correct.** When K^+ leave the guard cells, water follows, the guard cells become flaccid, and the stomata close. As a result, transpiration doesn't take place.

▌ **2. (D) is correct.** Water moves from a region of high water potential to a region of low water potential. The region of lowest water potential would be at the farthest end of the transpiration pathway.

BIG IDEA 4: Investigation 12, Fruit Fly Behavior

▌ **1. (C) is correct.** The amount of fertilizer is the variable factor, and the use of two similar plants in the same location receiving equal amounts of water implies the concept of a control. However, with such a small sample size (two plants) and no repetition, this is a flawed experiment.

▌ **2. (D) is correct.** However, this experiment has no control so any of the other choices are reasonable conclusions from the data. In order to reach a reliable single conclusion, you must design a new controlled experiment.

▌ **3. (B) is correct.** Much of the early movement is simply exploration, so data analysis should not begin until the pill bugs have acclimated. Choice C may seem reasonable, but it is not as good as B because it looks only at a single point in time.

▌ **4. (A) is correct.** It is the only statement that gives both the conditions and a measurable predicted result.

BIG IDEA 4: Investigation 13, Enzyme Activity

▌ **1. (C) is correct.** The rate of the reaction decreases when the number of substrate molecules has been reduced by the enzyme. There are fewer and fewer substrate molecules available, reducing the number of enzyme-substrate collisions. Above the maximum substrate concentration, the rate will not be increased by adding more substrate; the enzyme is already working as fast as it can. An enzyme can catalyze a certain number of reactions per second, and if there is not sufficient substrate present for it to work at its maximum velocity, the rate will decrease. Therefore, to keep the enzyme working at its maximum, you must add more substrate.

▌ **2. (B) is correct.** H_2SO_4 lowers the pH so that the globular shape of the protein is altered. The active site is distorted to the point that the enzyme no longer functions.

Statistical Analysis: Chi-Square Analysis of Data

▌ **1. (D) is correct.** There is no evidence for any type of linkage because both males and females show the traits in approximately equal proportions, and eye color and wings appear to sort independently. If the parents were homozygous for these traits, the offspring would not show different phenotypes from both parents.

▌ **2. (C) is correct.** This is obtained by using the formula x^2 the sum of $(o - e)^2/e$.

	o	e	$o - e$	$(o - e)^2/e$
Red eyes/normal wings	98	90	8	0.7111
Red eyes/no wings	22	30	8	2.1333
Sepia eyes/normal wings	26	30	4	0.5333
Sepia eyes/no wings	14	10	4	1.6
				$x^2 = 4.977$

▌ **3. (A) is correct.** The expected results are based on obtaining a 9:3:3:1 ratio from two heterozygous parents. There are three degrees of freedom. Because the Chi-square value is below 7.82, the results support the null hypothesis. Be sure you understand why A is correct and D is incorrect!

Sample Test

ANSWERS AND EXPLANATIONS

Part A

▌ **1. (A) is correct.** In a warming earth scenario, the biomes would tend to move upward on the climograph into the edge of the biome above them. Only choice A, coniferous to temperate biome, shows the upward, warmer move. The remaining choices more closely resemble the biome shifts of a cooling Earth.

▌ **2. (D) is correct.** An increase in atmospheric carbon dioxide acts to increase temperatures on Earth. The movement of biomes to the north would follow a long-term warming trend. For example, the temperate forest on its northern edge would push into coniferous forest while coniferous forest on its northern edge would push into the tundra. Do you see why tundra ecologists are worried about a warming, shrinking tundra biome?

▌ **3. (C) is correct.** To calculate the chance that two or more independent events will occur together in a specific combination, the multiplication rule is used. Multiply the probability that allele *P* will segregate into a gamete (1/2), by the probability that allele *R* will segregate into a gamete (1/2) by the probability that *s* will segregate (1/2). The product of the three probabilities yields the final answer: 1/8.

▌ **4. (A) is correct.** Recall from Investigation 4 that water moves from a region where water potential is higher to a region where water potential is lower. Keep in mind that the numbers are negative, so water will move from −0.15 MPa to −0.23 MPa, or from the root tissue to the sucrose solution.

▌ **5. (B) is correct.** In gel electrophoresis, the smallest fragments travel farthest; the largest fragments are closest to the well. Fragment b is shortest, followed by a and c. We would expect a gel with c closest to the well, then a, with b at the far end.

▌ **6. (D) is correct.** Choice A indicates incorrectly that chloroplasts function in cellular respiration, whereas choice B indicates incorrectly that all eukaryotes have a cell wall, and choice C incorrectly states that all prokaryotes have a double membrane. Only choice D, which states that mitochondria, chloroplasts, and prokaryotes have similar DNA and chromosomes, is correct and supports the idea of endosymbiosis. Endosymbiosis is an excellent topic for both multiple choice and essay questions; be sure you are familiar with this topic.

▌ **7. (C) is correct.** Mammals share branch point 3 with birds and branch point 2 with amphibians. The most recent common ancestor branch point is 3, thus mammals and birds are more closely related than mammals and amphibians.

▌ **8. (D) is correct.** The lizards and ostriches share the most recent branch point, number 4.

9. (D) is correct. Of the groups listed, hawks and other birds share the most recent common ancestor with snakes and lizards, branch point 4. Do not be confused by which group of animal is closest on the figure. Mammals are shown next to snakes and lizards, but they share branch point 3, a more distant branch point than 4.

10. (D) is correct. Think of this problem as two monohybrid crosses. With tail length, all offspring show the dominant long tail. Choices A, B, and D satisfy this requirement. The coat color gene shows a 3 yellow to 1 white ratio. Choices C and D satisfy this requirement. Only choice D satisfies both requirements.

11. (C) is correct. Because sarin inhibits the action of acetylcholinesterase (AChE), the enzyme that removes the signaling molecule (acetylcholine) from the synapse, the muscle fiber does not relax. This continuous signal results in a continued contraction and, therefore, paralysis.

12. (C) is correct. Both the leading and the lagging strand require the primer before DNA polymerase can begin replication. DNA polymerase cannot start replication without a nucleotide—even a ribonucleotide—already in place. The RNA primer is later removed and replaced with DNA.

13. (D) is correct. Allolactose is an inducer molecule. Specifically, it regulates gene expression in the following manner: When it is present in the cell, it binds to the repressor protein on the operator site of the *lac* operon. The binding of allolactose causes the repressor protein to change shape and fall from the operator site. The operon can now be transcribed, allowing mRNA to be formed. The *lac* operon is an example of an inducible operon.

14. (C) is correct. This is an autosomal recessive trait. In the first generation neither parent shows the trait, but they have children who do. Also note that if the trait were sex linked the female with the trait in the second generation would have a father with the trait. Need help with pedigrees? See the chapter "Mendel and the Gene Idea" in Topic 4.

15. (A) is correct. The pedigree pattern is consistent with an autosomal recessive trait, which means the trait is not on the X chromosome, eliminating choices C and D. Choice B indicates a dominant autosomal pattern, which is also not consistent with the inheritance pattern of the pedigree.

16. (D) is correct. This question would make a good short essay question, with your response centering on the three reasons cited in answer D. All three reasons given reflect a pathway that evolved early in the evolution of life on earth.

17. (A) is correct. A pattern of selection is an indication of the natural selection pressures on the population. In this population, goldenrod galls that are too small are unsuccessful or parasitized, whereas those that are too large are eaten by birds. The most successful galls are intermediate in size, forming a pattern of stabilizing selection.

18. (C) is correct. The graphs show patterns of directional, diversifying, and stabilizing evolution. With both extremes selected against, the pattern for goldenrod galls is stabilizing.

19. (B) is correct. Signal transduction pathways are often started by a hormone or other small molecule, but they can also be initiated by light. This is possible because the receptor is a protein (a phytochrome) that is activated by light, changes shape, and starts the transduction process. Not surprisingly, a number of pathways in plants are started with light as the stimulus.

20. (D) is correct. Activation of the cellular receptor protein (phytochrome) leads to the opening of the calcium ion channels and a temporary but marked increase in calcium in the cytosol. The high calcium levels activate protein kinase 2, which leads to the activation of transcription factor 2. Answer C does not take into account that the proteins from transcription factor 1 are still being produced. Answer D is the *best* answer.

21. (D) is correct. The guard cells are hypertonic because of the accumulation of K^+, a process of active transport (note from the figure that the K^+ is moving against its gradient) that requires ATP. Stomata open when guard cells actively accumulate K^+ from neighboring epidermal cells, causing the guard cells to become hypertonic to the surrounding fluid. This causes water to enter the guard cells, increasing water pressure (turgor pressure) resulting in a cell that bows outward, creating the hole or stoma.

22. (D) is correct. *Hypotonic* means having less solute and, therefore, more water than the comparison tissue. Because water is moving out of the guard cells in this figure, the guard cells are hypotonic to the surrounding cells. Their internal water pressure (turgor pressure) is decreasing, and they are becoming flaccid. Although the AP Biology Framework does not have many specific details about plants, this question is an example of taking knowledge from an area that is required, osmosis, and applying it to one of many possible illustrative examples. Be prepared for this and do not quit on a question that seems to be about an area you might not have studied. You will know the underlying principles.

23. (B) is correct. In a recombination event W and E will be most likely to stay together because they are only three map units apart, closer than any other two genes. The closer the genes are, the more likely they will stay together in a crossover event; the further apart genes are, the more likely they will be separated by a crossover event. This idea is the basis for making gene maps based on crossover percentages.

24. (A) is correct. The statement in choice A is a fundamental tenet of ecology: energy flows one way through ecosystems, but nutrients are recycled.

25. (D) is correct. Because DDT is not broken down by normal biological means, it accumulates in ever-higher concentrations as the poison moves through the food chain. This is referred to as biological magnification.

26. (C) is correct. Samples 1, 3, and 4 have the same number of restriction sites because they form the same number of bands. Because the bands are in different locations the restriction sites must also be in different locations, forming bands of different lengths.

27. (B) is correct. The solution on side B is hypertonic to the solution on side A. Solution B has a higher total solute concentration (total molarity of 1.2) than solution A (total molarity of 0.9). After 1 hour the NaCl concentrations would equalize (see the explanation for question 28), but note from the reading that glucose cannot cross the membrane. Even after one hour Side B would remain hypertonic, causing water to move from Side A across the membrane to Side B.

28. (B) is correct. Each solute moves down its own concentration gradient. NaCl is more concentrated on side A than side B and the membrane is permeable to Na$^+$ and Cl$^-$. This means we can expect Na$^+$ and Cl$^-$ ions to move down their concentration gradients from side A to side B.

29. (C) is correct. This question requires you to know that steroid hormones are lipids and so can easily diffuse across the plasma membrane phospholipid bilayer. Steroid hormones are bound by intracellular receptors, not by cell-surface receptors.

30. (A) is correct. Because steroid hormones are hydrophobic and can cross the plasma membrane, they bond with intracellular receptors forming transcription factors that help to stimulate the transcription of the gene into mRNA. Choices B and C both involve plasma membrane receptors, and choice D does not include the binding of the hormone to an intracellular receptor.

31. (B) is correct. The cell consumes O$_2$ as it receives electrons from the electron transport chain and forms water during the process of oxidative phosphorylation. The cell makes ATP through oxidative phosphorylation, so measuring the rate of consumption of O$_2$ by the cell is a good way to determine its metabolic rate.

32. (C) is correct. This question requires you to know the essential parts of a reflex arc: receptors, sensory neuron, interneuron, motor neuron, and effector. Structure 6 is a motor neuron, and it stimulates the muscle to contract.

33. (C) is correct. With other parameters such as light and temperature in the ecosystem staying more or less constant, an increase in precipitation will increase photosynthesis and, therefore, net primary productivity.

34. (C) is correct. Polyploidy is a common form of sympatric speciation in plants. Many plant species originated from accidents of cell division that resulted in extra sets of chromosomes being inherited. Note that sympatric speciation takes place without geographic isolation. Of the choices offered, only *T. turgidum* is a polyploid. You may have noticed that *T. aestivum* is also a polyploid but was not offered as an answer.

35. (A) is correct. To form homologous pairs, one homologue (chromosome) comes from the male and a matching homologue comes from the female. In sterile hybrids, there is no matching homologue because the organism contains only one copy of the chromosome. There is no second homologue to form the pair needed for meiosis. Notice in the diagram that the sterile hybrids have only one letter, representing one set of chromosomes, while the fertile species have two sets of chromosomes (two letters), allowing each homologue to have a potential match.

36. (D) is correct. The morpho compound will turn on genes *Q* and *R* in region 2 (gene *P* requires a high concentration, which is found only in region 1). Phogen will turn on *S* and turn off *Q* at medium to high concentrations. This leaves genes *R* and *S* on in region 2.

37. (B) is correct. Region 1 has a high concentration of morpho, allowing for genes *P*, *Q*, and *R* to be on. Without a functioning phogen, gene *S* cannot be activated nor can gene *Q* be inactivated.

38. (D) is correct. Eukaryotes are able to coordinately control genes in the same pathway because the genes all have the same combination of control elements. Copies of activators that recognize the control elements bind to them, promoting simultaneous transcription.

39. (C) is correct. The change in petal color causes a change in pollinator, which can serve as an evolutionary isolating mechanism, setting the stage for the evolution of new species.

40. (B) is correct. The coevolution of insects and flowers offers many strategies for successful pollination. With the change of petal colors also comes the potential for reproductive isolation as new animals may be attracted to the new flower.

41. (C) is correct. Choice A specifies an initial exposure, which does not result in a life-threatening response. Choice B is not correct because the innate response system does not produce antibodies, and choice D is incorrect because memory B cells produce antibodies on activation, not histamines.

42. (D) is correct. The graph shows a clear peak at the 7-mm mark along the x-axis. This question is based on the idea of optimal foraging, the analyzing of feeding behavior as a compromise between feeding costs and feeding benefits. Understanding how organisms use energy, how energy use affects evolution, and how organisms interact with their environment are all themes to guide your review.

43. (A) is correct. Behavior is best understood as a consequence of natural selection. Many behaviors important to survival are innate, so this statement is not supported. An organism's reproductive success depends in part on how the behavior is performed. Part of the behavior has a genetic basis, but the entire behavior does not have to be determined by genes.

44. (C) is correct. The removal of introns requires spliceosomes. Spliceosomes are complexes of snRNA and proteins that interact with certain sites along an intron, excising the intron and joining together the two exons that flanked the intron.

45. (C) is correct. Although the figure may seem complicated, ultimately the question is asking what complex converts single-stranded DNA to double-stranded DNA. In the list of possible answers, only the enzyme DNA polymerase can copy DNA to DNA.

46. (D) is correct. When species B is removed, species A cannot colonize the area, indicating that an abiotic factor could be preventing the colonization. When species A is removed, species B colonizes the area, indicating it cannot compete with species B or it would be growing and competing in the same plot as B.

47. (B) is correct. An ice bath or other procedure to lower body temperature helps prevent enzymes and other proteins from denaturing. Although many proteins in the body could be replaced without harm, damage done to brain enzymes and proteins may be permanent.

48. (C) is correct. Rotenone disrupts the electron transport chain, reducing its efficiency and preventing an effective H^+ gradient from forming. Without the H^+ gradient, ATP synthase cannot convert enough ADP to ATP to keep the organism alive.

49. (A) is correct. Cyanide binds to one of the electron carriers in protein complex IV, stopping the flow of electrons. Without a flow of electrons, the electron transport system can no longer function, and oxidative phosphorylation ceases. Cyanide is a favorite poison of spies because it binds irreversibly to the electron carrier, ensuring death!

50. (D) is correct. The reason the action spectrum for photosynthesis doesn't match the absorption spectrum for chlorophyll *a* is because chlorophyll *a* is not the only photosynthetically important pigment in the chloroplast. Two other photosynthetically important pigments in plants are chlorophyll *b* and the carotenoids. Choice B is a correct statement but does not explain the discrepancy between that absorption spectrum of chlorophyll and the action spectrum of photosynthesis.

51. The answer is (C). The high level of nucleotide matching in Exon 1 indicates that few mutations have accumulated in this exon over time. This usually means that any change from the original sequence has a negative selection impact on the individual, removing the nucleotide mutation from the gene pool. This would occur when the exon plays a specific, critical role in the functioning of the polypeptide.

52. The answer is (A). Mutations often accumulate at a higher level in introns because the majority of the nucleotides in introns do not play critical roles in the expression of the gene. If random changes in the nucleotide sequence in introns have no effect on natural selection, the changes in nucleotides accumulate over time.

53. (B) is correct. The diameter of the parent cell is 4μm. Using the formula $V = 4/3 \ \pi r^3$ and making the following substitutions, $V = (4/3) (3.14) (2)^3$, a value of 33.49 $μm^3$ is calculated. The diameter of the budding cell is 3μm. Using the formula $V = 4/3 \ \pi r^3$ and making the following substitutions, $V = (4/3) (3.14) (1.5)^3$, a value of 14.13 $μm^3$ is calculated.

54. (A) is correct. The volume of additional cytoplasm that must be synthesized is determined by subtracting the budding volume (14.13 $μm^3$) from the parent cell volume (33.49 $μm^3$) for a value of approximately 19 $μm^3$.

55. (D) is correct. The parent cell has a surface-area-to-volume ratio (50 $μm^2$/ 33 $μm^3$) of 1.5, whereas the budding cell has a surface-area-to-volume ratio (28 $μm^2$/14 $μm^3$) of 2. As the cell becomes larger the surface-area-to-volume ratio decreases, in this case from 2 to 1.5. Metabolically active cells tend to be smaller in size because the smaller size gives more cell membrane surface area to the volume of the cell. The improved surface-area-to-volume ratio allows for efficient transport of materials into and out of the cell.

56. (C) is correct. Species 4 has the greatest number of amino acid differences (two) when compared to the other species. Note the assumptions made in the question. Mutation rates for all species for all genes are not equal over time, and answering questions about relatedness between species would require much more data. The assumptions make the question answerable in the limited time of an exam.

57. (D) is correct. Plant leaves are green because they reflect and refract green light, which is not utilized in photosynthesis. Red light is used in photosynthesis, meaning the plant absorbs CO_2 for photosynthesis. Choice A requires you to know that normal light has all the wavelengths of the visible spectrum and, therefore, even more available energy than red light alone. The plant in normal light would use even more CO_2. Check the action spectrum for photosynthesis in your text (or look back at question 54), and be prepared to explain the peaks and valleys shown in the graph.

58. (D) is correct. A nucleotide insertion downstream and at the start of the coding sequence creates a frameshift mutation, causing the regrouping of codons and a completely new list of amino acids, leading to a nonfunctional protein. As you study different types of mutations, give emphasis to the *effect* of a mutation, and be able to predict and justify which type in a particular location would cause the greatest change in gene expression.

59. (A) is correct. The cytoplasmic determinants are produced by the mother and unevenly distributed across the egg before fertilization. After fertilization, the nuclei of the embryo are exposed to different sets of cytoplasmic determinants and, as a result, express different genes.

60. (C) is correct. In type 2 diabetes, the receptors for insulin no longer function efficiently, so body cells cannot take in as much glucose, which raises blood glucose levels. A careful reading of the stem will allow you to reject choices A and B.

61. (C) is correct. Notice that the x-axis shows increasing auxin concentrations in exponents of 10^2. This indicates an increase of 100 fold between the white lines. Be alert to the use of exponents and what this means to increasing or decreasing concentrations.

62. (D) is correct. An auxin concentration of 0.9 g/L is the tipping point between inhibiting or promoting stem (not root, the questions specifies stem) elongation.

63. (C) is correct. Let's examine each statement. Option A is not supported because an auxin concentration of 10^{-6} g/L promotes both stem and root elongation. Option B is not supported because very low concentrations of auxins promote, do not inhibit, elongation of the roots. Option D is not supported by the graph because auxin concentrations below 0.9 g/L always inhibit, do not promote, elongation. Option C is supported by auxin concentrations of 10^{-4} g/L, which promotes stem elongation but inhibits root elongation.

Part B Grid-In Questions

Tip from the Readers: Where rounding is an issue with Grid-In questions, answers are accepted over a range that would allow for proper rounding. Where possible, we advise rounding at the end of your calculations to the requested whole number or decimal place.

1. The answer is 0.04 mls of O_2 consumed/minute. The germinating corn at 22°C consumed 1.6 mls of O_2 at 20 minutes and 0.4 mls of O_2 at 5 minutes. This gave the following equation for germinating corn: 1.6 − 0.4 /15 = 0.08 mls O_2/minute. The germinating corn at 12°C consumed 0.8 mls of O_2 at 20 minutes and 0.2 mls of O_2 at 5 minutes. This gave the following equation for germinating corn: 0.8 − 0.2 /15 = 0.04 mls O_2/minute. The difference is 0.08 − 0.04 = 0.04.

2. The answer is 17,190. The graph shows that radioactive decay to 1/8 requires three half-lives. With each half-life given at 5,730 years, a total of three half-lives would be 17,190 years.

3. The correct answer is −7.84 (bars). The formula of solute potential is −iCRT. In this case, the formula is −(1.0)(0.32)(0.0831)(295) = −7.84. If you find these problems difficult, go to the lab section of this book to Investigation 4, Diffusion and Osmosis, where you can find an explanation of water potential and how to work water potential problems.

4. The answer is −3.9 kcal/mole. Note that you must grid in the negative sign to get credit for this one. The coupled reaction requires +3.4 kcal/mole but obtains −7.3 kcal/mole from ATP, which leaves −3.9 kcal/mole. Be sure you recognize that endergonic reactions have a positive delta G and that exergonic reactions have a negative delta G.

5. The answer is 49.0%. The 68% that shows banding represent $p^2 + 2pq$, which is not an expression we can work with. However, it also means 32% have no banding and that equals q^2, so q equals the square root of 0.32 or 0.57; therefore, p equals 0.43. The heterozygote is represented as $2pq$, so 2(0.43) (0.57) = .4902, changing to a percentage by multiplying by 100 and rounding to the nearest tenth yields 49.0%. *In this example, an answer of 49 would be counted wrong because it is not given to the precision specified in the question.* Read carefully!

6. The answer is 46.44. $N = (19)(22)/9 = 46.44$.

> *Each question includes a sample answer, our evaluation of the answer with test-taking hints, and a rubric for you to use in evaluating your own response. We strongly suggest you write a practice response to each question and grade it using the rubric.*

Question 1 Sample Response

1. **(a)** The cell membrane of a typical animal cell is composed of three main components that are involved in transport across the membrane: phospholipids, which are two fatty acids joined to two glycerol hydroxyl groups and a phosphate group connected to the third glycerol hydroxyl group; proteins, both integral (embedded in the cell membrane) and peripheral (associated with the outside of the membrane); and cholesterol, a hydrophobic steroid embedded in the hydrophobic portion of the phospholipids. Carbohydrates are also an important macromolecule found on cell membranes, but they are not involved with cell transport.

   Phospholipids form a hydrophobic foundation for the rest of the molecules in the cell membrane. Some very small nonpolar molecules, such as O_2 and CO_2, can pass through the lipid membrane unaided, but hydrophilic and large molecules cannot pass through the membrane without utilizing protein channels.

   Proteins are involved in providing channels for the passive transport of water and certain other solutes across the membrane. Proteins can also act as pumps that use ATP energy to actively transport substances against their concentration gradient.

   Cholesterol is also found in animal (but not plant) plasma membranes, where it functions as a fluidity buffer. At high temperatures, such as human body temperature (37°C), cholesterol makes the membrane less fluid. At lower temperatures, cholesterol prevents packing of phospholipids, helping to maintain fluidity. Maintaining proper fluidity is necessary for the transport of materials across the plasma membrane.

   (b) Glycoproteins found on viral envelopes bind to specific receptor molecules on the surface of a host cell. This promotes entry of the capsid and viral genome into the cytoplasm, where cellular enzymes digest the capsid and release the genetic material. This type of entry is a form of receptor-mediated endocytosis.

   Lipid-soluble hormones, such as steroids, diffuse through the cell membrane to bind to a specific receptor protein. Often, the protein receptor/hormone combination acts as a transcription factor, turning on specific genes.

   Water enters the cell through a process called facilitated diffusion. This means that water crosses the cell membrane down its concentration gradient with the help of specific transport proteins termed *aquaporins*. Transport proteins are specific for the molecules they assist across the membrane and do not require an input of energy.

   Oxygen molecules (O_2) diffuse across the membrane because they are very small and hydrophobic.

The student clearly addresses all parts of this question but digresses in the first paragraph to describe phospholipids and types of proteins in the membrane. This is outside the scope of the question, and you should avoid doing this because there is not enough time to add extraneous details and still answer every question well. This student would have done just as well if the entire first paragraph were omitted! Remember to always read the question carefully, answer all parts of the question, and organize your answer so it is easy for the person grading your response to follow your answer.

Question 1 Rubric

(a) **Identify three** components of a typical animal plasma membrane, and **explain** the role each of these components plays in regulating the cell's internal environment. (**6 points maximum**)

Identify (1 point for each macromolecule)	**Explain** the role in regulating the cell's internal environment. (1 point for each explanation)
Phospholipids	Create a hydrophobic barrier that prevents movement of hydrophilic molecules into the cell.
Proteins	May span the membrane and provide a channel across the membrane for a hydrophilic solute
Cholesterol	"Fluidity buffer," resists changes in membrane fluidity caused by changes in the temperature; proper fluidity allows for working proteins and diffusion across the membrane

(b) **Describe** how each of the following can enter an animal cell. (**4 points maximum**)

Object entering the cell	**Describe how object enters the cell.** (1 point each)
Viral RNA	An animal RNA virus enters the cell by fusing its envelope or outer membrane with the plasma membrane.
Steroid hormone	Steroid hormones are hydrophobic and can diffuse through the plasma membrane.
Water molecules	The polar water molecule diffuses into the cell through aquaporins, protein channels embedded in the plasma membrane (facilitated diffusion).
O_2	Diffuses through the plasma membrane as O_2; is hydrophobic

2. (a) Species richness, the number of species in the community, and relative abundance, the proportions of the community represented by the various species, both contribute to species diversity.

(b) Community 1 has a distribution of species A at 5 trees / 20 total trees = 25%; Community 2 has a distribution of species A at 16 trees / 20 total trees = 80%.

(c) Community 1 is considered more diverse because although species diversity is equal between the two communities, the relative abundance is more equitable in Community 1. Compared to a community with a very high proportion of one species, a community with a more even relative abundance, such as Community 1, has greater species diversity.

(d) If the blight damaged species A, the structure of Community 2 would be most seriously affected. This is because Community 2 has a much higher relative abundance of species A (species A makes up 80% of the individual trees in Community 2, compared to 25% in Community 1). Loss of species A from Community 2 would result in large light gaps, more erosion, and greater loss of nutrients from the community. Communities with greater species diversity are more stable. Community 1 is more diverse and more stable; thus, it is better able to recover from environmental insults and repel invasive species.

Question 2 Rubric

(a) **Describe** the factors involved in species diversity. (**2 points maximum**)

- **1 point** for **species richness** or definition: number of different species in the community
- **1 point** for **relative abundance** or definition: proportion each species represents of all individuals in the community

(b) **Calculate** the percentage of *each* community represented by species A. (**2 points maximum**)

- **1 point** for the calculation in Community 1: 5 trees of species A / 20 total trees = **25%**
- **1 point** for the calculation in Community 2: 16 trees of species A / 20 total trees = **80%**

(c) Which of the two communities in the figure is more diverse? **Explain** how two communities that contain the same number of species can differ in species diversity. (**2 points maximum**)

- **1 point** for stating that Community 1 is more diverse
- **1 point** for explaining that Community 1 has greater **relative abundance** than Community 2 because it has a more equal distribution of individuals of each species

(d) **Predict** and **justify** the impact on community stability in each forest community of a disease that affects species A. (**4 points maximum**)

- **1 prediction point** for stating that Community 1 will have less damage to its community structure than Community 2
- **1 justification point** for noting the higher relative abundance of species A in Community 2 than in Community 1 (80% of species A in Community 2 compared to 25% of species A in Community 1)
- **1 justification point** for naming a specific environmental impact that would be more severe in Community 2. Examples include but are not limited to: increased light penetration, increased erosion, increased susceptibility to invasive species, and increased loss of nutrients.
- **1 justification point** for the overall conceptual statement that more diverse communities are more stable communities; thus, Community 1 is more diverse and more stable.

Question 3 Sample Response

(a) The control is *a* which has no deletion in the any control element and therefore produces 100% of reporter mRNA. The deletions in *b*, *c*, and *d* each result in different amounts of reporter mRNA compared to the control. *b* produces about 175% of the control, *c* produces about 140% of the control, and *d* produces about 40% of the control.

(b) The normal role would be to activate gene expression; without the control element, activators are not able to bind to the enhancer, and the level of gene expression decreases *c*. Element *b* would have the greatest effect on promoting tumor growth, because its deletion results in the greatest increase of gene expression.

This response clearly identifies and addresses each part of the question and earns all possible points.

Question 3 Rubric (4 points)

(a) **Provide evidence** that all three possible control elements are actual control elements.

- **1 point** *b*, *c* and *d* are all control elements; each increases or decreases the amount of mRNA

(b) If deletion of a control element causes a reduction in gene expression **identify** and **explain** the normal role of that control element.

- **1 point**—normal role is activation of gene expression
- **1 point**—allows enhancers to bind the activator

(c) If similar results were obtained in a study of control elements of a type of tumor cell, **explain** which element, if deleted, would have the greatest effect in promoting tumor growth.

- **1 point**—element *b* causes the greatest increase in gene expression, which would promote tumor growth

Question 4 Sample Response

4. (a) The amount of inorganic phosphate increases very slowly in the first 5 minutes, then there is a rapid increase of this product until about 25 minutes. After 25 minutes, the rate of product formation slows and finally no additional product is produced after 30 minutes.

(b) The rate of the reaction is (270 μmol/mL – 10 μmol/mL)/(20 minutes-5 minutes) = **18 μmol/mL/minute**.

(c) As the enzyme activity slows (when the slope reaches zero), there is no additional $\textcircled{P}_i$ being released because the cells have used up the substrate.

(d) Your blood sugar level will increase as glucose is released from your liver cells into your bloodstream. This is an example of negative feedback.

*All the rubric points are included in this essay. When asked to describe a pattern, as in part (a) be specific about each part—don't simply say it increases and then decreases, for example. Cite the data! When asked to make a calculation, always show your work and **be sure** to include units in your answer.*

Question 4 Rubric (4 points)

(a) **Describe** the pattern you see in the graph.

- **1 point**—description of *each* phase of the graph

(b) **Calculate** the rate of the reaction to the nearest whole number in the time interval between 5 and 20 minutes.

- **1 point**—(270 μmol/mL – 10 μmol/mL) / (20 minutes-5 minutes) = **18 μmol/mL/minute** (no credit for answer without units; may accept 17–19 μmol/mL/minute).

(c) When the substrate (glucose 6-phosphate) is first added to the liver cells, it is transported into the cells and processed by the enzyme (glucose 6-phosphatase). Then the product is released from the cells into the buffer. **Propose a hypothesis** to explain the slope of the line between 25 and 40 minutes.

- **1 point**—The rate of product decreases because the substrate is consumed.

(d) If your blood sugar level is low from skipping lunch, the following reaction will occur in your liver cells:

Glucose 6-phosphate
Glucose 6-phosphatase
Glucose + P i

Predict how this reaction will affect your blood sugar level. What type of feedback is this?

> • **1 point**—blood glucose will increase/negative feedback (both parts required to earn point).

Question 5 Sample Response

5. Template sequence from problem: 3′-TAC TTC AAA CCG ATT-5′.

(a) The mRNA sequence would be 5'-AUG AAG UUU GGC UAA-3′.

(b) The amino acid sequence would be met-lys-phe-gly-stop.

(c) The substitution would cause the second codon to become AAA, but because both AAG and AAA code for the same amino acid, lysine, there would be no change to the polypeptide chain.

(d) Deletion of the second cytosine would be a frameshift mutation, and all codons after the first one would be different, resulting in many changes to the original amino acid sequence.

The student clearly addressed each part of the question. This is a typical 4-point question with a relatively narrow focus. Although the student could have figured out each of the changed mRNAs and amino acids in part (d), for example, it was not called for in the question. Limit your answers to what is being specifically asked in order to have time to answer every question on the test!

Question 5 Rubric (4 points)

The DNA template strand of a gene contains the sequence

3′-TAC TTC AAA CCG ATT-5′.

(a) Draw the mRNA sequence, indicating 5′ and 3′ ends.

• (**1 point**) Correct mRNA sequence: 5'-AUG AAG UUU GGC UAA-3′

(b) Predict the amino acid sequence from this gene.

• (**1 point**) Correct prediction: met-lys-phe-gly-stop

(c) What would be the effect of a mutation that substitutes a thymine for the second cytosine?

- (**1 point**) The second codon would be AAA. Because it also codes for lysine, there would be no effect in the amino acid sequence.

(d) What would be the effect of a mutation that deletes the second cytosine? (**1 point maximum**)

- Only the first amino acid in the chain would be unchanged.
  and/or
- This would be a frameshift mutation.

Question 6 Sample Response

6. (a) If the seedlings are rotated 180° away from the window, over several days they will change the direction in which they are growing and all lean back toward the window. This is because a plant responds to light by the movement of auxin from the light side of the stem tip to the dark side of the stem. The auxin hormone activates enzymes in the cell wall that pump hydrogen ions (protons) into the cell wall, causing a drop in pH. The lowering pH activates other enzymes in the cell wall to break cross-links between cellulose fibrils, which weaken the cell wall. This weakening of the cell wall allows turgor pressure from the central vacuole to stretch the cell walls on the dark side, making the cells larger on the dark side and, in the process, turning the plant toward the light. Growth of a plant toward a light source is known as *positive phototropism*.

(b) This response describes a process that enables a plant to gain maximum exposure to light, which is the energy source for photosynthesis. Plants that perform more photosynthesis have more energy to devote to life processes, including reproduction.

The student gives a very detailed explanation of why the seedlings move toward light. Because this is only a 3-point question, this amount of detail exceeds what would be expected. You will see this reflected in the rubric.

Question 6 Rubric (3 points)

A tray of germinating oat seedlings is placed in a window that has light shining through it most of the day, and it is given adequate water and soil nutrients. After 3 days, the tray is rotated 180°.

(a) Predict and explain what will occur. (**2 points maximum**)

- Prediction that the seedlings will all bend toward the light
- Explanation that a hormone (auxin) is distributed in response to uneven light. This increase in the hormone on the dark side causes cells to elongate on the dark side of the seedlings, causing the seedling to bend toward light.

(b) What is the evolutionary significance of this response? (**1 point maximum**)

- Maximum light exposure results from this bending, which increases the amount of photosynthesis/maximizes use of energy.

Question 7 Sample Response

7. Three pieces of evidence that glycolysis was the first metabolic pathway for the production of ATP include:
   1. Long ago, Earth's atmosphere contained almost no oxygen, and only relatively recently have the current atmospheric levels of gases come to be what they are. Glycolysis does not require oxygen, so it is possible that prokaryotes (which evolved before eukaryotes) used glycolysis for making ATP at a time when no free oxygen was present in the early atmosphere.
   2. The second piece of evidence is that glycolysis is a very common method for making ATP conserved across organisms in the three domains: Bacteria, Archaea, and Eukarya. This commonality implies that glycolysis originated very early in the evolution of metabolic pathways.
   3. The final reason has to do with the site of glycolysis—that is, it takes place in the cytosol and not in an organelle. Prokaryotic cells, which evolved first, are much simpler than eukaryotic cells, and they contain no membrane-bound organelles (not even a nucleus). Therefore, if glycolysis were to take place in an early prokaryotic cell, it would have to evolve in the cytosol. For instance, it would have to evolve such that it did not rely on a specialized membrane to function.

   This response gives the required three pieces of evidence and good reasoning to support them.

Question 7 Rubric (3 points)

It is theorized that glycolysis was the first metabolic pathway for the production of ATP. Glycolysis begins the process of making ATP by breaking glucose into two molecules of pyruvate. **Justify** this claim with three pieces of evidence that support this point. (**3 points**)

- Glycolysis does not require oxygen. Oxygen was not present in the early atmosphere.
- Glycolysis occurs across all domains; enzymes of the pathway are widely conserved.
- Glycolysis occurs in cytosol and does not require membrane-bound organelles.

Question 8 Sample Response

8. (a) A substitution mutation can result in a different amino acid being incorporated into the protein. Because of R-group interactions, the protein may fold differently and therefore function differently.

(b) Malaria kills many people in sub-Saharan Africa, but individuals who are heterozygous for sickle-cell disease are less likely to die of it than people without the mutant form of hemoglobin. Because these people are able to live and therefore reproduce, the sickle-cell allele will continue to be passed on.

(c) The frequency of the allele would be lower in a population in Alaska because malaria is not found there. There would be no selective advantage to having the mutation, and because it has a negative effect in individuals who receive two copies of the allele, the allele would become less common over time. The value of the sickle-cell allele will decline over time, dropping from 0.07 to 0.06 to 0.05 and down toward 0.01.

The student addresses each part of the question. In part (c) the student would not have received credit without the last sentence. If you reread the question, it asks for a frequency, so a wise student will give a number, not simply say "lower."

Question 8 Rubric (3 points)

Sickle-cell disease is caused by a single base-pair substitution in the amino acid sequence for the β-globin gene.

(a) **Predict** how this change might alter the overall structure of the protein. (**1 point maximum**)

- changes interactions between amino acids
- changes the secondary or tertiary structure resulting from alteration in folding
- changes the quaternary structure of hemoglobin

(b) Explain why this mutation is common in sub-Saharan Africa. (**1 point maximum**)

- Individuals who are heterozygous for the sickle-cell allele are less likely to die of malaria (a common disease in sub-Saharan Africa) and so pass on the mutant allele.

(c) If the frequency of the allele is 0.07 in sub-Saharan Africa, predict a biologically plausible frequency for the allele in a population of Native Americans in Alaska. (**1 point maximum**)

Any value less than 0.07. (Because the allele would not offer an advantage to individuals in Alaska.)

Index

C

calcium ions, 56, 263
Calvin cycle, 84, 85f, 88–90, 89f
CAM photosynthesis, 91
cancer, and cell cycle control, 139–140
canopy, 279
capillaries, 238
capsid, 140
carbohydrates, 30, 42, 49, 235
carbon and molecular diversity, 29–30
carbon cycle, 292
carbon dioxide (CO_2)
    alternative mechanisms of fixation, 90–91
    Calvin cycle, 88–90
    citric acid cycle, 80
    resource acquisition and transport, 251f
carbon fixation, 84, 90–91
carbonic acid (H_2CO_3), 29
carnivorous plants, 220
carnivores, 291
carpels, 197
carrier protein, 51
carrying capacity, 282
catabolic pathway, 71, 76–77
catalysts, 73
Cell, The (Topic 2), 41–69, 395–399
cell body, 256
cell-cell signals, 139
cell communication, 53–57
cell cycle, 57–62
cell cycle control system, 61
cell death, programmed, 255
cell differentiation, 138
cell division, 138
cell division, chromosome duplication and
    distribution during, 58f
Cell Division: Mitosis and Meiosis
    (Investigation 7), 328–332, 439
cell-mediated immune response, 244
cell plate, 61, 105
cells, 41–69, 395–399. *See also* animal
    cells; eukaryotic cells; plant cells;
    prokaryotes
    competent, 334
    daughter, 103
    embryonic stem, 149, 255
    guard, 214, 345
    memory, 243
    plasma, 243
    somatic, 58, 101
cell-surface receptors, 248
cell types, and differential gene expression,
    138–139
cellular innate defenses, 241
cellular membranes, 48–49
Cellular Respiration (Investigation 6),
    324–327, 438–439
cellular respiration, 77f, 324–327,
    438–439

cellular respiration and fermentation,
    76–82
cellulose, 31, 47
cell wall, 47
central nervous system (CNS), 257, 260
central vacuoles, 45
centrioles, 47
centromere, 58
centrosomes, 47
cephalization, 200
cerebellum, 261
cerebral cortex, 262
cerebrum, 261
channel protein, 51
chaparral, 278
characteristics, shared, 188–189
Chargaff, Erwin, 124
Chase, Martha, 124
checkpoints, 61
chemical bonds, 26, 27
chemical cycling, 290
chemical energy, 71
chemical force, 51
chemical reactions, 27
chemical synapse, 259f
chemiosmosis, 81
chemiosmosis and light reactions, 88f
chemoreceptors, 262
Chemistry of Life, The (Topic 1), 25–39,
    391–394
chiasmata, 103
Chi-square analysis, 354–357, 442
Chi-square table, 358
chitin, 31, 198, 201
chlorophyll, 83
chloroplasts, 46, 83
cholesterol, 32
chondrichthyes, 202
chordate characteristics, 201f
chorion, 203
chorionic villus sampling, 113
chromatin, 44, 126
chromosomal basis of inheritance, 113–117
chromosomal mutations, 165
chromosomes
    inheriting, 101
    made of DNA molecule and proteins,
      126, 128
    in sexual life cycles, 102
chromosome theory of inheritance, 113–114
cilia, 47
circadian rhythms, 224, 266
circulation, 237–240
circulatory system, 237–238
cisternal space, 44
citric acid cycle, 79f, 80
clade, 188
clade Deuterostomia, 201
cladogram, 188, 316

class, 186
cleavage furrow, 61, 105
climate change, 277–278, 295
clonal selection, 242
cloning, 144–145f
cloning vector, 146
codominance, 110–111
codones, 129
coelom, 200
coenzymes, 74
coevolution, 220
cofactors, 74
cohesion, 28
cohesion-tension hypothesis, 216
colonization of land, 175
colonization of plants, 195–196
commensalism, 193, 287
common ancestor, 186, 314
community, 286
community diversity, 289
community ecology, 286–289
Comparing DNA Sequences to Understand
    Evolutionary Relationships with
    BLAST (Investigation 3), 314–316, 437
competent cells, 334
competitive exclusion principle, 286
competitive inhibitors, 74
complete dominance, 110
complete metamorphosis, 201
compounds, 25
concentration gradient, 50
conformation, 29
coniferous forest, 279
conjugation, 192
conservation biology and global change,
    294–296
consumers, 83, 288
continental drift, 164, 175
contractile vacuoles, 45
controlled experiment, 349
convergent evolution, 164, 187
coral reefs, 279
corepressor, 136
cork cambium, 212
corpus callosum, 262
cotransport, 51, 215
countercurrent, 246
countercurrent exchange, 232, 239
covalent bond, 26
crassulacean acid metabolism. See CAM
    photosynthesis
Crick, Francis, 124
CRISPR-Cas9 system, 141
crossing over, 103
    genetic variation, 106, 166
    linked genes, 115
    synapsis and, 105
cryptic coloration, 287
cyclic AMP, 56

eudicots, 197
eukarya, 191
eukaryotes
  as animals, 199
  appearance on earth, 174–175
  fungi, 198
  multicellular, 151–152, 175
  single-celled, 194–195
  versus prokaryotes, 190–192
eukaryotic cell cycle, 61
eukaryotic cells, 41–43, 44, 131–132
eukaryotic gene expression, regulation, 136–138
eukaryotic organisms, 189
eutherians, 202
evapotranspiration, 291
evidence, endosymbiotic hypothesis, 174–175
evo-devo, 152, 175
evolution, 161–184, 410–420
  animal diversity, 199–200
  bacteria and archaea, 190–194
  colonization of plants, 195–196
  descent with modification, 161–165
  fungi, 197–199
  and genetic variation, 106
  history of life on earth, 173–176
  invertebrates, 200–201
  origin of species, 170–172
  phylogeny and tree of life, 185–190
  of populations, 163, 165–170
  protists, 194–195
  scientific support, 163–165
  seed plants, 196–197
  theory of, evidence for, 163–164
Evolutionary History of Life, The (Topic 7), 185–210, 420–423
exaptations, 176
excitatory neurotransmitters, 260
excretion and osmoregulation, 245–247
exergonic reaction, 72
exons, 131
exoskeleton, 201
experimental questions, AP Biology Exam, 7–9
exponential population, 282
external fertilization, 251
extinction rates, 289
extinctions, mass, 175
extinction vortex, 295
extracellular digestion, 233
extracellular matrix (ECM), 47
extraembryonic membranes, 203
extreme halophiles, 193
extreme thermophiles, 193
extremophiles, 193

F

facilitated diffusion, 50, 51
facultative anaerobes, 82, 192

family, 186
fats, 31, 235
fatty acids, 31
feathers, 202
feedback inhibition, 75
feedback regulation and coordination, 248
fermentation, 76–82
ferns, 196
fertilization, 195
  alleles shuffled through sexual reproduction, 166
  angiosperm life cycle, 220–221
  animal reproduction, 251
  embryonic development, 254
  land plant colonization, 195–197
  and meiosis, 103
  random, 107
  in sexual life cycles, 101–103
first law of thermodynamics, 72
fission, 250
fixed action pattern (FAP), 265–266
fixed allele, 166
flagella, 47, 191
flower, 197
flowering, photoperiodic control of, 224f
fluid mosaic model, 48
F_1 (first filial) generation, 107, 108f
food chain, 288
food vacuoles, 45
food webs, 288
forensic applications of DNA technology, 150
formulas and equations, 358–359
fossil record, 164, 174
founder effect, 168
fragmentation, 250
frameshift mutation, 134
frass, 341
free energy (ΔG), 72
free-response questions and answers
  AP Biology Exam, 10–12, 18–20
  Topic 1: The Chemistry of life, 39, 394–395
  Topic 2: The Cell, 69, 399–400
  Topic 3: The Energy of life, 100, 405–406
  Topic 5: Molecular Genetics, 160, 414–415
  Topic 6: Mechanisms of Evolution, 184, 419–420
  Topic 7: The Evolutionary History of Life, 210, 422–423
  Topic 8: Plant Form and Function, 230, 425–426
  Topic 9: Animal Form and Function, 276, 430–431
  Topic 10: Ecology, 303, 434–435
freshwater biomes, 279
fruit, 197, 220

Fruit Fly Behavior (Investigation 12), 348–352, 441
F_2 (second filial) generation, 107, 108f
functional groups, 30
fundamental niche, 286
fungi, 198–199
  mutualistic relationships, 211, 219
  origin on Earth, 175

G

gametes, 58, 101, 102
gametic isolation, 171
gametophyte, 195
gap junctions, 48
gas exchange, 237–240
gastric juice, 234
gastrovascular cavity, 237
gel electrophoresis, 146, 148f, 337–338f
gene cloning, 144–145f
gene expression, 128
  eukaryotic, 136–138
  from gene to protein, 128–134
  regulation, 134–140
  studying with DNA technology, 149
gene flow, 168
gene idea, Mendel and, 107–113
gene of interest, 335
gene pool, 166
genes, 101
genes of operon, 135–136
gene therapy, 149
genetically modified (GM) organism, 150
genetic disorders
  caused by chromosomal alterations, 116
  dominantly inherited, 113
  recessively inherited, 111–112
genetic drift, 168
genetic engineering, 144–148
genetic material. *See also* DNA (deoxyribonucleic acid); RNA (ribonucleic acid)
  bacterial transference, 192
  DNA as, 123–125
  self-replicating RNA, 173–174
  virus, 140
genetic profiles, 150
genetic recombination, 115
genetic variation, 106–107, 165–166, 170
genetics, Mendelian
  and behavior of chromosomes, 113–114
  and complex inheritance patterns, 110–111
  exceptions to inheritance patterns, 117
  law of independent assortment, 107–108, 109f
  law of segregation, 108f
  laws of inheritance, 107–109
  meiosis and sexual life cycles, 101–107
  probability laws, 110

P

paleontology, 164
pancreas, 234–235
pandemic, 143
paramecia, 45
paraphyletic, 189, 194
parasitic plants, 220
parasitism, 193, 237
parasympathetic division, 261
parental types, 115
parthenogenesis, 250
passive diffusion, 50
passive immunity, 244
passive transport, 50, 52f, 214
pathogens, 193
pattern formation, 139
PCR (polymerase chain reaction), 146, 147f
pedigree, 111
pentose (5-carbon) sugar, 33
pepsin, 234
peptide bonds, 32
peptidoglycans, 191
perception, 263
peripheral nervous system (PNS), 257, 261
peroxisomes, 46
p53 gene, 139
P (parental) generation, 107, 108f
pH, change in, 33
phages, 140
pharmaceuticals, and DNA technology, 150
pharyngeal slits, 201
phenotype, 108
pheromones, 251, 266
phloem, 212
phosphate group, 33
phosphofructokinase, 82
phospholipids, 31–32, 42, 48
phosphorylation cascade, 55
photic zone, 279
photometer, 346
photons, 84
photoperiodism, 224
photophosphorylation, 84
photorespiration, 90
Photosynthesis (Investigation 5),
    321–323, 438
photosynthesis, 82–91
    adaptation to hot, dry climates, 90–91
    Calvin cycle, 88–90
    lab investigation, 321–323, 439
    leaf anatomy, 213
    light energy conversion to chemical
        energy, 83–84
    overview of, 84, 85f
    relationship with respiration, 340–341
photosystem I (PS I), 86
photosystem II (PS II), 86
photosystems, 85
phototropism, 223
pH scale, 28

phylogenetic trees, 186–188, 187f, 203
phylogeny and tree of life, 185–190
phylum, 186, 200–201
phytochromes, 223
pigments, 85
plant cells
    cell plates, 105
    central vacuoles, 45
    chloroplasts, 83
    cytokinesis, 61
    resource acquisition and transport,
        214–218
    structure, 43f
    water potential, 319f
Plant Form and Function (Topic 8),
    211–230, 423–426. See also plant
    cells; plants
plants
    angiosperm reproduction and
        biotechnology, 220–221
    attacks by herbivores and pathogens, 225
    colonization of land, 195–196
    crop modification, 221
    flowering, 220–221
    hierarchical organization, 211–212
    hormones, 223
    leaf anatomy, 345f
    mechanisms for substance transport,
        214–216
    meristem cell division, 212
    origin on Earth, 175
    responses to internal and external
        signals, 222–225
    seed, evolution of, 196–197
    soil and nutrition, 219–220
    structure, growth, and development,
        211–213
    vascular, resource acquisition and
        transport, 214–219, 215f
plasma, 239
plasma cells, 243
plasma membrane, 49f
    bulk transport, 52
    eukaryotic cells, 41–42
    receptors, 53, 222
    selective permeability, 48
plasmids, 145, 191, 333, 334f
plasmodesmata, 47, 218
platelets, 239
pleiotropy, 111
pluripotent, 149
point mutations, 134, 165
polar, 27
polar covalent bonds, 26
polar molecules, 50
pollination, 220
poly-A tail, 131
polygamous, 267
polygenic inheritance, 111
polymers, 30

polypeptide, translation as synthesis,
    132–134
polyphyletic, 189
polyploid, 172
polyploidy, 116
polysaccharides, 30
population
    conservation, 295
    density, dispersion, and demographics,
        280–281
    ecology, 280–285
    evolution of, 163, 165–170
    exponential model, 282
    formula, growth rate, 283
    genetics, 166
    growth prediction, 282f
    growth regulation, 284
    Hardy-Weinberg equation, 166, 309–313
    increase in, 285
    logistic model, 282
positive-feedback loop, 248
positive-feedback systems, 232
positive gravitropism, 225
positive phototropism, 223
posterior, 199
postsynaptic cell, 257, 258
postzygotic barriers, 171
potential energy, 71
predation, 287
predator, 287
pressure flow, 217, 218f
pressure potential (Ψ_P), 318
presynaptic cell, 257, 258
prey, 287
prezygotic barriers, 171
primary consumers, 288, 291
primary electron acceptor, 86
primary growth, 212
primary immune response, 243
primary producers, 288, 291–292
primary productivity, 340–341
primary structure, 32
primary succession, 288
prions, 143
probability (p), 355
probe, 146
producers, 83
productivity, 340–343, 342f
products, 74
prokaryotes, 189, 191f
    biosphere, roles in, 193
    diverse set of lineages, 192–193
    earliest living organism, 174
    genetic diversity, 191–192
    impact on humans, 193–194
    nutritional and metabolic adaptations,
        192
    structural and functional adaptations, 191f
prometaphase, 59
promiscuous, 267

tundra, 279
turgor pressure, 216
Turner syndrome, 116
type I diabetes mellitus, 245

U

uniform dispersion, 281
unsaturated fatty acids, 31
Urey and Miller experiment, 173
urinary formation, key functions, 246f
use and disuse, 162

V

vaccines, 143
vacuoles, 45
Van der Waals interactions, 27
vascular cambium, 212
vascular plants, resource acquisition and
    transport in, 214–219, 215f
vascular tissue, 212
veins, 238
ventral, 199

ventral nerve cord, 201
ventricles, 238
vertebrae, 202
vertebrate brain, 261–262f
vertebrate neuron, 256f
vertebrates, 202–203
vestigial organs, 163
villi, 234
viral envelopes, 140
viruses, 140–143
visual signals, 266
voltage gradient, 51

W

warning coloration, 287
water
    adhesion and cohesion, 28, 216, 344
    and plant colonization, 195–196
    properties of, 27–28
    structure of, 27
    transport, 49–50
water potential (Ψ), 215, 318–320

water-soluble hormones, 248
Watson, James, 124
waxes, 31
white blood cells (WBCs), 239

X

X chromosome, 102
X-inactivation, 115
X-linked genes
    disorders, 115
    transmission of recessive traits, 114
x-ray crystallography, 124
xylem, 212
xylem sap, 216

Y

Y chromosome, 102
yeasts, 198
yolk sac, 203

Z

zygote, 103, 199